CALL OF THE LAND

Call of the Land

A Novel of High Adventure in 4-H Club Work

By

HAROLD M. SHERMAN

M. A. Donohue & Company

CHICAGO • NEW YORK

Dedication

To the Founders and Pioneers in the Organization and Development of the Inspired 4-H Club idea and program of Farming and Home-Making—carried on under direction of the National Extension Service, conducted co-operatively by the State Agricultural Colleges and the United States Department of Agriculture.

To the County Agents, the County Club Agents, the Home Demonstration Agents and the Legion of Local Leaders who always have and are devoting themselves so tirelessly in the Service of Youth.

To the Civic and Business Leaders, the Civic and Farm Clubs, and the Business Organizations—all of whom, in their Support, are Contributing so enormously to enable Youth to earn while learning and to earn what it learns.

And last—but FIRST—to that wonderful Peace Army of Eternal Youth— the Boys and Girls of Yesterday, Today and Tomorrow—who comprise 4-H—upon whom our hopes for "Making the Best Better" in a World so much in need of such Service—are placed.

These hopes could not be entrusted to finer Heads, Hearts and Hands.

Acknowledgements

The Author is immensely indebted to the courtesies, hospitality, information, guidance and experience in the field of 4-H so generously extended and outstandingly provided by the following:

Kenneth Anderson, *Associate Director, National Committee on Boys and Girls Club Work, Inc.;* Mr. and Mrs. W. A. Anderson and Son, Bill, Jr.; Judge Jacob M. Braude, *Boys' Court, Chicago;* Jack Carter; Andrew Daum; Mr. and Mrs. T. D. Davis and Sons, Jimmy, Larry and Harold; Mr. and Mrs. Ralph R. Dawson; Harry Dehls; The Fender 4-H Club, *Its Entire Membership;* Glenn A. Green; William J. Good; Hendrix Lackey; D. S. Lantrip; T. E. Luther; N. V. Morris; Guy L. Noble, *Managing Director, National Committee on Boys and Girls Club Work, Inc.;* Glenn C. Rutledge; Elizabeth Simpson; J. M. Thomason; Leslie E. Troeger, *Editor, National 4-H News;* Thomas E. Wilson, *Chairman, National Committee on Boys and Girls Club Work, Inc.*

And many others whose helpful suggestions and co-operation have contributed much to this novel of "fictionized fact".

All characters in this novel, with the exception of Judge Jacob M. Braude, Thomas E. Wilson and Russell A. Firestone, as named, are entirely fictitious and based upon a composite study of achievements in the field of 4-H and have not been based upon any real life persons, as such—nor have any specific situations, as related.

HAROLD M. SHERMAN

Chapter I

HIDDEN VALLEY was at the railroad station.

If you had been an inhabitant, you could probably have called most of its 801 citizens by name. This was the biggest concentration of its population gathered in one spot since the boys from Rock County, of which Hidden Valley was the County seat, had left for war.

But now the war was over and Dave Carson was coming home. He was bringing with him all the medals which a grateful nation could bestow and his home folks wanted him to know how proud they were of him.

Frank Carson's boy! Son of one of the best known and best liked farmers in the County, whose beef cattle were famous for miles around. It was open range in Arkansas but not for Frank Carson's herd. He kept it fenced in and fed and handled his cattle by the latest approved methods of the Extension Service of the Department of Agriculture. Pretty silly, going to all this trouble, lots of folks thought. Foolish spending out all that extra money for special fencing and feed when the State abounded in rich, free pasture lands and cattle could get fattened up on other people's property without costing a cent.

But Frank, he'd always gone in for modern ways. Why he even had a wind-charger and electric lights on his place and was figuring, when all this war priority business was over, on fixing himself an indoor toilet with bath tub! Such a thing was almost unheard of on the Stony Creek Route which led up into the hills out of Hidden Valley!

Frank was at the station with his bright-eyed wife, Emma. She was wearing a new store dress they had driven all the way to Little Rock to get for the occasion. No Mail-Order-House clothes this time. You couldn't ever be too sure of a becoming style or fit, and Mrs. Carson had to look just right before all these people and her boy. She was only sorry for one thing—that it was the middle of February and her winter coat kept her from

1

showing the green-figured dress off to advantage, but since it wasn't too cold she did manage to leave her coat open so that those of her acquaintance might observe that she had on something new. As for Frank—you couldn't get him to dress up for anything. He'd spend money for cattle and barns and new equipment but when it came to clothes—well, a clean pair of overalls and his old worn windbreaker were good enough.

"I don't want Dave to have any trouble recognizing me," he had said to her before starting for the train. "A woman's different. If she's recognized too quick, then she's not been keeping up with the fashions."

Mayor Ed Brannigan stood beside the Carsons on the station platform. This welcoming party had been his idea. An event like this would mean more business for the town since it brought people in from all over the County. They would stop to shop after the ceremony was over and most of them would trade in one or more of Ed Brannigan's places of business, for he owned almost half the town.

There was the Brannigan General Store on the choicest corner of the Square, facing the old stone Court House. Right next to it was the Brannigan Drug Company and, adjoining it, Brannigan's Feed and Seed Store. They were of pine construction, made of timber milled by the Brannigan Lumber Company. At the far end of the block was the Bank of Hidden Valley which did not bear Brannigan's name, but he was its president and principal stockholder. And, if a stranger had to stay in Hidden Valley over night, he had only one choice of hotel—Brannigan's Dew Drop Inn. This was located on the opposite side of the Square, the only three story building in town. It had a wide veranda where the rocking chair brigade sat whenever weather permitted, passing judgment on all the town's activities, seen and unseen.

Brannigan, himself, liked to know what was going on. That is why he built a big white house in a pine grove on the highest elevation above Hidden Valley. Here he could lounge on his porch, day or night, or—by turning over in his bed on the second floor and looking out the window, survey in a sweeping glance, the entire Brannigan Empire.

"Well, Frank," Mayor Brannigan was saying to Farmer Carson, "I'm only sorry *I* didn't have a boy to fight for my country. All *I* could do was stay home and sell War Bonds, raise money for the Red Cross, and help the Government line up all the timber in this section to keep production going." He turned now to include Mrs. Carson as he patted them each on the shoulder. "But I envy you folks. Parents of one of Rock County's greatest heroes! The name 'Carson' will live long after 'Brannigan' is gone and forgotten!"

The father of the returning war hero looked up the street from the depot at the row of Brannigan stores.

"I'm not so sure about that," he said, dryly.

There was the distant wail of a train whistle which echoed in the hills just outside the town. The steel rails commenced to sing. A babble of excited chatter broke out. Members of Hidden Valley's High School Band of twelve pieces got their instruments in position. White-haired old Professor Hoyt, who had taught Dave Carson how to play the drums, raised his baton. They would let Dave hear the familiar strains of his High School song as the train pulled in. He had entered the Service in his Senior year.

"Now, boys!" admonished Professor Hoyt, in a quavering voice. "All of you watch me and don't any of you start ahead of time. We want to make this the best we've ever played it!"

Those nearest the tracks cried out: "Here it comes!"

Frank Carson took his wife, Emma, by the arm. They looked at each other. There were tears in their eyes. A group of Dave's High School friends brushed against them.

"Hi, Mr. Carson! . . . Hello, Mrs. Carson! . . . Bet you're happy! . . . Gee, it'll be great to see Dave!"

The little three-car train on the Branch railroad out of St. Louis was wheezing to a stop. Dave Carson would likely be the only passenger for Hidden Valley. There was the baggage car . . . now the smoker . . . and here the passenger coach—on the end!

Hardly anybody on the train. Some curious older passengers looking out the windows, with half-alarmed, wondering expressions at sight of the crowd and the great din which was going up.

Dave would be on the rear platform, smiling and waving as he'd been when he went away. Only he *wasn't* there. Instead, a dark-eyed, dark-haired youth of perhaps eighteen, who swung down, suitcase in hand, with an amused grin as he said: "Well, you've got the band out and everything! Is this all for *me?*"

Professor Hoyt gave a signal and his musicians lowered their instruments.

"You know it ain't!" shouted someone close to him. "Who are you and what're *you* doing here?"

"My name's Roy Willard," introduced the strange youth with an irritating nonchalance. "Is Sue Kendall in the crowd?"

A girl's voice cried out in surprise. "Why—why—this isn't . . . you weren't supposed to arrive till tomorrow! Father wasn't expecting . . . !"

"So I'm here today," called the youth. "Am I supposed to go back and ride on these tin cans again?"

Sue came toward him through an opening lane of fellow townspeople who eyed her questioningly.

"Oh, it's all right," she assured, "only there must have been a mix-up somewhere. We're all here to meet Dave Carson."

The strange youth laughed, dropped his suitcase and took out a cigarette, which he tapped against the palm of his hand. "Yeah, I know," he said. "I've already met your hero. He's been helping take care of a soldier's baby on the train—and the kid didn't want to let him go. Here he is now!"

As he spoke, the young man for whom all Hidden Valley and half of Rock County had been awaiting, came backing through the door of the shabby old coach, onto the rear platform. He was wearing over-seas cap, there was an Airborne insignia on his shoulder, and over this same shoulder had been slung a bulging khaki duffel-bag. Dave's free hand was raised in farewell greeting to someone in the coach.

"Goodbye, Honey," he was calling.

"Daddy! Daddy!" cried a baby voice.

Dave, grinning, gave a helpless shrug of his shoulders and turned to face a laughing crowd of home folks.

"Hello, everybody!" he saluted. "I got a little tied up in there. That kid thinks every soldier's her father!"

"Now!" cried old Professor Hoyt, excitedly. "Give it to him!"

And Hidden Valley's High School Band *did*! It was joined by the voices of students, young and old, as Dave stood on the platform, looking down, with the words coming up to him which once had seemed to mean so much.

"When we leave the dear old High School
    And face the world alone,
We'll think of days we've spent here
    As the best we've ever known . . ."

The locomotive snorted and the wheels of the little engine spun around on the rails as it gave a tug on the cars. Dave leaped to the ground and was swallowed up in the avalanche of his friends which immediately engulfed him. He was hugged and kissed and whacked on the back and hand-shaken until he good-naturedly, but breathlessly, fought his way free, crying: "Hey, folks—let up! Give me air! . . . Where's Mom and Dad?"

Dave's chestnut brown hair was ruffled, his face was streaked with lipstick, his tie was askew and even his trim fitting uniform with the over-seas Service ribbons and medals on it had been pulled out of place. He looked about the circle of eager, admiring faces, seeking only one. A woman was suddenly thrust forward through the crowd, her chestnut hair streaked with gray.

"My boy!" she said, and held out her arms.

Dave's blue eyes had a light in them like an Arkansas sunrise.

"Mom!" he cried, and took the little woman in his arms. He held her close for a moment as she cried, softly, against his coat sleeve, and then he stepped back to look at her. "Gee, Mom!" he exclaimed, "Isn't that a *new* dress?"

Mrs. Carson laughed and nodded, dabbing at her eyes. "He hasn't changed any," she said, happily, looking up at the strong man in the windbreaker beside her. "I couldn't ever wear anything new without his noticing it right off!"

Dave's hand now reached out for his Dad's. They clasped in a grip which could only exist between a son and a father, without a word being spoken.

And then the big figure of Mayor Ed Brannigan pushed in between them.

"Well, Dave, my boy! We're glad to have you back!" he boomed. "Mighty proud, too—every dang one of us! You've put Hidden Valley on the map of the World and we've come here to do you honor. Get in my car, Dave. We're parading up to the Court House Square where we're having a little program, celebrating your return home!"

He took Dave by the arm and motioned to the crowd.

"Form in line, folks. Make a procession! Professor Hoyt, get your band out in front. Come on, everybody, let's go!"

Dave disengaged himself to grab his father and mother as they were being pushed away. A rotund farm youth, in blue shirt and overalls, picked up Dave's duffel-bag which had been dropped at his feet, and flung it over a broad back.

"I'll carry this for you, Dave," he volunteered, joyfully.

"Porky O'Connor!" recognized Dave. "Man, oh man—aren't you ever going to stop growing?"

Porky grinned. "I'm raisin' pigs, now, Dave—and I'm gainin' weight faster'n *they* are!"

A golden-haired girl with liquid blue eyes, caught at Dave's sleeve. "Hello!" she said.

Dave stopped. They had been enroute to Mayor Brannigan's car at the side of the station.

"Carolyn!" he greeted, as their eyes met and her face took on a tinge of color. "Say, *you've* grown, to—I don't mean like Porky here—but, well—what's become of those pig-tails?"

Carolyn laughed, a trifle fussed. "Oh!" she said. "I've been wearing my hair like this for about a year."

She turned sidewise to exhibit a long, wavy bob which the sun attractively spotlighted for her.

"It's all right," said Dave. "I approve of it." Then, catching sight of her two sisters, behind her, Dave called: "Hi, Eleanor! ... Hi, Doris! ... You three sisters still singing together?"

"We sure are!" chorused Eleanor and Doris.

"That's something I've got to hear!" said Dave.

"You will!" promised Carolyn, shyly. "We're on the program."

"That's swell!" said Dave. "I'm beginning to like this!"

Mayor Ed Brannigan interposed, impatiently. "I don't want to seem to be rushing you, Dave, my boy, but we're due to be on the radio in less than half an hour and we've got to get things going. Mr. and Mrs. Carson—you ride with Dave and me in my car. It's only a couple of blocks but the folks on the street and around the Square can see Dave better."

Brannigan owned the only Cadillac in town. It was a seven passenger Deluxe which he never risked on the hills or gravel roads of Rock County. He had bought it specifically to carry local and state politicians and visiting celebrities around the Square on such auspicious occasions as this. A liveried chauffeur, imported from Batesville, added the last touch of swank. He now had the car door open and was helping his passengers to seats.

"I'll sit back here between your father and mother," proposed Mayor Brannigan, magnanimously. "And you sit just ahead of us, all by yourself. Don't want to disappoint anyone who wants to get a good look at you!"

The returned war hero submitted graciously and smiled and nodded or waved at the many friends who hailed him from all sides. The little procession got under way with the Color Guard from Hidden Valley High School proudly leading off, holding high the great silk American flag and standard, one of Brannigan's gifts to the school. Behind them marched the School Band with old Professor Hoyt keeping pace, despite a touch of rheumatism which caused a slight limp. The band struck up the old tune, "Hot Time in the Old Town Tonight." Dave grinned, then became soberly reflective.

Things hadn't changed any. The little community he had

loved and left may have hung gold stars in some of its windows but the same people were doing the same things in the same old way, and thinking mostly the same thoughts as the day he departed Hidden Valley, now over two years ago. But, if the community hadn't changed, Dave knew that *he* had. That High School song had moved him deeply before he had gotten out into the world and seen and experienced what it was really like.

. . . We will think of days we've spent here
As the best we've ever known. . . .

"That's wrong," Dave thought to himself. "That's looking backward and nobody can do that today—young or old. We've got to look ahead. There wouldn't be anything to live for if we really believed that our days spent in High School were the best we'd ever know!"

They were entering the Town Square and there was the old stone Court House bedecked in flags and bunting. The little portable platform, too, which was rolled into place on the ground near the Court House steps for political rallies and special events like this. Backless wooden benches, seating about a thousand, were set up on the lawn and extended across the roped off gravel highway. These seats were filling rapidly as paraders broke ranks and sought out places of vantage.

The merchants of the town had decorated, too, and Jed Peters, town printer, had been enterprising enough to print up a "Welcome Home" card with Dave's picture in uniform upon it, taken from a snapshot he had sent his mother, just after his first B-29 bombing mission over Berlin. These cards were in every window and some had been nailed to the front of the platform, draped in red, white and blue. Hidden Valley had certainly done itself proud in paying tribute to a local son. Dave's eyes grew misty.

Walking along behind the limousine, carrying his own suitcase, Hidden Valley's new arrival took note of all that was happening. The girl beside him did not appear too happy to be in his company and was staying with him more through a feeling of compulsion than desire.

"You look like I'd spoiled your day," he said to her as they reached the Square. "This isn't any shindig of mine. I didn't even ask to come here. If you'll tell me how to get out to your place, I'll beat it on ahead and you can go with your gang. You say your Dad's out there. He's the one I'm supposed to see, anyhow!"

Sue Kendall's face was troubled. It was not an unattractive face but there were lines of care in it beyond her years. She had black hair, glossy, wild and almost untamed. Her eyes of greenish hue, were striking in their intensity. Her body, though well proportioned, was seriously underweight, as if overworked or undernourished, or both.

"We don't have a car," she said, "and no one will be going out our way until after this program is over—and it's too far for you to walk—so you'll just have to wait."

"Okay!" accepted her unexpected companion, in none too agreeable a spirit. "But I can tell you right now, I'm not going to enjoy this any more than you are!"

They were moving down the sodded aisle toward a few seats which were left on the side. The strange youth kicked over his suitcase, sat down and put his feet on it. He took out a pack of cigarettes and extended it to Sue.

"Have one?" he offered.

"No, thanks," she said. "I don't smoke."

Roy Willard placed a cigarette between his own lips.

"Doesn't look like folks do much of anything out here," he observed.

Mayor Brannigan was mounting the platform, followed by Dave and his parents. A great cheer went up, accompanied by a burst of applause.

"How come all this fuss over one soldier boy?" demanded Roy. "There are men coming home by the thousands in Chicago and nobody turns out to meet 'em!"

"That's because it's Chicago," rejoined Sue, loyally. "There's too many people there. But everybody knows everyone else out

here—and Dave and his folks, well—they're sort of special.
Dave's one of the swellest fellows . . ."

"Yeah," said Roy. "A regular Mama's helper. You should have
seen the way he handled that squalling kid on the train. The
mother was going nuts until he came along and made up to her
little girl. She was calling him 'Daddy' in no time. He ought to
get a medal for *that!*"

Sue eyed this city fellow at her side. "You don't like people
much, do you?" she asked.

"I don't like 'em well enough to be a nursemaid for their
brats," said Roy. "If that's the way to be popular, count me out!"

The program was beginning. Herb Bevins, long, lanky editor
and publisher of the Hidden Valley News Weekly, was Master
of Ceremonies. He was Mayor Brannigan's righthand man in
affairs of this kind and could always be depended upon to
eulogize the town's leading citizen in appreciation of the generous
amount of advertising which the various Brannigan enterprises
regularly carried in his paper.

He now approached the loud speaker system and cleared his
voice in it to be sure the device was working before starting his
opening remarks.

"Can you hear me out there?" he coughed, looking in the
direction of Brannigan's General Store and a group of spectators
on the roof.

"Yes!" some blustering voice shouted back. "And it sounds
like you've got a bad cold!"

The crowd laughed.

"Fellow citizens of Hidden Valley and Rock County!"
addressed Editor Bevins. "We are gathered here, on this eventful
day in February of 1946, to welcome back from the Service of
his Country, one of our finest and most heroic young men. I'm
sure Dave Carson must be gladdened at sight of so many of his
home-town folks—the old familiar faces—friends and acquaint-
ances of a life-time—who are here to testify to their love and
admiration for him. But I am no silver-tongued orator. It is not
for me to pay tribute. There is only one man in Rock County

who has the power of expression to speak in our behalf and I will be calling on that gentleman soon to do Dave honor."

He nodded in the direction of Mayor Ed Brannigan who sat with arms folded across his expansive chest, gazing fixedly over the heads of the audience, looking off toward his home on the hill.

"But, first, I want to call upon three talented young ladies, who have been making quite a reputation for themselves in these parts, as a singing trio. I refer, of course, to Hidden Valley's version of the Andrews Sisters—the Hiltons—Carolyn, Eleanor and Doris!"

The three girls—golden-haired Carolyn; brown-haired Eleanor, and Doris, the red-head, ascended the steps to the platform, making a little curtsy to Dave as they did so. They then turned toward the audience, smiled, and sounded a chord between them.

"Should auld acquaintance be forgot
And never brought to mind?
Should auld acquaintance be forgot
And days of auld lang syne? . . ."

The harmony of the three voices brought cheers from the crowd at the finish and the girls encored with "The Atchison, Topeka and the Santa Fe", which brought their 'outdoor house' down.

Editor Bevins let the crowd subside and then said: "We should have opened this occasion with prayer but the Reverend Samuel Hascom, of the First Christian Church, was not here in time. He spent the night at the bedside of Noah Walters, whom you all know has been sick for some while. On the way in this morning, Reverend Hascom suffered an injury—to his *car*—and was delayed. He will now give the invocation . . ."

Reverend Hascom was a short, chubby, bald little man, jolly on most occasions. He had endeared himself to the peoples of all faiths in the County by his genuine service in the field. A murmur of sympathy had gone through the crowd, not so much at mention of Noah Walter's illness but at announcement of the accident to the Reverend's car. This was a tragedy everyone had in common, sooner or later, on the gravel and dirt roads of Rock County. They listened respectfully, although quietly amused, as Reverend Hascom thanked God Almighty for His manifold blessings. When he began to enumerate them, one by one, Mayor Ed Brannigan became extremely restive, glancing several times at his watch and then motioning to Editor Bevins who came tiptoeing across the platform, behind the minister.

"There's less than two minutes before we have to go on the air," he whispered. "And we've got only so much time. Can't you signal to him to cut it short?"

Editor Bevins shook his head, despairingly. "I can't," he said. "He always prays with his eyes closed!"

Mayor Brannigan ground an expensive set of uppers. "You shouldn't have called upon him at all," he said. "He's going to ruin this whole affair!"

When a clergyman's heart is overflowing with gratitude, despite his own personal afflictions, and he is confronted with an opportunity to pronounce a blessing at such an important function as this, he is seldom mindful of radio time, or *any* time, for that matter!

Mayor Brannigan tried a warning cough and waited expectantly. No result. Reverend Hascom had finished thanking God for the bounties bestowed upon Rock County and the State of Arkansas and was now calling upon the Creator to "guide and protect our great country." This meant that he still would refer to the ravaged nations of Europe and the deplorable conditions in the Far East, and only God and Reverend Hascom knew how long that would take!

Mayor Brannigan coughed again. He did more. He took out a metal case containing his glasses, removed the spectacles and dropped the case with a loud clatter on the platform. Reverend Hascom opened one eye and Mayor Brannigan caught it. The gesture he gave the good Reverend was unmistakable.

"For all other things, oh God, we thank Thee," concluded Reverend Hascom, and sat down.

He had already transgressed upon the radio time of station

KARK of Little Rock which was making a remote control pick-up of this special event of Hidden Valley. As soon as he had finished, the loud speaker system, hooked up around the Square, was cut in on the radio broadcast by the technician who had been sent to the town to handle all details.

"Your program's been announced!" he cried, yanking off his ear-phones. "Editor Bevens has been introduced. There's nothing but dead air. They're waiting for him to speak!"

Mayor Brannigan was on his feet, copy of speech in hand, gesturing to his Master of Ceremonies.

"Ladies and gentlemen!" he gulped. "I regret that time does not permit me to properly introduce our esteemed Mayor, who has done so much for the town of Hidden Valley. As our foremost citizen, he has been selected to make the address of welcome to the Country's greatest war hero. Without further ado, I give you now, the Honorable Edward F. Brannigan!"

This was the cue for applause and the audience supplied it. Mayor Brannigan smiled, bowed and slipped on his glasses.

"My good friends in Hidden Valley and Rock County," he began. "And all others within the reach of my voice. This is indeed a glorious and unforgettable moment in the history of our Community. We have gathered here today to welcome home a young man who left his parents' farm, two years ago, in answer to his Country's call.

"Dave Carson, son of Frank and Emma Carson, joined the Air Corps and went overseas as a Tail Gunner with a B-29 Crew, which took part in the final all-out assault upon Berlin.

"He participated in thirty-one raids over enemy territory, being credited with shooting down seventeen of their planes.

"On his last mission, the B-29 Bomber suffered a direct hit, two of its motors being shot away. With the pilot killed and the co-pilot mortally wounded, the big ship rapidly losing altitude and a constant target for anti-aircraft as well as pursuing attack planes, Tail Gunner Dave Carson crawled through the wreckage, lifted the dead pilot from his seat at the controls, and took over the flying of the crippled Bomber!

"Under direction of the wounded co-pilot, he brought the Bomber safely home, crash-landing it at its base in England! By this time he, himself, and all members of the Crew had received severe wounds.

"For this unparalleled act of heroism, Dave Carson was advanced in rank and awarded the Order of the Purple Heart, the Distinguished Service Cross, with Oak Leaves, and he has just stopped off in Washington, enroute home, to have bestowed upon him by the President of the United States, himself, the Congressional Medal of Honor.

"We here, at Hidden Valley, his home folks, wish to add our praise to the plaudits of a grateful and admiring world . . ."

Mayor Brannigan paused for breath and gave a nod to his visible audience in the Town Square. There was a tremendous burst of applause and loud cheers.

Dave, on the platform in the front row beside his parents, sat, head down, unmoving. He should have been accustomed to public acclaim by this time, having received so much of it from the press and the people of New York and Washington. But now, he realized it was hardest of all to take in a community where he was known. Somehow these tributes, however well-intentioned, seemed like so many words strung together, signifying nothing of value beyond the passing moment.

Dave hadn't wanted this but he couldn't help himself. He didn't feel like a hero—he never had. He had just done what any one of thousands of American fellows would have done in a like spot. And, if given his choice, he would have preferred to have slipped quietly into town and disappeared into the bosom of his family and close friends for a few days, forgetting that he'd ever been to war.

"I tell you, Dave Carson," said Mayor Brannigan, looking up from the reading of his speech to address him personally, "There is nothing in Rock County too good for you. We can't do enough for our returning Service men and especially for those who, like yourself, have brought such honor to our beloved community.

And now . . .!" He cleared his throat and looked toward the back of the platform, motioning to Editor Bevins who was awaiting his cue. "And now . . ." he began again into the microphone, "As a little token of the love and respect that the citizens of Hidden Valley and Rock County hold for you, and so you may always remember the occasion of your home-coming, we are proud to present to you this gift of a handsome combination phonograph and radio set, equipped for battery and electricity, with the choice of twenty-five records . . ."

Mayor Brannigan looked back over his shoulder at Editor Bevins and two of his own employees from the General Store who were carrying the truly beautiful console on stage. They set it down in front of the dais containing the microphone and speaking stand, so that all in the audience could see. There was a loud murmur of admiration and applause.

Mayor Brannigan beamed. "Well, Dave," he said, in a tone of great cordiality, "the time has come for *you* to say something. We want to hear the story of your great experiences from your own lips. You are back in your own country, my boy, where you can speak freely of what is in your mind and heart . . ." He gave a majestic wave of his arm. "These are your home folks. Ladies and gentlemen of Hidden Valley and Rock County and the listening audience, you are now to hear direct from Dave Carson, our hero and the nation's hero . . . Lieutenant Carson!"

Mayor Brannigan had played his role well. He stepped back from the microphone, joining in the standing applause as every man, woman and child was on his feet cheering Dave.

The returned war hero lifted his head and glanced for a moment at his father and mother sitting beside him. Mrs. Carson reached over and patted her boy's hand. Dave rose slowly to his feet. As he turned toward the microphone, he saw Carolyn seated on the back row of the platform, with her sisters. She guardedly blew him a kiss. The din of the ovation was continuing as Mayor Brannigan stepped down and extended his hand.

"It's all yours, my boy," he said. "The world's waiting to hear from you."

The muscles in Dave's face were twitching. He forced a smile and stepped up on the dais as Mayor Brannigan returned to his seat on the front row of the platform and leaned over, patronizingly, to offer another word of congratulation to the Carsons.

A hush suddenly fell over the Town Square. Dave was standing quietly behind the microphones, a stalwart figure, appealing in his mature boyishness, obviously struggling to control his emotions and not yet daring to trust his voice.

He had given no thought as to what he might say when called upon. In the vastly greater communities of New York and Washington, where he had been feted by the best these cities had to offer, Dave had modestly confined himself to brief expressions of appreciation. But here it was different. Perhaps, as Mayor Brannigan had suggested, he could *really* let the home folks know how he felt about some things. Perhaps he could find words, on an occasion such as this, to speak—not so much for himself as for all boys who had left their homes in farm and city and gone off to war, and who now were returning hopeful of the opportunity to help make a better world and to establish homes for themselves.

Dave wet his lips and tried to still the palpitation in his throat. He gripped the sides of the little table and leaned toward the microphones.

"Thank you, Mayor Brannigan, for the nice things you had to say about me—and thank you, everybody, for the gift of this wonderful combination set." He paused and drew a deep breath, shaking his head. "But you didn't need to do this for me. I know the spirit in which it was meant but I didn't go off to fight for my country to win a radio or get prizes for killing people, when I came home."

A sharp gasp of surprise and shock went through the audience and Mayor Brannigan half rose from his chair. Even Mr. and Mrs. Carson exchanged startled, questioning glances.

"I did the best I could," Dave continued, "as any other real American in my place would have done. Only I'm lots luckier than a great many of them who didn't come back and who didn't live to enjoy any gift like this." He gestured toward the console in front of him. "Mayor Brannigan has asked me to tell you the story of my experiences. You'll have to excuse me on that. You've read enough about me and what happened in the papers, anyhow.

"I just dreamed of getting back home and trying to think this was all a nightmare and that we never had a war and that I could take up right where I left off and just enjoy living out here in these wonderful hills, in God's country."

There was a deathly silence over the Town Square, broken only by a fretful baby's cry on the outer fringe of the crowd. Mayor Brannigan had folded his arms and was staring straight ahead into space.

"*That* was my dream," Dave went on. "But I know, now, that it can never work out. I have seen too much. I have seen what war did to Europe . . . I've seen the farm lands in Italy . . . and France . . . and the Netherlands . . . and in Germany. I've seen the poor farmers there, their cattle all slaughtered or carried off, their lands inundated with floods, their barns and homes blown to pieces, their families scattered or killed.

"That's not a nightmare, folks. That's a *reality*. And *I* had to help destroy some of those people and their lands so we could chase the Germans back to their own country and lick Hitler and finally win this war.

"But it'll be some years before thousands of these farmers can raise good crops or cattle again, or get back their spirit, if that's ever possible. *That's* what I see when I go to bed nights. *That's* why I can't take much credit for what I've done.

"We've got to help those people, somehow. We've got to help the whole world. I just don't know how right now but I won't sleep well till I find a way. Because, if we *don't* find a way— there's going to be another war and it won't be too long in coming! Humans just can't stand such misery and hunger without any hope for the future.

"You folks in the hills know what I mean when a cloudburst

or a freeze or a drought wipes out your crops—or a disease takes your cattle and chickens. But you always know you can manage to get through, somehow, and next year things will be different.

"That's not true, today, in lots of countries of the world. You don't hear much about this yet because it doesn't make pleasant conversation, but I . . . !"

Mayor Brannigan stood up, pointing to his watch and motioning at Hidden Valley's hero.

"I guess my time is running out," said Dave. "I'm sorry, folks, if I've sort of put a damper on this 'welcome home party' you've planned for me—but if you really want to know what's in my mind and heart, that's it! . . . Here's Mayor Brannigan. I think he'd like to say something. Thank you!"

Dave stepped down from the dais and Mayor Brannigan passed him without speaking. There was only scattered applause as stunned townspeople focused their attention upon Hidden Valley's foremost citizen and what he might have to say to this unexpected, impassioned outburst. Dave slid quietly into his chair beside his father and mother who appeared at a loss as to how to conduct themselves.

"Well, folks," said Mayor Brannigan. "You've just heard from our war hero, Dave Carson. From what he had to say, it appears he went away a boy and came back a *man.* We can understand how he feels but neither he, nor all of us, can solve the problems of the world. We'll do well to solve all the problems of this very community. If Dave *really* wants something to do along that line, he can start right here at *home!* I could say more—but time will not permit."

He had scarcely finished than the allotted time for this "special event" expired and their program was cut off the air. The crowd applauded and stood up as the High School Band struck up "The Star Spangled Banner".

"Don't go away, folks," shouted Mayor Brannigan, at its conclusion. "Come up and meet Dave. We're serving coffee and doughnuts just inside the Court House. Form in line and get something warm. It's getting right snappy out here!"

Chapter II

THE INFORMAL RECEPTION for Hidden Valley's returned war hero was held in the Court Room. It ordinarily seated two hundred people but the benches had been cleared out to make room for all those who wanted to crowd in to shake Dave's hand.

There were young and old in line and babes-in-arms. People in Rock County who had "knowed" his folks long before he was born. Quiet, hard-working, God-fearing humans from the back hill country, who had wrestled with Nature and stony soil and native ignorance of modern farm methods in the raising of their crops and livestock. But they loved their wild picturesque surroundings, the great over hanging cliffs, the gushing springs of sparkling, clear water; the untamed wilderness of flower and bush, the whispering friendliness of stately pines, the constant symphony of bird and animal sounds, the sun's rising and settings, and the moist, fragrant fertility of their rich lands.

They used to say of this soil that you could drop a kernel of corn and turn your back and up would spring a corn stalk seven feet high!

Every kind of flower and plant and shrub and tree seemed to grow and thrive in Arkansas. Thrive, that is, until its planters wore out the soil and then, not knowing how to rotate their crops, had moved on to other land, despoiling it the same way. They just hadn't realized what they were doing and many didn't comprehend it yet. But farmers like Dave Carson's father did and had been doing something about it.

"Good to see you back, Dave," these home people said, as their calloused hands gripped his. "Glad you made it all right—*my* boy didn't get back . . ."

"That colt you used to ride? . . . He done broke his leg an' we had to shoot him!"

"We got a new barn since you left—built of timber right off our place . . ."

19

"Remember old man Rose? He shot himself over Widow Brenner . . . No, she ain't married yit . . . Says no man's gonna git a share of her holdin's no more!"

"Good huntin' on my place, Dave—but I guess you won't want to be usin' your gun fer a spell . . ."

"I'm in the Second Grade, and I can count to ten an' spell my own name back'ards. Yes'n I kin pull a pail o' water, too!"

"Me? Oh, I'm doin' all right. Stepped up production while you were gone. My hound dog had a litter of pups, half collie; our cat had kittens, half bob-cat; an' my wife had twins—*all mine!*"

"Are you comin' to the Square Dance Saturday night at Kelly's Corners? They got the hottest old-time fiddler—worth walkin' ten mile to hear him play 'Turkey-in-the-Straw' . . . !"

"No, Dave—Billy Pierce ain't here no more. He up an' left with his folks. They bought themselves an Eighty in Texas an' are takin' to raisin' cotton."

"Bet this town'll seem pretty slow to you after all the places you've been!"

"So long, Dave—we'll be seein' you around!"

At the end of the long line of greeters and well-wishers, a small group had been patiently waiting. It was comprised of the Hilton sisters, Sue Kendall and the new Hidden Valley arrival, Roy Willard. He had been introduced to the three girls by Sue and was seated now on his upended suitcase, smoking an ever-present cigarette.

"You say you come from Chicago?" Carolyn was asking.

"Yeah—that's my home town," said Roy.

"And that's one place I've always wanted to go," said Eleanor. "I don't expect I'll ever make it, though. No one in our family's ever been to a big city except Dad and *he* says he never wants to go again!"

Roy blew out a cloud of smoke and aimed his cigarette at an old brass cuspidor along a spattered wall.

"First time I've ever seen one of those things," he said. "Hit it the first time, too. That's pretty good." He looked up at Eleanor, who was eyeing him curiously, frankly fascinated by what, to her, passed for sophistication. *"You'd* like it in a big city," he added. *"All* you girls would. And the way you sing, you could get somewhere."

"Do you really think so?" asked Carolyn, pleased.

"I *know* so," said Roy, positively. "I've heard the best in the business. If I had you girls in Chicago right now, I'd introduce you to a booking agent friend of mine and I'll bet he'd have you on the stage and radio in no time!"

The three Hilton sisters looked at one another.

"Oh, I don't think we're *that* good," said Doris, the youngest of the trio, doubtfully.

Roy nodded. "You'd need more training, of course—and experience. But I'm telling you—you've got what it takes. If you girls hang around this town much longer, you're crazy!"

"But we just sing because we enjoy it," said Carolyn. "We've never even thought of being *professionals!"*

Roy shrugged his shoulders. "Okay! It doesn't mean anything to me. But maybe ten years from now, when it's too late, you'll wish you'd done something with your talents. I don't see enough in Hidden Valley to keep me here over night if I didn't *have* to stay here for awhile."

He gave a sidewise glance at Sue Kendall, whose cheeks were flaming.

"Roy—I mean, Mr. Willard's come here to help out on the farm," she explained. "His father and my Daddy were boyhood friends in Tennessee but Mr. Willard's folks moved to Chicago and Daddy got married and came here. But since mother's died and he's got so crippled up with arthritis—and I've had all the work to do on the place—he's been thinking for some time, it's too much . . . And so, when Mr. Willard wrote and asked Daddy if he could arrange for Roy to stay with us for awhile . . ."

"Skip it!" said Roy, cutting in. "Who cares about all those details? I've been shipped down here and I suppose I've got to make the best of it. But this isn't my kind of life any more than living in a big city is yours—so don't expect me to like it!"

The bluntness of Roy's comments made the girls feel almost as though they should apologize for their town and county. They had never experienced such open disdain for a community they had been brought up to love and respect. Each began to wonder if she had not over-rated the region in which she lived. A big city, admittedly, held so many advantages, conveniences and opportunities of different kinds, as well as wonderful entertainments which could never be enjoyed up here in the hills.

"We'll keep practicing," said Carolyn, after an awkward pause. "Maybe, some day, we'll get to Chicago—or even New York. Who knows?"

Sue, noting that Dave was at last free from hand-shakers and hangers-on, touched Roy's arm. "We can see him now," she said.

Roy took up his suitcase as the little group moved forward. Dave, seeing them approaching, advanced smiling to meet them.

"Well," he greeted, face perspiring. "I'm glad *that's* over! How are you all? . . . Sue—I meant to ask about Tom. Are you two married yet?"

Sue shook her head and tears rimmed her eyes. "No," she said. "We're not even engaged now. Tom said, for me to be caring for *one* cripple was enough . . ."

Dave regarded her, soberly. "Why, I hoped Tom would be all right by this time. I missed him here today. You mean to say he's still not up and around?"

"He's never walked since the infantile paralysis hit him," reported Sue.

Dave glanced at the stranger to Hidden Valley who was standing by, with an attitude of disinterest.

"Tom Dodds is one of my best friends," he explained. "We were figuring on entering the Service together. He was nuts about aviation. Made model airplanes—and flew them, too! But the day we were going to enlist, Tom took down sick. I had to leave and I didn't find out, till later, what he had."

"Pretty tough break," said Roy. "Can't tell, though—if he had gone to war, he might have been killed."

Sue's eyes flashed. "He'd *rather* have been killed, or even crippled—just so it was fighting for his country! . . . But he can't see any reason for being stricken like he was—no good to himself . . . or—or anybody!"

"That's life," said Roy, with an air of superior wisdom. "Some folks get all the good breaks . . ." He looked at Dave. "If I were *you*—I'd begin to worry about my luck running out!"

Dave nodded. "I know, it usually balances up, sooner or later." Then, turning to Sue, "I'm sure sorry to hear this about Tom. I'll have to drop in on him on the way out. Are his folks in town?"

"No," said Sue. "They stayed out with him. They told me this morning he was too depressed to be left alone."

"Tom won't go anywhere and he doesn't want to see anybody," volunteered Carolyn. "He's really a case, Dave. He may not even want to see *you*."

"He'll see me," said Hidden Valley's returned war hero, "or I'll know the reason why!"

Frank and Emma Carson edged toward their boy. The reception was all but over. Folks in from the County were now thinking about doing their shopping and getting back home. There wasn't much to keep them in Hidden Valley aside from trading—no picture theatre or bowling alley or social center. No place for one to meet friends, except on street corners or at Wade's Bar and Pool Room, which wasn't any place for a lady. The merchants all said, "Hurry back, please!" but, unless there was an auction being held in the Town Square, with bargains in second-hand furniture, or a barker, with a smooth tongue, selling four pair of women's stockings for a dollar—sight unseen —and throwing in some wisecracks with each sale, most of the farmers made their purchases and "hurried back" *home*.

"You about ready to leave, dear?" asked Emma Carson, taking Dave's arm.

Dave smiled and squeezed her hand. "Yes, Mom—guess I am. It'll certainly seem good to get on our place again!"

"It'll be grand to have you there," said his mother.

Dave glanced at Carolyn. "I hope to be seeing you soon," he said.

"Me, too!" she replied, and blushed.

"I sure enjoyed hearing you girls sing," Dave complimented. "Almost forgot to tell you—there's been so much going on around here."

The three Hilton sisters laughed and started to move away, but Sue Kendall stepped forward.

"Oh, Dave," she requested. "I'd like to ask a big favor. I was going out with the Durfees but they only had room for one. Could you and your folks give Mr. Willard and me a lift?"

"You bet we can!" spoke up Frank Carson. "Our car's parked over by Petander's Grocery. You young folks can have the back seat to yourselves."

Sue's face registered great relief. "Thanks an awful lot. I hated to trouble you a day like this but . . ."

"Think nothing of it," admonished Dave. "I want to find out some more about Tom, anyway. Say, Mr. Willard, how about letting me carry your bag for you? My stuff's already in the car."

"It's not heavy," refused Roy. "I'm traveling pretty light. Don't expect to stay too long."

They were walking now across the Town Square. As they passed Brannigan's General Store, the Mayor, himself, was standing talking with County Judge George Middleton, who was often twitted for his "weighty decisions" since he, for years, had been just under three hundred pounds.

"Hello, Dave!" called the Judge. "I couldn't navigate through that crowd to shake your hand so I'll do it now. I was just discussing your speech with the Mayor, here. You certainly got some things off your chest!"

"Yes," said Dave, slowly. "I'm not so sure now that I said the right thing."

"Well, don't let it worry you," laughed the Judge. "The public doesn't remember what a speaker says over night. If it did, they could hang a lot of politicians!"

Dave looked past the Judge at Mayor Brannigan. "I hope you

don't think I didn't appreciate all you and everybody have done for me," he half apologized. "This has really been swell!"

Mayor Brannigan made a strange sound in his throat. "Well, you had me wondering for a bit," he replied. "I've had my men put the phonograph and radio set in the trunk compartment of your father's car. We couldn't get it closed but if you'll drive carefully over those roads, I guess you'll make it all right."

"Many thanks, Ed," said Frank Carson. "That machine's going to give my boy a lot of pleasure—the rest of us, too!"

"Yes," added Emma Carson, helpfully, "We haven't had a phonograph since the old Victor gave out."

"That so?" said the Mayor, "something must have been wrong with our sales department! . . . Well—you've got one now and it hasn't cost you a cent! I've put in about half a hundred records. You can pick out twenty-five and bring the rest back." He held out his hand to Hidden Valley's returned war hero. "Dave, my boy—when you're in town one of these days, drop in and see me. Do you know what you're going to do yet?"

"No," said Dave, as he shook the hand of the town's foremost citizen. "I haven't thought ahead that far. All I've been able to think about was getting back on the place, in my own clothes and my own bed. But I reckon I'll just stay on the farm and help Dad get in the spring planting and take care of his live-stock—if he still wants me."

Dave felt a strong, warm hand on his shoulder.

"That's what I was hoping I'd hear you say," Frank Carson said, softly.

Tom Dodds had his bed by the upstairs window in his room which overlooked the Stony Creek Road and the sharp, rising turn-off at the end of his parents' property which led to the old Kendall place, Eighty Acres, a half mile back in the hills. Cars or trucks seldom ventured up this road and, since the Kendalls had no automobile of their own, and Matt Kendall was bed-ridden anyway, his dark-haired daughter was usually the only one seen on it.

She always traveled by foot, either catching the school bus or riding to town, six miles, with the mail truck. Sol Egbert, the mail carrier, would often bring supplies to save Sue a trip into Hidden Valley, and leave them by her mailbox on the Stony Creek Route.

In years past, Tom had hiked up the Kendall road, many times, transporting supplies and staying to romance with Sue. They had made a striking appearing couple and everyone in the County who knew them, called it an *ideal match*.

They sympathized with courageous, uncomplaining Sue Kendall who, since the age of eleven, upon the death of her mother, had managed to do the farm chores, to milk the cow, to care for the chickens and goats, to collect the firewood, to go to school and to look after a father who had wasted away with arthritis until he could no longer walk.

The Kendalls were as poor as their land and Old Matt as unyielding in his ways as the stones on his place. But there was something in that daughter of his that everyone liked—and especially the young fellow on the adjoining Eighty who had asked her to marry him and had promised to make a home for her invalid parent.

That was two years ago. Tom Dodds had relived it, time and time again in his mind, as he had looked out the window and glimpsed the figure of the girl he had loved, coming and going on her solitary missions.

On occasion, as the impulse struck him, Tom would unlock a drawer in his desk and take out a little house plan that he and Sue had drawn up together. The lumber, the doors, the window sashes, the cross beams, the roofing, the siding, the stones, the cement—everything they needed to build it had been bought and delivered and was still stored in his father's barn.

They had been going to erect their dream house in the pine grove on the cliff above Stony Creek where the Kendalls' line bordered the Dodds'. It mattered not that Sue was only turned sixteen and Tom but a year older. Sue was far advanced for her years and sandy-haired, blue-eyed, broad-shouldered Tom was already recognized as one of the brightest young men in the County.

"He'll get along," experienced farmers said, when they saw the corn he was raising and his herd of hogs.

So the idea of an early marriage for these two young people was smiled upon by the community. It seemed a happy solution for the body and soul-crushing burden Sue had been carrying.

It didn't do any good to relive these moments because they always ended in futility. Why he, a healthy young man, who asked nothing of God or his neighbors but the opportunity to work hard and make a place for himself in the world, should have been struck down and left an invalid, just as helpless in his way as Matt Kendall, was a question for which there was no human answer.

It wouldn't have been so bad if what happened to him had not all but wrecked another life, too. He could never forget how Sue had clung to him, insisting that they be married anyway and that she'd somehow care for both her father and himself. But, of course,—this just wasn't possible. An able-bodied man was needed on the Kendall place—a man who could lift Sue's burden from her and bring her the happiness and release from ceaseless toil and devotion which she had so richly earned.

Tom had never once doubted the decision he had made when he knew his emaciated body would be crippled for life. He must free Sue from her promise, she would have to learn to forget him so that she might develop a new heart interest elsewhere.

He still carried in his wallet their much folded and worn marriage license, issued to them three days before he had intended to enlist. If accepted for the Service, they had planned to be married and have their honeymoon on the farm for the ten days before he would be called. The building of their home would have to wait until his return from the Service but they would have the joy of knowing that they belonged to each other and both would be buoyed by their dream of the future together.

Dave Carson, his bosom pal, was to be best man and Carolyn

Hilton, bridesmaid. Swell kids, these two, and sweet on each other. But they weren't ready to marry yet. They'd probably go to college first, that is, if the war didn't last too long, and if Dave got back. Tom remembered how he'd good-naturedly argued with Dave and Carolyn, since Dave was enlisting with him, to try to get them to make it a double wedding. But, no soap. They thought it was wisest to wait. That was their decision and they were sticking to it.

If this hadn't chanced to be the day of Dave's home-coming, Tom might not have tortured himself with these bitter recollections. His parents had offered to carry him to the car and drive him to town so he could join in the welcome to Dave but Tom, who had not permitted himself to be taken from the house since he had been brought back from the Little Rock Hospital, had refused.

"Dave won't want to be messing with me," he told them. "If this hadn't happened, perhaps *I'd* have been coming home today, too. Dave and me together. We always did things together up till then. No, I'd be a load around anyone's neck, the way I am. It's hard enough to sit here and think about the burden I am to you folks but it's worse to have to face it, that I'll never be any better. Sometimes it seems I just can't stand it another day. Sometimes I feel you'd be better off if I . . . !"

When moods of depression and melancholy hit Tom like this, Dad and Mother Dodds were afraid to leave him long alone. They had tried every way they knew to help lift his chronic despondency, to no avail. Today, however, their son's spirits had hit a new low.

"Unless he gets some new interest in life," Fred Dodds said to Anna, his wife, "We're not going to have our boy much longer. I confess, I'm rather at my wits' end and we've about exhausted our resources on doctors' bills. I haven't wanted to tell you this but Ed Brannigan refused to renew my mortgage at the bank. Said he was sorry but I'd have to pay up when it came due. I was hoping he'd even let us have a little more money on the place. Right now, dear, I don't know where we're coming out at."

Mrs. Dodds shook her head, despairingly. "If there's ever an answer to prayer, we should get it pretty soon," she said.

There was the sound of a car on the road. This didn't happen too often at any time of the day or night, for the hills up Stony Creek way were not densely populated.

Farming in this mountain country was just plain hard work. It had its compensations for those who loved unrivalled scenery, unequalled drinking water and unsurpassed fresh air. But they paid for this in back-breaking toil, willingly given, to make the rocky soil yield a living. However, only mountain goats and those accustomed to driving in this region, could negotiate most of the roads cut through to their places.

Even the Stony Creek Route, a county highway, was next to impassable after heavy rains, with yawning washouts which could swallow up a car without warning, or landslides of rock, massive enough to crush it or block its path.

This gravel road, in good condition, was so full of ruts and so filled with sharp stones as to chew up a tire in a few months' time. In dry weather, you could see a cloud of dust approaching long before you could see the car. If you were a stranger to these parts and didn't close all windows on passing, you would grind Arkansas sand between your teeth and shake it from your hair and clothes for hours afterward. The hills, themselves, were so steep and so long that the sounds of cars groaning and straining as they climbed could be heard echoing through the valleys, for miles. From this it can be seen that a trip into town and back, even for the natives, was always a thrill and an adventure!

"Folks probably going home from Dave's celebration," said Mrs. Dodds, stepping out on the front porch.

"It's Frank Carson's car," recognized Fred Dodds. "It's got one cylinder that hasn't been hitting. I can't understand why he hasn't had it fixed."

"My, I'll bet the Carsons are happy!" said his wife. "This has been a big day for them." She stepped inside the front door and called upstairs: "Oh, Tom! The Carsons are just going past! Do you see them?"

"I don't want to see them!" Tom flung back. "Don't want to see anybody!"

Mrs. Dodds wearily returned to the porch. Her husband pointed.

"They're stopping down by the Kendalls' road," he reported. "There's some young fellow getting out with a suitcase. Wonder who *he* is . . . ? There's Sue . . . and there's *Dave* . . . ! They're looking up this way!"

"They're waving at us!" cried Mrs. Dodds, and lifted her arm in greeting.

The Dodds house was set back on a rise, about an eighth of a mile from the highway. It had its own special drive which wound around through a little grove of cedars to a levelled off place in front of their home. The Kendalls' road was on beyond their drive-in, some three hundred yards. Its juncture with the Stony Creek Route was plainly visible, especially this time of year.

"Tom!" called his mother. "You *must* look out! There's some strange young man starting up the hill with Sue. Dave's coming this way. I think he's running up to see you!"

There was no answer from upstairs but the creak of bed springs indicated that Tom was changing his position.

"I won't stay long," Dave assured his parents as he started toward the Dodds' home. "Goodbye, Sue . . . So long, Mr. Willard . . . Hope you get to liking it better out here. I'll be seeing you both around!"

Frank and Emma Carson sat in their car and watched their handsome-figured son stride easily up the road and turn in to the Dodds'.

"He's a wonderful boy," said Frank, huskily. "That's the best thing we ever produced on our farm."

Emma rested her head against her husband's windbreaker. "And he's so thoughtful," she said. "I know he's just dying to get home and yet he's still taking time to say 'Hello' to Tom."

Frank Carson knuckled a tear from the corner of his eye.

"Remember, Mother, how we thought maybe Dodds' son was lucky to have been taken ill so he wouldn't have to risk his life by going to war?"

She nodded, unspeaking.

"Well, there he lies up there, unable to ever walk again, and there goes *our* boy, back home safe after all he's been through. I tell you, Mother, there're some things in this life you just can't understand. The Dodds are God-fearing, God-loving people, just like us . . . and here our cup is full and running over . . ." He lowered his head and offered a silent prayer of thanksgiving.

Emma touched his arm and gently shook him. "Look, Frank . . . look at there . . . !"

Their boy had reached the Dodds' porch and Mrs. Dodds had opened her arms and hugged him to her as though he were her own son. Tom's father had Dave by the hand and soon they could see that something Dave had said had them both laughing. They went in the house together, Mrs. Dodds with a handkerchief to her eyes, and the Carsons could faintly hear her calling: "Tom, Dave's here! He's coming up to see you!"

Dave had his hand on the stair post and a foot on the first step. He was being restrained by Tom's mother who whispered: "He's all changed, Dave, so don't expect to see the same Tom. I don't know whether he'll even talk to you. He won't let us bring anyone to the house any more. Says the sooner everybody forgets him—that he's even alive—the better!"

Dave nodded and patted Mrs. Dodds reassuringly on the shoulder. "Let me tackle him in my own way," he said.

The Dodds looked at one another, resignedly. Dave went up the stairs. He stopped outside Tom's door and knocked on it.

"Hi, Tom," he called.

"Stay out!" cried a voice.

Dave pushed the half-closed door open. Propped against the pillows in a bed near the window was the fellow he had used to pal around with. Both had been fine physical specimens two years ago and Dave, today, was even more so. They were the same age, with birthdays only a month apart. Dave had been nineteen in January and Tom's birthday was coming up this month, either the twenty-third or twenty-fourth ... which was it?

As Dave looked at Tom he steeled himself against the betrayal of shock. Tom wasn't much more than a lanky frame of skin and bones. His legs, with knees drawn up, even hidden beneath the coverlet, revealed their gaunt outlines. Tom's cheekbones were prominent and his blue eyes, now intense and seething with rebellion and resentment, were deep in their sockets. As Dave stood in the doorway, smiling his old smile of greeting, Tom feelingly repeated: "I told you to *stay out!*"

"I didn't hear you," grinned Dave, and walked in. He crossed to the bed and put out his hand but Tom withdrew his bony fingers and thrust his thin arm under the covers.

Dave looked down at him. "Okay," he said. "This is a break for me. I've only shaken hands with a couple thousand people today. You're very considerate."

Tom scowled. "I told Mother not to let you come up!" he said. "I'm not seeing anybody. Now will you please *get out of here?*"

Dave pulled up a chair and sat down.

"Oh, no! You don't get rid of an old pal *that* easy! Who are you trying to fight—the world? *I* didn't cause what happened to you—so don't take it out on me. I thought you'd be up and around by this time. What're you lying there in bed for?"

Tom stared at Dave in shocked astonishment, then hurled back the covers with an angry gesture. His body, pitifully depleted from the hips down, was exposed.

"Well, *what of it?*" fired Dave. "I've seen some of my buddies without any legs at all—or arms, either! They've *really* got something to gripe about! You can still move those arms and legs, can't you? They're still attached to your body. You'd better get over feeling sorry for yourself and start doing something about it!"

Tom made fists of his bony fingers and beat on the sides of his bed. "Get out of here!" he screamed.

"Not till I finish what I'm going to say," defied Dave. "I've had a lot of respect for you, Tom. I couldn't have thought more of you than if you'd been my brother—but I've just ridden up here with Sue and she's told me about you—how you've been acting—how you've broken off your engagement –how. you won't even see her or anybody else, any more. I've found out one thing since I've been to war—you've got to learn to *take* it in this life . . . !"

Tom had stiffened. He was sitting upright, supporting himself with a great effort, eyes burning with indignation. "I won't hear any more!" he shouted. "Shut up! Go away! Let me alone!"

"You're *yellow!*" accused Dave. "Those germs didn't affect your spine, did they? You've still got your *backbone!* A fine soldier *you'd* have made. It's a good thing you *had* to stay home. We'd never have licked Hitler with guys like you on the firing line!"

There was an emotional explosion inside of Tom and he burst into great wracking sobs. Dave sat quietly, watching him. He could hear Mrs. Dodds tiptoeing, nervously, in the hall. She finally looked in, anxiously, and Dave motioned her out. Tom's sobs came from deep down in his body, as though they had been pent-up there, for a long time. He cried himself to exhaustion and sank back against the pillows.

When he was through, he reached out a tear-moistened hand toward the returned war hero of Hidden Valley.

"Thanks, Dave," he whispered. "I needed that. It's done something to me. Come and see me again. I'll try to treat you more decent—next time."

Roy Willard shifted his suitcase from one hand to the other.

"It's more of a climb up this hill than it looks," he said to Sue. "Or else this bag is heavier than I thought!"

Sue smiled. They were nearing the top of the Kendalls' hill which commanded a picturesque view of the countryside in all directions. She had been observing this young fellow from the city, closely. He had started out so jauntily as though this half mile walk over rough, rocky ground would be nothing at all. She now noted that he was growing increasingly short of breath but was doggedly trying to continue.

"Would you like to put your suitcase down and rest a moment?" she asked.

"Naw!" declined Roy, scornfully. "How much further is it?"

"Only a quarter of a mile," said Sue.

"We've gone about a *mile* already," said Roy, giving her a side-wise glance. "Or are the miles in Arkansas longer than other States?"

Sue almost laughed aloud but she replied, politely: "No, they just *seem* longer."

The air was chilly but Roy was not. This was more exertion than he had put forth since he played on the school althletic teams. But he'd be hanged if he'd let a mere girl show him up when it came to a little cross-country hike like this! He shifted the suitcase to the other hand again and continued on.

"Why didn't you folks ever get a car?" he asked, after a moment.

"Couldn't afford it," was Sue's short answer.

"Then why didn't you move?" said Roy.

"Couldn't afford that, either," Sue replied.

"What have you got up here on this hill?" demanded Roy, "*Diamonds?*"

Sue was amused. "No," she said, "Just an old place that we love. It's pretty run down," she added, apologetically. "Gone to *wrack and ruin,* as some folks would say, but I just haven't been able to keep it up. The fences are down or rotting away, the barn's in better condition than the house, and about everything needs fixing."

Roy shifted the suitcase once more and then, feeling a blister on the palm of his right hand, gave up and put the bag down, sitting on it.

"All right!" he snapped. "*You* win! I'll take city living for mine. This hill is a killer. I don't know a Boy Scout in America who could stand it." He slid over to one end of his suitcase.

"Here," he invited, "Aren't you tired? Don't you want to sit down, too?"

Sue did laugh outright this time. "This isn't so bad," she reassured, "once you get used to it!"

Roy grimaced and rubbed the calves of his legs. "There are some things in this life I don't *want* to get used to," he said, "and this is *one* of them!"

Sue was standing in the roadway, looking back over the route they had come. Far below could be seen the Dodds' house. It would not be so visible when the trees leafed out in another two months or so but, now, the woods were barren and bleak and a grayish-blue haze hung in the distance.

Roy, following her gaze, asked curiously: "It's none of my business, but when Dave Carson asked you, in the car, to go with him to see your old boy friend, why didn't you do it?"

Sue didn't answer for a moment. She just stood, still gazing in the same direction. "There's an old saying," she finally replied, " 'When a flame dies out, it never burns again.' "

Roy eyed her, thoughtfully. "I get it," he said. "You mean, you can't rekindle an old flame. Well, I never worry about that, I just go out and strike me a new one!"

Sue faced about. "Are you rested now?" she asked. "We're almost there. You'll see our place, such as it is, just around the bend."

Roy arose and lifted his suitcase. Then he set it down again.

"Wait a moment!" he said. "There's something I want to know. Just what kind of a guy is your old man?"

Sue hesitated, her face coloring. "What a question! . . . I don't know how to answer that."

"I mean," explained Roy, "is he soft or hard-boiled? Is he strict or easy-going? Does he lay it on the line or beat around the bush? I want to know what he's going to expect of me!"

Sue shook her head, uncertainly. "Daddy doesn't say very much. He hasn't discussed you with me. He just said he'd received a letter from your father, asking permission to send you down here to stay with us, if we could make a place for you—and promising that you would work for your board and keep."

Roy walked around in a circle and kicked at the ground with

his feet. It was hard and half-frozen and he hurt a toe.

"That's pretty sweet!" he blurted, with feeling. "A nice little railroading job!" He shot Sue a questioning glance. "You know what I *really* am, don't you?"

Sue's eyes met his, unfalteringly. "Daddy said you'd been in jail several times," she replied.

Roy, looking down, hammered a heel at the unyielding earth. "Yeah," he said, bitterly. "I'm a bad boy . . . a delinquent . . . a graduate of a Reform School . . . a jail bird . . . a last-chance Charlie, who's out on probation and who's slated for a real ride, if he slips again. That's me! . . . That's the nice little prize package my Dad's wished on you people." He shrugged his shoulders. "Well, at least you're taking me in with your eyes open. I don't see how anyone's going to get a bargain out of this!"

There was a moment of silence between them, and then Sue said: "You don't seem so bad to me—so far. Let's be getting on to the house. Daddy can't wait on himself and I've already been away from him the longest I've been since Mother died."

It was late afternoon and winter clouds were drawing a hazy curtain over the sun. A long, somber shadow dropped its mantle on the hill. Roy grabbed up his suitcase for the last time and they rounded the bend toward the house.

Matt Kendall lowered his field glasses. He could only hold them to his eyes for short periods of time because he no longer had any grip in the stiffened, swollen joints of his calcified fingers and hands. He could lift the glasses by pressing his gnarled fists against them at the sides. But now he dropped them in his lap and leaned back on the pillow of his easy chair.

"So she's finally a-comin'!" he spoke aloud, something he often did when alone, "And she's got the boy with her. Seems to me he wasn't due until tomorrow. I'll have to check Bert Willard's letter." He fumbled in the pocket of an old, worn bathrobe and hooked out an envelope, shaking a folded sheet from it. Then he reached for his spectacles on the little table nearby which contained a pitcher of water and a plate of half-eaten sandwiches. The spectacles slipped from his grasp and landed on the floor at his feet.

"Damn!" he cursed, softly. "There go my eyes! Well, it's commencin' to get dark, anyway."

He stuffed the letter back in his pocket without trying to put it in the envelope. "They should be here in about fifteen minutes," he figured. "Sue could make it quicker but that boy with his suitcase will take longer." A harder tone came into his voice. "It's high time she was gettin' back—leavin' me here alone since ten this mornin'! She should of knowed better. First time she's ever done this. If that boy has been the cause ... !"

He wrestled with the field glasses again and got them up to his face. "Not a bad lookin' young feller," he ruminated " 'ppears to be good and strong. That's what we need here—somebody good and strong. Lots of work to be done that a girl can't do. But now, Sue'll have more time to wait on me."

He lowered the glasses and set them on the table.

"I'll straighten the boy out," he added, with a glint of satisfaction, "by givin' him so much to do he won't have no time for devilment."

He could hear Sue's voice at the door now and see the knob turning. "I know it doesn't look like much," she was saying, "but if we could ever get it painted and a new roof, it would really be quite nice."

The door swung open and Sue looked in upon her father. Behind her, half a head taller, his dark eyes curious and alert, was Bert Willard's son, suitcase in hand.

"This place doesn't need paintin'!" said the bent figure in the easy chair, by the window. "Where're you gettin' these expensive ideas? Come in and shut the door—both of you! That draft's goin' right through me!" Then, fixing his eyes on the advancing youth, he snapped: "I s'pose, of course, you're Bert Willard's son!"

"Yes, Daddy," spoke up Sue. "This is Roy. He said he figured coming a day early wouldn't make any difference to us."

She crossed over to kiss her parent on the cheek, which he

scarcely regarded as he kept his attention focused upon the new arrival.

"You take after your father considerable," he appraised. "I ain't seen him since we were boys together. Kinda strange he'd think of me after all this time but I guess, after all you've been up to, he was hard put to find anybody who'd take you in!"

Roy's suitcase dropped to the floor with a bang. There was fire in his eyes as he blazed: "Now see here, Mr. Kendall, I didn't come all this way to take any more abuse. I've been getting enough of that at home. I'm willing to go through with this because I can't help myself just at present . . . but don't hold what I've done over me, Mr. Kendall—I just won't stand for that!"

Sue's face was white and drawn as she stood between her father and the boy from the city. Folks didn't oppose Matt Kendall's will for very long. There wasn't any living with him, if they did. She should have warned Roy about his temperament but she, somehow, couldn't bring herself to do it. Seemed like her Daddy had gotten worse with the years, as his arthritis had crippled him, more and more. It was just his way, Sue had told herself, in trying to excuse him, of fighting back against this awful affliction.

"Listen here, young man," said the boyhood friend of Roy's father. "I want you to understand, right at the start, that I'm doin' you and your Dad a mighty big favor, lettin' you come here! You oughta know, by this time, that there's few people anywhere that's willin' to take you in, except—perhaps—the penitentiary. I'm not holdin' anythin' ag'in you so long as you do what you're s'posed to do around here.

"If you was in prison, they'd probably put you on the rock pile." He laughed, a dry, hard laugh. "Well, we got plenty of rocks in Rock County and at least *half* of 'em's on my farm! . . . You've come here to work and straighten yourself out . . . and if I kin send a good report to the Judge every three months, you'll git off probation inside a year. But it's all up to you, Mr. Willard. You kin like it or not, just as you please.

"We live plain and simple here. Not too much to eat or to put on our backs or keep us warm—but we allus git along, somehow. You kin have what *we* have but you got to pull your part of the load." He paused for breath and wet his lips with a smacking sound. "That's my say, young man, so you'll know your place, right from the beginnin'!"

Roy had remained standing in the center of the unfinished living room, the muscles in his jaws bulging. He was about to make a heated retort when he chanced to glance at Sue. There were tears streaming down her face and she had an appealing finger pressed against her lips.

"Okay," said the son of Matt Kendall's boyhood friend. "Where do you want me to bunk?"

Sue's face brightened and she swallowed a little sob in her throat. "I'll show you," she said. "Just come back here. We've cleared out this little store-room off the kitchen for you."

Roy picked up his suitcase and strode after her, passing within inches of the man who was doing his father a favor.

"This used to be my bedroom before mother died," said Sue, stepping aside to let Roy enter. "I sleep in the big bedroom now and Daddy stays all the time in the living room between the chair and his cot. I hope this will be all right."

Roy slid his suitcase between the wall and the scarred wooden bedstead, with the patch-work coverlet. "It's no room at the Hotel Stevens," he said, "but it'll do for me. I've been in lots worse places than this!"

An irascible voice sounded from the living room. "Sue, come here!"

An apprehensive look crossed her face. "Just make yourself at home," she said, with a forced smile. "I'll show you around later."

Her father's voice again, in a higher pitch: "Sue! Did you hear me?"

"Yes, Daddy—I'm coming!"

Sue re-entered the living room as Roy looked after her, gritted his teeth and shook his head.

Matt Kendall pointed a twisted finger at his eye glasses on the floor. "Pick up my specs." Then, as Sue knelt to do so, he said in a hoarse whisper, next her ear: "Now, see here, young lady— don't you be gettin' any gay ideas just because we have a young man in the house! You tend to your chores, same as always— and I'll manage him. He'll be doin' the heavier work soon—but you've been neglectin' your father lately . . . such as not comin' home early, as you did today . . . !"

Sue stood up and laid the spectacles on the little table. She picked up the water pitcher and the sandwich plate.

"But, Daddy—I couldn't get a ride out this way till the Carsons went home, after things were over . . . !"

Matt Kendall's eyes gleamed and his thin lips set in a hard line. "*Carsons!* All stuck up—now that their boy's bein' paid all this attention! And you ridin' out with *them* . . . ! I'm not wantin' to be under obligation to Frank Carson. He's been agitatin' to git new roads and 'lectricity out this way—which means raisin' taxes! We're well enough off as we are!"

Sue's mouth quivered. A defiant look flared in her green eyes, and died away. She bit her lips and left the room.

Chapter III

AT THE CARSON place there was the smell of fried chicken and baking biscuits in the air. It was sunset time—the time just before supper when Dave and his Dad used to lay off work and stroll down by the Pine Bluff on the great cliff overlooking their rich bottom-lands and the mountains beyond. Mother was always putting the finishing touches on her meal about then and after they'd had a good, quiet talk and watched the sun slip out of sight, they would wait for her five minute bell to call them back to the house and the nightly reward for their labors. The stock was usually in hand and most of the chores done for Frank Carson was an efficient farmer and had good help in his hired man, Jud Emery.

Tonight was cool and crisp, with a clearing sky in the west, a harbinger of a better tomorrow. The country-side was naked but Dave's memory clothed the old familiar landscape in all the seasons of the year. It seemed so good to be out here again, in his old denims, enjoying this understanding comradeship which had always existed between his father and himself.

"Son," said Frank Carson, biting on the stem of his pipe and looking off across the hills, "I was a bit surprised at you today—the way you spoke to the folks in town. All you said may have been true but I don't think you made too many friends by it. I know, for a fact, that Ed Brannigan was fit to be tied."

Dave did not try to conceal his chagrin. "I'm glad you brought this up, Dad. It's been worrying me ever since I said it. I just spoke the way I felt, without thinking. So few people in our county have ever been outside it. They don't know how the rest of the people in this world are living—and they don't even know how well off they are, themselves. But they could so easily be a lot better off, with a little effort. They could have all the conveniences of the city, right in their own homes!"

Dave's eyes glistened as new feelings assailed him. "I've been

41

in wonderful hotel rooms with baths and toilets and running water and electric lights and telephones. I've walked up Broadway where they have more light bulbs in one big sign than in almost the whole state of Arkansas! ... But when I got back here and compared the misery I'd seen abroad with the good things *we* had, I guess I just went overboard. I knew, though, almost as soon as I sat down, that I'd made a boner."

Frank Carson nodded. "I'm afraid you made an enemy of the biggest man in Hidden Valley," he said. "Folks don't like criticism, especially handed out in public. Ed Brannigan expected compliments and you gave him brick-bats. It's a hard thing to say but the folks around here don't give a tinker's dam right now to what happens to the starving people of Europe. They just want to forget the war and get the bothersome priorities and rationings out of the way and be permitted to live their own lives again." Frank Carson put a kindly hand on his son's shoulder. "There's one thing you'll have to learn, Dave, if you want to be spared a lot of heart-ache. You can't change human nature over night!"

Dave was thoughtfully watching pink and purple streamers of light, tracer bullets from the setting sun.

"You're right, Dad," he said, softly. "I'm through trying to change the world. But I'm *not* through trying to change this County! Ed Brannigan cut me down to my size when he told that crowd if I really wanted to do something, I could start right here at home. Well, that's just what I'm going to do!

"You've been fighting, for years, to get better conditions, not only for us here on the farm, but for everybody else. You've got a fine reputation as a progressive farmer, but there's lots of modern conveniences you haven't got, simply because the people around here won't co-operate.

"If I'm going to stay out here in the country and get married and have a home of my own, I want my wife and family to enjoy the things I've seen other people enjoying. There's no reason why they shouldn't!"

Frank Carson smiled. "More power to you, Dave," he said.

"You sounded then like *me* talking—thirty years ago. But you have a far greater opportunity than I. If you think you can really do something for this community—if you've got any good ideas—go to it! . . . I'll help you all I can."

Big Jim Watson was the County Agent in charge of the Extension Service for the United States Department of Agriculture in Rock County, Arkansas. He had his offices in the basement of the County Court House. It was here that he dispensed information on Agriculture and Home Economic subjects and sent out bulletins and pamphlets on crop and livestock raising. The latest improved methods of farming were available to all in the rural community who wished to make use of this knowledge.

It was a sad but true commentary on human nature that there were still many fine, well-meaning farmer folk in the County who were sure that their old ways of working the land were best and rebelled against accepting any help or advice from these "high-falutin' County Agent fellers" who were "allus tryin' to nose into your business." Since Rock County was set so far back in the hills, it had remained the most backward in development and county agents there had encountered more resistance than co-operation.

Into Big Jim's office on this morning after Hidden Valley's home-coming celebration for Frank and Emma Carson's son, came the returned war hero, himself.

"I'm Dave Carson, Sir," he announced.

Big Jim Watson grinned, as he looked up from his desk.

"Well, I might not have recognized you at that, with your uniform off. Besides, we've really never met. I came here after you left for the Service." He extended his hand. "Glad to meet you, Dave. Sit down. What's on your mind?"

Dave was in overalls and hunting jacket. He hung his cap on the back of a chair and sat on its edge, leaning forward, intently.

"Mr. Watson!" he said, excitement in his voice. "I didn't sleep much last night. I got to thinking of what Mr. Brannigan said about doing something for this town and county. I realize we can't do anything worth-while for the rest of the world until we've improved *our* conditions and set a better example at home." He flashed a quick, self-disparaging smile. "I guess I must have sounded like a world crusader yesterday," he apologized. "Well, I didn't mean it that way. I know now, Mr. Watson, that I can't do much of anything alone. Nobody can. And when I got to thinking it over, wondering how a person could go about changing things for the better, I suddenly thought of the 4-H Clubs and what they've been doing in other parts of the state and country."

Dave paused, drew a deep breath and then asked: "Mr. Watson, is there any reason why a 4-H Club can't be organized here in Hidden Valley?"

Big Jim's face had been lighting up in anticipation of this query. "Dave," he said. "I've been waiting a long time for some-one like you to develop the urge and initiative to come in here and make such a request. I tried to get a 4-H Club started in Rock County several times but the war had taken most of the young fellows with natural leadership ability and it seems like everybody, young and old, was too busy with other things to give my proposal any real thought.

"*Of course* a 4-H Club can be organized! All it takes is five enthusiastic, determined young men and women like yourself— and a good adult Local Leader, to start it going!"

Dave looked up at a map of Arkansas which hung on the wall beside the County Agent's desk. It had numerals written across each County.

"Is that where the 4-H Clubs are now?" he asked.

Big Jim nodded. "Yes, they're all over the State." He pointed to a section of eastern Arkansas. "This area is peppered with fine Negro organizations that are doing a great work. It's about time the farm boys and girls of Rock County got busy!"

"I'm ashamed to say," Dave confessed, "that I don't know too much about the 4-H Club work. I'm afraid you'll have to start at the beginning and give me a little background."

Big Jim reached in the drawer of his desk. "Well, I can start you off with some literature which you can study when you get home. You know, of course, that this 4-H Club work for rural boys and girls is a part of the National Agricultural Extension System. It covers every State in the Union, Puerto Rico, the Territories of Alaska and Hawaii—and it's becoming International with 4-H Clubs being formed in China, Italy, Greece, Czechoslovakia and Brazil—just to mention a few foreign countries now introducing our work.

"We have a National 4-H Club Congress, representing some fifteen hundred of the pick of 4-H Club members, which meets in Chicago in the first week of every December. Within a few years, the way things are going, with the need for improved farm methods throughout the world, we expect to be holding an Annual International 4-H Club Congress, as well!"

Dave stood up, smacking his fist on Big Jim's desk. "This is it!" he cried. "It's the answer to everything! . . . Tell me, Mr. Watson—what can I do to get this thing going, locally? What does it cost to belong?"

Big Jim smiled. "There aren't any dues, Dave. You pay for your membership in service to your community. Every boy and girl picks out a project and works at it. The purpose of the Club is to teach young people the latest and best practices in Agriculture and Home Economics, to show them how to work together and how to better themselves by helping others."

"What age do you have to be to join?" asked Dave.

"Anyone can belong who's between ten and twenty-one," said Big Jim.

"That gives me just about two years yet," Dave figured. "What's the first step? Should I go out and round up some of my friends?"

"You can," said Big Jim. "And, if you like, *I'll* sound out a few farm families for you. You've got to get the fathers and mothers behind their sons and daughters, too, if you want to make a real success of this thing."

"Let's see," said Dave, thinking out loud. "I'm sure I can get you at least five members right off. There's the Hilton sisters and Porky O'Connor and Sue Kendall and—I was going to say—Tom Dodds. That's natural because we used to be in on everything together. Of course, he's out now . . ." Dave hesitated, as a sudden thought hit him. "No, maybe not. Maybe Tom *could* fit into this Club somehow. Do you suppose . . . ?" He paused again and considered as Big Jim eyed him, curiously. "Would it be possible, Mr. Watson?" continued Dave, "if I could interest Tom in joining, for the Club to meet at his place?"

Big Jim nodded. "Certainly would. You can meet wherever you choose, around at different farm homes, if you like, until you are able to get a Club House of your own."

"I'd like to have Tom with me," said Dave. "It would seem like old times. He's been trying to shut the world out and I think, if he just got with the gang again, it would make a difference. Dodds' home would be as convenient as any place, seeing as how most of the ones I've suggested live along Stony Creek Route."

"Then, why don't you plan it that way?" proposed Big Jim, "And I'll work along with you to set up the first meeting. But there's one thing we've got to have before we go much further and that's a good Local Leader—some farm man or woman who will be present at meetings and be ready to help and advise on your projects and activities at all times. I have just the person in mind, if you'll let me suggest him."

"Go ahead," invited Dave.

"Your *father,*" said Big Jim. "There's not a better man in the County. I believe he has fewer enemies and more friends than almost anyone I know here. Just his name, alone, connected with the formation of a 4-H Club, would enable us to get some boys and girls whose parents wouldn't let them join, otherwise. I know your father's a busy man but every worthwhile person is busy. Do you suppose, Dave, you could get him to accept the job?"

Dave stood up. "I'll go back to the farm and see him about it."

Chapter IV

THE FOLLOWING SATURDAY afternoon, cars of every vintage, early and late models, came from both directions on the Stony Creek road and began turning in at the Dodds' driveway. The private gravel approach was soon congested and those still arriving parked their automobiles or trucks at the side of the Stony Creek Route, proceeding to the Dodds' home on foot.

From his bedroom window, upstairs, the astonished son of Fred and Anna Dodds watched this strange and growing assemblage of Rock County boys and girls, some as young as ten years, and others up to the age of twenty. He had known most of them before he became a shut-in but had not seen or heard from many of them since. Why they should be converging on his home now was a mystery.

Tom, at first amazed, then panicky, finally became enraged. Whoever was behind this had an awful lot of nerve. He could hear voices downstairs, laughter, the increasing rustle of excitement. Every once in awhile he could distinguish his parents' voices as they greeted new-comers.

"Mother," he finally called, and when she apparently hadn't heard, he shouted again: *"Mother!"*

"Yes, Dear." sounded Mrs. Dodds' voice from the foot of the stairs. "I'm coming right up."

He followed the sounds of her footsteps to the door. As she came in, wearing her best afternoon dress, he demanded: "What's going on here?"

"Why, it's just a meeting of farm boys and girls who are going to organize a new club," she informed.

"Well, why all the secrecy? Why haven't *I* known about this?"

"Because, Dear—Dave arranged it and he asked us not to tell you. Said he wanted it to be a big surprise."

Tom's face went white with fury. "It's a surprise, all right. One I don't like. I don't thank Dave for this. You keep everybody

47

downstairs! I won't see 'em! . . . Shut the door. Keep all this
noise out. This is a dirty trick to play on me!"

"But everyone's come here, expecting to see you," his mother
replied. "That's why the meeting's being held at our house—so
you can attend!"

Tom was momentarily speechless. Before he could say more
his mother, struggling to control her emotions, hastened from
the room.

A car was honking down on the road. Tom turned over in
bed and looked guardedly out the window, so he would not be
seen. It was the Carsons arriving, Dave—with his father and
mother! Dave was waving to someone and looking up toward
the Kendall place. Tom knew before that person came within his
range of vision, that it must be Sue.

So *she* was coming, too! What kind of a get-to-gether *was*
this, anyway? Began to look like about all the young people he
knew were turning out! Must be between twenty and thirty here
now—several grown-ups with them.

Tom had a sudden thought. Maybe this club business was all
an excuse—maybe Dave had cooked up a birthday party! . . .
But this wasn't his birthday . . . it wasn't until next week . . .

Yes—Dave had been waiting for Sue! His folks had gone on
ahead . . . Tom could hear them in the hall, downstairs, talking
to his father and mother . . . Sue and Dave were laughing at
something and pointing to the different makes of cars as they
turned in at the Dodds'!

Sue looked as though she'd grown taller but she was still far
too thin . . . over-working as usual. She'd have looked much
different, by this time, if only . . . ! She was pretty, though—
her wonderful green eyes, the color of summer green wheat,
blown by the breeze; and her tumbling wave of black, curly
hair . . . ! Tom felt an invisible vice closing in on his heart. It was
cruel—what they were doing to him. Terrible and unthinking!
. . . If he could only die now—and get away from all this!

"Is everybody ready?" he heard Dave ask, as he came in the
door.

"Yes!" shouted a chorus of voices.

"Okay! Then wait just a minute till I go upstairs and get Tom!"

There were footsteps taking the stairs, two at a time, then a hearty rap on the door which swung inward to reveal his old pal, Dave—in a tight-fitting suit of civvies.

"Almost busted a seam coming up here," he grinned. "I'll have to have Mom let this suit out." Then, as Tom glowered at him, he added: "*What?* Aren't you dressed yet? Snap it up! Everybody's waiting!"

Tom turned his head away, unanswering, and Dave strode into the room. He went straight to the closet and felt around among the hangers, taking out a blue bathrobe.

"Here it is—just the thing," he said, tossing the garment on the bed. "Now where do you keep your shirts and ties? Same old place?" He crossed to the dresser and pulled open a drawer. "Boy, I could use some of these white shirts, myself! Well— what d' you know!" He took out a tie. "Here's my birthday present to you, three years ago! . . . Looks pretty snazzy yet. Very appropriate, too—Green and White! That's the 4 H Club *colors!*"

Tom turned his head to look at Dave. "So *that's* what this is all about!" he said.

"Yeah!" grinned Dave. "Get that pajama top off and let me sneak this shirt on. You're going to be in on the biggest thing ever started in this County!"

Tom held up a shaky restraining hand. "No, Dave, I can't," he said, brokenly.

"What d' you mean, you *can't?*" rejoined Dave. "We've done everything together all our lives—and you're going to be with me on this! You've laid around and taken it easy long enough!"

Tom swallowed hard and fumbled with trembling fingers at the top button of his pajamas. Dave's strong fingers were there to help and the pajama top came off, revealing the bony structure of a body which had once been as robust as his.

"I'm afraid this shirt will be too large for me, now," said Tom. "The collar will probably go around my neck *twice!*"

"Who cares about that?" said Dave. "It's not the size of your neck that counts—it's the size of your *heart!*"

He pushed Tom's slender arms into the shirt sleeves and buttoned the collar loosely at the neck. Then he ran the tie under the fold and did a neat four-in-hand.

"Nothing wrong about that," he said, as he stepped back to survey the effect. He grabbed up a mirror off the dresser. "Here— take a look! There's nothing the matter with you that a little beef in the right places won't cure!"

Tom examined himself and shook his head. "I haven't been this near dressed in almost two years," he said.

Dave picked up the bathrobe, then laid it down again. "Well, how about going all the way?" he said, as he saw how Tom was reacting. "Where are your pants?"

"In the closet, somewhere," said Tom.

Dave crossed over, rummaged around and came out with two pairs of pants. He inspected each, made a choice and threw the other pair over the back of a chair. "These'll do!" he declared.

Tom's eyes filled with tears. "They belong to the suit I was going to be married in," he said.

Dave threw back the covers. "Here—let me pull 'em on for you. Got to save time!" He circled Tom's body at the waist with his powerful left arm, lifted him up and adroitly pulled the pants on over the withered legs. "Now all we need is a belt and your slippers—and you're all set!"

He turned back to the dresser, jerked out several drawers, and produced a belt.

"My slippers are on the closet floor," informed Tom. "I haven't worn them for a long time, either."

"What're you doing—saving 'em for your old age?" razzed Dave. He got the slippers—blue ones to match the bathrobe— and dropped them beside the bed. "Guess you'll have to sit up so we can slip your belt on and stick your shirt tails in," Dave directed. "Here—let me turn you around—like this!" He grasped Tom and placed his body on the edge of the bed as he spoke, keeping a supporting hand against his back.

"I see you've got some crutches over there in the corner," observed Dave. "Ever use 'em?"

Tom clutched Dave's arm, terror-stricken. "No—Dad just got them in case I was ever strong enough to . . . Don't let go of me, Dave! Hold on!"

Dave had reached down to shove the slippers on Tom's feet and he was now pulling the belt up to the last notch. "I'm not letting you go, don't worry," he reassured. "You're doing swell. Get into this bathrobe and we're ready to go!"

Tom's eyes were alight with excitement. He was breathing heavily. Even this amount of exertion had been quite exhausting to him.

"Atta boy! Now slip your arm around my neck while I make a saddle!" He lifted Tom easily off the bed and walked with him across the room, then stopped before the closed door. "Say, Tom," he requested. "Can you reach the knob?"

Tom's trembling fingers closed over it and the door came open.

"Gang way, everybody!" called Dave, as he headed for the stairway, "Here we come!"

Thirty-one boys and girls and some of their parents, from Rock County, of various ages and sizes, were packed in the Dodds' living room. A card table had been placed in front of the stone fireplace, at the far end, with chairs left vacant for officers who would be elected as the Club was formed. Near the fireplace was Mr. Dodds' old, comfortable reading chair, with footstool prepared for the fellow who had not been down stairs in almost two years. As Dave appeared in the doorway with him, there was a tremendous shout of greeting.

"Hi, Tom!" sounded from everyone's throat.

"Hello, gang," he replied, and his voice broke.

Dave carried him down a narrow aisle between the chairs and placed him in a sitting position so that he could see and be seen by all.

"Take a look around, Tom," he said, "and tell me if you know everybody here."

Tom's deeply sunk eyes made the rounds. They came to rest upon a man, his wife and little boy who must have been not more than five years of age.

"I don't recognize those people," he said.

Dave laughed. "No, Tom. That's Mr. and Mrs. Jim Watson and son. He's the County Agent. 'Big Jim' and 'Little Jim' . . . !" The Watsons smiled and nodded.

Tom's eyes continued to roam from face to face of those assembled, almost hungrily devouring their features, noting the change in each person from the time he had seen them last. It was almost as though he had come to life after having been dead to his community for a long period.

"Well," said Dave, "we'd better get started. I'd like to call on Mr. Watson to come up here and take over as temporary chairman and show us how to get under way."

The genial County Agent rose to his feet and joined Dave at the front of the room.

"There's nothing much to it," he said. "Most of you have signed your membership application blanks and gotten your parents' consent to join this 4-H Club, so the first thing you need to do is hold an election of officers. The positions open are for President, Vice-President, Secretary-Treasurer, Reporter and Song Leader. You will probably want to appoint other committees and officers later as you plan the work of the Club—but nominations are now in order for President!"

There was an attitude of tense interest in the room. Some of the boys and girls, especially the younger ones, were uncommonly shy and backward. Each was now waiting for the other to speak first. There was an embarrassed silence. Big Jim smiled.

"Start the nominations, somebody. You ought to be able to pick a good President out of this crowd!"

"Mr. Chairman!" said a voice.

All turned in the direction of the speaker.

"Please stand when you address the chair," requested the County Agent.

A rotund, chubby-faced figure stood up. There was a titter of laughter. Porky O'Connor glared, good-naturedly, at his ridiculers. "I'd like to nominate Dave Carson," he said. "Dave got us together and I think he ought to be our first President!"

There was a burst of applause in support of this suggestion.

"All right," said Chairman Watson. "Are there other nominations?"

"Mr. Chairman!" called a girl's voice. A golden-haired young woman stood up in the back of the room.

"Yes, Miss Hilton," recognized the chairman.

"I move the nominations be closed," she smiled.

"Second the motion!" chorused a dozen voices.

"The motion has been made that the nominations for President be closed," repeated Big Jim. "All those in favor, signify by saying 'aye'."

"AYE!" acclaimed those present.

Big Jim smiled and motioned to Dave. "Will the first President of the Hidden Valley 4-H Club come forward and take the chair?" he invited.

Dave, grinning, walked around the card table as Big Jim put out his hand in congratulation and then returned to his seat.

"Speech! Speech!" yelled several.

Dave's face sobered. "Looks like I'd gotten myself in for it," he said. "But I truly consider this a great honor because I believe this 4-H Club we are forming is going to make a fine name for itself in this County. We've got a big job to do on our farms and for the town.

"Before I forget it, I want to thank Mr. and Mrs. Dodds for opening up their home to let us meet in. They said we could come here once every two weeks. How about giving them a big hand?"

The applause almost lifted the living room ceiling.

"I guess the next order of business," said Dave, as the noisy appreciation subsided, "is to finish the elections—so I'll now ask you to make nominations for Vice-President!"

"Mr. President!" called several voices.

Dave looked from one section of the room to the other. "Which one of you addressed the chair first?" he inquired.

"*I* did!" said a voice, and a lanky youth stood up.

"All right, Ben Andrews!" recognized Dave.

"I'd like to nominate Tom Dodds!" said Ben, and sat down.

"I second the nomination!" cried a number.

"Mr. Chairman! . . . Mr. Chairman!"

"Wait a minute, here!" Dave commanded. "One at a time! Jerry Deakin—I guess *you* were first!"

Jerry, short and freckled, grinned as he got to his feet. "I move that the nominations be closed," he said.

There was a booming assent to this proposal and Tom Dodds was unanimously elected. The usual cry of "Speech! . . . Speech!" went up, and all turned expectantly to hear from the thin-faced figure in the blue bathrobe.

Tom tried to speak but he had no voice. He wet his lips and tried again.

"I appreciate this," he said, slowly, in a low, halting tone. "But I'll have to ask you to excuse me . . . I'm not well enough . . . I couldn't really be any help to you . . . !"

Tom was howled down and the elections went on with Sue Kendall being chosen as Secretary-Treasurer, Porky O'Connor for Club Reporter, and Carolyn Hilton as Song Leader.

"Now that the elections are over," announced Dave, "I'd like to have our Secretary-Treasurer, Sue Kendall, come up here and take over this Record Book and call the roll!"

Sue had been seated half way back on the side. As she advanced toward the card table and Dave, who awaited her, she said: "I don't know if I'll be able to keep this position. I didn't sign up till this afternoon and I've not yet gotten my father's consent."

"Oh, you'll get that all right," assured Dave, handing her the secretary's minute book. "I guess the names are all in there. Everybody stand, please, when your name is called, and say 'Here'!"

Sue started the roll call. When she came to one name, she hesitated and cleared her throat. Then, getting it out quickly, she said: *"Tom Dodds . . . !"*

For just a moment their eyes met and Tom looked away as he answered, faintly: "Here!"

When the roll call was finished, Sue looked about the room and asked: "Did I skip anybody?"

A young hand shot up. "You skipped *me!*" piped a youngster's voice.

Everyone laughed. It was Little Jim, five-year-old son of the County Agent.

"Little Jim Watson!" called Sue, importantly.

The youngster jumped to his feet, face beaming. "Here!" he cried.

President Dave Carson, taking over, said, smilingly: "We're not doing things in any special order this first meeting. I haven't even called on you members to recite your 4-H Club Pledge. How many of you have learned it?"

Almost every hand shot up. "All right," said Dave. "Then let's stand up and give it. Everyone watch me. Let's start together."

All members arose and stood by their chairs. Dave raised his right hand to the side of his head and said, "I pledge . . . !"

Each boy and girl in the room followed Dave's motion and joined with him in saying:

"I pledge my head to clearer thinking . . ." Their right hands lowered to a position over their hearts.

". . . my heart to greater loyalty . . ."

The hands now extended, palms upward, as they pledged:

". . . my hands to larger service . . ."

They suddenly snapped to attention, a little raggedly this first time, but their voices were strong as they finished:

". . . And my health to better living—for my club, my community and my country!"

There were cheers and applause as Dave complimented: "That's great, gang! How'd you like that, Tom? Wasn't that *something?*"

All eyes turned to the young man in the blue bathrobe who had been watching proceedings intently. He nodded his head and said, in a choked voice: "That was wonderful!"

Dave nodded. "That's a lot to live up to and our Club Motto is even tougher. How many of you can tell me what it is?"

There was an instant shout: *"To Make the Best Better!"*

Dave laughed. "What a gang! You sure must have studied the 4-H Club bulletins I left with you!" Then, looking at the fellow who had been his life-time pal, he said: "I guess Tom is the only one who wasn't prepared in advance but you can see for yourselves he's right on the beam, wearing the 4-H colors in that Green and White tie!"

Tom smiled and lifted the tie ends for all to see.

"Something else you don't know, Tom," Dave went on. "The National 4-H emblem is a Four-Leaf-Clover with a letter 'H' on each leaf. Remember that time, about five summers ago, when we ran onto a whole patch of four-leaf-clovers?"

Tom nodded and his eyes moistened.

"We said, then, that we'd have *good luck* the rest of our lives," Dave continued. "Well, we have had, mostly. We've got swell parents and a nice home and wonderful friends—and what we *don't* have, we still have a chance to get!

"The H's on this 4-H emblem stand for Head, Heart, Hands and Health. I can't think of a symbol I'd like better than a Four-Leaf-Clover. It's going to bring us *all* good luck and achievement—the 4-H Way." Dave paused and looked around. Then, addressing County Agent Watson, he asked: "Let's see. What do we do next?"

Big Jim Watson stood up. "I think the time's come, Dave, for you to introduce to the members the man who is going to be their Local Club Leader. They'll want to get to know him and work with him."

"Okay," Dave smiled. "Well, folks, I now take great pleasure," he said, "in presenting to you the most wonderful man in this world—*my Dad!*" He turned to look at his father who was seated quietly in a back row, beside his mother.

As Frank Carson got slowly to his feet and started down the aisle, there was warm applause. Dave stepped aside and sat down to give his father the floor.

"I want you young people to know," he began, "that I've never had any honor conferred upon me which compares with this—of being asked to be your Leader. It's going to be a great responsibility but I'll get a great kick out of it.

"The longest part of my life has been lived. The days of my plantings are about over. But, perhaps I can help plant some seeds in your lives that will take root and grow so you can develop into better farmers, better home-makers, better citizens, better leaders and better men and women.

"It isn't easy to grow up in the world like it is today, but we have a chance here, working together, to gain an understanding and appreciation of ourselves and each other and of nature which will help us solve the problems of our farm, our home and our community. This will mean, in time, a higher standard of living for everybody in Rock County and more happiness than we've ever had before."

Frank Carson paused for a moment. His listeners had been paying him rapt attention.

"I want each one of you members," he continued, "to do a lot of careful thinking about the projects you are going to choose to work at. Be sure, in your mind and heart, that you really want to do what you set out to do. You can't succeed in life unless you put your whole soul behind things.

"Some of you may want to pick a beef project. I mention 'beef' because the raising of beef cattle has been one of my projects for years. Others of you may choose a project like bee raising, making and designing clothes, poultry raising, improving your home or your community, conserving the soil, gardening, raising of pigs or sheep, preserving of food, growing of fruit, forestry, or any one of almost countless things you can do with your lives as you develop the ability."

Frank Carson paused again, debated a moment and then concluded: "I guess that's all I have to say at this time—except that, as your Leader, I want each one of you to call upon me at any time of the day or night, for any help I can give you. And that goes for Mother Carson, too. If any of you girls, especially, would rather take your problems to her, you'll find her a very understanding and helpful person, as I have all these years.

"Mother," he called, "will you please stand up and take a bow?"

Emma Carson gave a little murmur of protest but she stood up, smiling, and was greeted with applause as her husband returned to his seat beside her and squeezed her arm, affectionately.

"Well," said Dave, resuming the chair. "I guess this about winds up our first business meeting. You members, as soon as you've decided on your projects, get in touch with Mr. Watson at the County Agent's office and let him give you your *project record books*. They're furnished free by the Agriculture Extension Service and you know, if you don't keep good and accurate records, that you can't qualify for any of the awards. You can't tell, either, whether you're making or losing money on your project if you're raising pigs or crops or canning fruit or anything like that. When we really get going, we're going to check your records at every regular club meeting so we can get a line on your progress . . ."

"And now," announced Dave. "We've come to the entertainment part of our program. I gave the Hilton sisters a copy of the National 4-H Song Book and told them to pick out a 4-H song to sing to us. They've been working on it for the last two days as *their first project.*" Dave directed a glance at the location where the girls were seated. "Carolyn, Eleanor and Doris—will you come up here, please, and do your stuff?"

The three attractive Hilton sisters came down the aisle and turned about to face their audience. They struck a chord by humming to themselves. Then Carolyn said: "This 4-H song is entitled, 'Dreaming' . . ." She placed her head close beside those of her two sisters, as they began:

"My home must have a high tree above its open gate,

"My home must have a garden where little dreamings wait;

"My home must have a wide view of field and meadow fair,
"Of distant hill, of open sky, with sunlight everywhere . . ."

The sentiment of this simple song was touching hearts as the girls sang. Sue Kendall seemed particularly affected. She glanced once at Tom and found his hollow eyes looking at her. Each, self-consciously, looked away.

"My home must have a friendship with every happy thing,
My home must offer comfort for any sorrowing;
And every heart that enters shall hear its music there,
And find some simple beauty that every life may share . . ."

Sue Kendall suddenly leaped to her feet and ran, crying, from the room.

"Sue!" called Tom, and reached out gaunt fingers after her.

The Hilton sisters broke off their song. Everyone sat momentarily shocked. Then Dave, joined by the Dodds and his parents, hurried out—but Sue had already grabbed up her coat from the table in the front hallway, and was running sobbing down the hill toward Kendall Road.

Frank Carson placed a restraining hand on Dave who was about to take after her.

"Let her go son," he said, feelingly. "This is one time when nobody else can help."

Chapter V

MATT KENDALL had his field glasses trained on the Dodds' home as his daughter came running out and hurried up the hill.

"Well, she's mindin', this time, and comin' home early!" he said, in a tone of grim satisfaction. "But that must be some shindig at the Dodds' place! Never saw anythin' like it in my life. Enough folks there for a *funeral!*"

He turned to glance out the other window toward the barn where the new farm hand had been chopping up wood all afternoon—dead tree trunks, fallen limbs and underbrush he had cleared from the Kendall woods that morning.

"That boy will be good and tired tonight," chuckled Sue's father. "But he's a danged good worker, if what he's done today is any sample. With some one like him around to collect the wood on the place, we won't have to buy any more to burn. That'll make quite a savin'."

The chronic invalid leaned back in his chair to await his daughter's arrival. She was over the brow of the hill now, but had slowed her pace. Looking below, with his naked eye, Matt Kendall could see no signs of anyone else leaving the Dodds' home as yet. The cars and trucks were parked thick along the drive-in and Stony Creek road.

"She's just got time to get everythin' done before dark," her father estimated. "It'll take a little longer with her breakin' the boy in, but once he gets the hang of things, it's goin' to be a lot better here for me."

Matt Kendall watched for the door knob to turn. She was coming up the walk now. He could count her steps to the door although she could no longer be seen. From gate to door, at her normal stride, it was just *twenty-seven steps*. He had listened to the crunch of gravel under her feet, time and time again.

She was his life, coming and going, living and breathing and acting for him. At times, when she had to be away at school or in town shopping, she left him fortified with food and drink and things to read and anything else he needed, within reach. She had been a dutiful daughter, his legs and his arms and his only contact with the outside world beside the little battery radio and a few farmer folk who dropped by at infrequent intervals. But the Kendall place, being off the main road, and its drive-way in such bad shape, discouraged many callers.

The door knob was turning now but Sue had hesitated outside as though not wanting to come in. Matt Kendall sensed this, as he sensed most things. And, when she entered, on noting the redness of her eyes, he greeted her with the question: "Well, Sue. What happened? Why did you run away from Dodds'? Nobody else has left yet. Not a one but you." He could see her stiffen and her lips tighten.

"Nothing happened, Daddy. I just wanted to leave, that's all. I promised you I wouldn't stay long."

Matt Kendall eyed her intently. "What kind of goings-on was it? There hasn't been that many people at the Dodds', ever! You just told me a few of Tom's friends were dropping in for a little visit. It's a danged sight more'n *that!*"

Sue slipped off her coat and took a folded piece of paper from the pocket.

"Yes, Daddy," she said. "It *is* more than that. They've organized a 4-H Club and I've joined up—and they elected me Secretary-Treasurer!"

This announcement struck Matt Kendall like a whip lash across the face.

"So that's what all the fuss was about!" He painfully shifted his position in the chair, groaning as he did so. "You *joined,* did you say? How are you goin' to have any time for any club doin's?"

"That's the nice part about it, Daddy," said Sue, hopefully. "I can work on *projects* right here at home and they'll only take a few minutes each day." An eager glow came into her eyes. "I want to beautify our place, fix up the yard . . . plant some flowers and shrubs . . . clear out the weeds and seed it with grass . . .

then fix up our house, inside and out . . . And I want to make myself some new clothes, too. It won't cost much, Daddy. I can make some of them out of those pretty feed sacks . . . and then, too, we can begin getting better returns out of our goats and chickens by using more scientific methods . . . !"

Matt Kendall was as near the suffering of a stroke as he had ever been in his life. His body shook with mounting rage as he pounded the chair arm with a gnarled fist.

"Stop it!" he cried. "Don't you say any more! . . . Who's been puttin' you up to all this fancy business? I've heard of this 4-H foolishness before! A clever scheme of the County and State to get farmers to spend more money. Work on 'em through their children! . . . Well, if you've joined an outfit like that, you can resign right now! I won't have you wastin' your time and my money!"

Sue unfolded the piece of paper in her hand and advanced toward her father.

"I won't ask you for a cent, Daddy. I'll do everything you want me to do—as I always have—and I'll do this work, too. I can manage." She handed him the paper. "Here's my Membership Application. I've filled it out. All the other fathers and mothers have given their consent in writing. Won't you please sign up for me, too?"

Matt Kendall took the paper between his twisted fingers and slammed it down on the table.

"I most certainly will *not!*" he said.

Sue burst into tears. "Daddy, that's the only thing I've asked you for since I can remember. Couldn't you just do something for me that I want very much, this *once?*"

Her father nodded, grimly. "Yes, if you knew what was good for you, I could! We've made a livin' on this place without all those expensive, new-fangled ideas and I'm not goin' to let you . . . !"

"But, Daddy," broke in Sue, appealingly. "I've been reading some circulars they gave me which tell about home improvements and dress-making and new methods for raising chickens and goats—and I think we can save and make *more* money—once I learn how to . . . !"

"The Carsons are behind this, ain't they?" fumed Matt Kendall.

"Well, yes, partly," admitted Sue. "Dave Carson's President of the Club and his father's the Local Leader!"

"I thought so!" raged the crippled form in the easy chair. "That Frank Carson's been tryin' to manage everybody on this Route for years—and now that his son's back from war, with all this publicity, he figures that he and his boy together can organize and put it over on us. You're not mixin' up in anythin' like this, young lady—and that's final!"

Matt Kendall reached over, took up the Membership Application, tore it in two, and dropped it in the waste basket under the table.

The spirit had gone out of Sue's eyes. She turned toward her bedroom door, choking a sob.

"Better hurry and change your clothes," her father called after her. "It'll be dark before you get your chores done."

"I don't care if it is!" she cried.

There was a rap on the outer door and Bert Willard's son stepped in.

"Well, I finally got all that wood sawed up," he announced, "and I've got a blister on my left hand the size of half a dollar. Do you have any Band-Aid?"

"Do I have any—*what?*" demanded Matt Kendall.

"You know—a piece of adhesive tape—something to stick over this till it gets a chance to heal."

Matt Kendall chuckled. "Don't worry about a little thing like that. You'll have *callouses* on your hands in a few days. That's what you need—toughenin' up. Why, when your Dad and me was boys together . . . !"

"Yeah!" said Roy, drily. "You were twice as tough as I am. You didn't pay any attention to blisters and you had callouses a mile high!"

"That's enough out of you!" snapped the boyhood friend of Roy's father. "Sue's gettin' dressed to show you the night chores.

You've made a good start today. Just keep it up and we'll get along all right."

There was a sudden far-off series of distressed animal sounds. "What's that?" questioned Roy.

"That's one of those new kids!" identified Matt Kendall, excitedly. "He's in trouble somewhere. Somethin' must be after him!"

Sue came running from the bedroom. She was dressed in old shoes, overalls and leather jacket.

"The goats should be coming in now," she said, "But that sounds like the kid's still out in the brush! Come on, Roy— and help me find him!"

She started out through the back of the house with her new farm hand following. The kid had continued its crying. It sounded almost human.

"He's hurt!" Matt Kendall called after them. "It's that stray dog again! Better take the gun!"

Sue grabbed up the double-barrelled, 20-gauge shotgun which hung over the kitchen door and ran outside with Roy at her heels. She paused, for an instant, to get the direction of the kid's cries and then set out past the barn. She slipped the bar in the fence gate, leading into the pasture and raced across the field, noting as she did so that the herd was in. Roy had difficulty keeping pace with her.

They slid down into a steep, rocky ravine together. There, below them, was a little kid lying on its side, blood gushing from a gaping tear of its hide, across the back of its neck and down over both shoulders. Just leaving the scene was a large, savage-looking mongrel dog.

Sue braced herself against a rock ledge, raised the shotgun, and fired. The little kid's attacker leaped into the air, slid off a stone shelf, and rolled down an embankment.

"Good shot!" exclaimed Roy.

She handed him the gun, without a word, and rushed forward to kneel beside the wounded kid, gathering it up, lovingly, in her arms.

"Oh, you poor thing!" she cried. "I'll have to get you to the barn and fix you up, right away!"

Roy looked on, aghast. "Wouldn't it be better to shoot it?" he asked, "and put it out of its misery?"

Sue gave him a reproving look as she stood up, cuddling the kid to her in so comforting a fashion that his whimpering ceased.

"No," she said, "I can sew his hide together and perhaps it'll be all right."

She started to climb up out of the ravine with the new farm hand beside her.

"What are you going to sew it with?" he asked, appalled.

"Just ordinary needle and thread," said Sue. "It's all we've got."

There was nothing more said as they hurried back to the barn but, once inside, Sue turned to Roy and directed: "I'm going to need your help. Get that old chair over there. Bring it here in this light and sit down . . . Now—hold this kid on your lap while I run to the house and get what I need! . . . I'll be right back."

The boy from the city nervously followed instructions. He felt the trembling body of the little kid against his knees and arms. The sight of the raw flesh of shoulder and neck sickened him.

"Hurry up!" he called.

Sue was already flying between barn and house. She dashed through the back door and kitchen, into her bedroom.

"Was I right?" asked her father, excitedly.

"Yes, Daddy—it was that same dog!"

"Did you get him?"

"I got him!"

Sue rushed into the living room with her sewing basket and a towel flung over one arm.

"What's happened?" demanded Matt Kendall.

"The kid's badly chewed up. I'm going to see what I can do!" she cried, as she hurried out.

Roy was greatly relieved to see her. "I don't believe you can ever sew this up," he said. "I think the poor little thing is going to die."

"Here," commanded Sue. "Lift the kid up so I can put this towel on your knees!"

The little animal cried out as it was moved. It had a piteous expression on its face. Sue, meanwhile, had opened her sewing box on the barn floor. She grabbed up a spool, broke off a length of coarse, white thread, doubled it, and ran it through the eye of a needle.

"You'll have to hold the kid as still as you can," she instructed Roy. "This is going to hurt him but it can't be helped." She knelt beside Roy and examined the great tear in the hide. "This looks like quite a job," she said. "I'll have to run the needle through both flaps of flesh, then pull the edges together and tie the thread and cut it."

Roy gritted his teeth. "All right," he said, taking careful hold of the kid, "Let's get going!"

Sue, starting at one end of the tear, lifted up the hide and attempted to push the needle through. The little kid cried out.

"There, there," she said, "I'll be as gentle as I can, baby!"

Roy turned his head away as the needle went through the flesh and, presently, Sue said to him: "There—that's *one* tied! See—the hide pulls together all right."

Roy looked just as she snipped the thread with her scissors and prepared to repeat the process. Each time the needle punctured the unusually tough hide, the little kid set up a quavering wail.

Finally, when they were almost finished, Sue encountered a portion of the hide which resisted the needle and threatened to break it.

"My, my!" she said. "I've never run into anything like this! I'm afraid I'll have to get a pair of pliers!"

She got to her feet and ran across to a tool shelf, returning with an old pair.

"This is something I can't do alone," she told Roy. "You take these pliers and when I get the point of the needle pushed through, you get hold of it and pull it the rest of the way."

The boy from the city was wet with perspiration. His face had a chalk-like look. Sue bent to her task. The little kid screamed. *"Now!"* she cried.

Roy gripped the needle with the pliers and pulled steadily. Sue caught the needle as it came through.

"That's fine!" she said.

The process was repeated as the kid squirmed and kicked and cried, but presently it was all sewed together with bunches of stained knotted thread in a jagged line across its neck and shoulders.

"There you are, baby," said Sue, petting its head as she got up. "In a few days, if all goes well, you should be as good as new." Then, to Roy, who gave an unconcealed sigh of great relief, "Hold it just a moment longer. I'll let the goats in the barn, and find this kid's mother, and put her in a separate stall, and let her take care of her baby."

"Don't make it long," begged Roy. "I've had about all of this I can take!"

Sue hurried to the barn door at which the herd was waiting, flung it open, and the goats charged in. It was the work of minutes to locate the nanny and confine her in a solitary stall. Then Sue quickly returned to Roy who was leaning back in his chair, with one hand to his head. The little kid was lying quietly on his lap, apparently content to remain.

"All right, baby," soothed Sue, taking her patient from Roy. "I've done all I can for you. You and your mother will have to do the rest." She crossed to the stall.

Roy got shakily to his feet and followed her. He looked in as she set the little kid down. It ran, at once, crying, to its mother. The nanny lowered her head in an affectionate greeting and tenderly nuzzled her offspring. The little kid, with a relieved cry, went happily in search of its evening meal.

Sue glanced wearily at Roy as her features relaxed in a smile. "Well, that's that!" she said.

"And that's *plenty!*" said Roy, feelingly. "One more stitch and you'd have had *me* for your next patient!"

Members of Hidden Valley's newly formed 4-H Club stayed on at the Dodds' for refreshments. Most of them gathered around the figure in the blue bathrobe and expressed their joy at seeing him again. There were bright spots of excitement and pleasure in Tom's cheeks but he soon motioned to Dave and whispered in his ear.

"Awfully sorry. This has been swell—but I'm all in. Please get me back to bed."

Dave lifted his chum in his arms as everyone cleared a way for him.

"Goodbye, gang!" Tom called, making a feeble attempt to wave. "See you next meeting!"

Dave mounted the stairs with his burden.

"So long, Tom!" rejoined his fellow members. "Take care of yourself!"

Once in his room, safely back in bed, and with his clothes off, Tom indicated to Dave that he wanted to talk.

"Pull up a chair," he requested.

Dave did so, and sat down. "Quite a nice party, wasn't it?" he grinned.

Tom nodded, soberly. "Yes, Dave. You've started something, this time. I only wish I was well and on my feet. We could really go to town with this outfit!"

"We're going to town, anyway!" declared Dave. "We're not going to let anything stop us. You can still use your head and heart and hands right where you are. And, one of these days, you'll have your *health* back!"

Quick tears sprang into Tom's eyes. "You don't really believe that," he said. "You're just trying to make me feel good."

Dave gave him a steady look, "I don't believe in miracles," he admitted, "but I believe there's no limit to what a guy can do for himself if he just makes up his mind to do it!"

Tom gazed hard at the ceiling. Then he held up thin arms and examined them, critically. After a moment, he pushed back the covers and studied his emaciated body and legs. Finally, turning back to Dave, he said, with a wan smile: "Do you think

I can ever put any real meat on this carcass?"

"You can, if you feed up right," declared Dave. "But you'll have to exercise, too. I don't know much about infantile paralysis —but I *do* know if anybody'd lie in bed as long as you have, even with *nothing* the matter with them, they wouldn't have enough muscles left to get around on. They'd be darn near as helpless as you are!"

Tom took a moment to consider this statement. "It's going to be a long climb," he said, in a low voice, filled with emotion, "but, thanks to you, Dave—I'm going to try to make it!"

His pal of a life-time reached over and patted his shoulder. "That's what I hoped you'd say. You *can't* lose from now on."

Dave got up, prepared to leave.

Tom made a detaining gesture. "Just a minute," he said. "There's something I want to ask you."

Dave, who had turned toward the door, came back, looked down and smiled. "Okay—shoot!"

Tom hesitated, moistening his lips. "Who was that fellow with the suitcase, who rode out with you and Sue, the day you came home?"

"Oh," said Dave, "his name's Roy Willard. I don't know much about him yet. Sue just told me he was the son of a boyhood friend of her father's."

"Is he—staying at the Kendall place?" asked Tom.

"So far as I know," said Dave.

"Going to stay long?"

"I guess so. I think they plan on breaking him in as a farm hand."

Tom's eyes flashed. "Matt Kendall will never pay for a hired hand. He's too close and tight-fisted. I found that out when I was . . . !" He paused, as feelings almost overcame him, and then finished, in a whisper, ". . . going with Sue."

"Well, then—probably he's working for his board and keep," surmised Dave. "I've only just met him. I couldn't tell you much about it."

"Do you know where he came from?" persisted Tom.

"Yeah—he's a city guy from Chicago."

Tom shook his head. "A lot of help *he's* going to be on the farm!"

Dave grinned. "Well, he's got a pretty good build and with Sue to teach him . . ."

Tom squirmed in his bed. "Maybe I can begin sitting up a little each day," he said, changing the subject. He looked toward the crutches in the corner. "It'll probably be quite awhile before I can get strong enough to get around on them."

"Won't hurt you to try in a little while," encouraged Dave. He started again for the door. "I've got to get downstairs and talk to some of the members, before they get away, about their projects. I'll be seeing you."

Tom nodded. "What did you say that fellow's name was?" he called.

Dave stopped at the door. " 'Willard'," he informed. " 'Roy Willard'."

"Oh! . . . oh, yes . . . that's right! . . . Well, I sure hope he turns out to be a real help. I've been worrying about Sue. She mustn't lose *her* health, *too!*"

It was dusk and the splash of color the sun had painted in the sky was fading, as Sue Kendall finished the round of her nightly duties with the new farm hand. He was getting accustomed to the routine and had even tried, tonight, to milk the cow. They were headed now for the house with Roy carrying the pail of milk and Sue, the lantern, as he said: "That funny sound the bossy made when I took hold of her—do you suppose she was saying *'ouch'?*"

Sue laughed. "Or something worse than that!" she answered. "You'll be lucky if she ever forgives you!"

"I don't see why cows weren't born with faucets, anyway," said Roy.

"Oh, you'll catch on how to do it after a few times," reassured Sue. "And the cow won't mind at all."

"You mean—she won't kick me or step in the pail or switch her tail in my face any more?" asked Roy.

"No!" said Sue. "She's really a *lady,* when you treat her like one!"

They had reached the back porch and Roy set the pail of milk on the table.

"You folks all done?" called Matt Kendall, from the living room. "I'm gettin' hungry!"

Sue went to the doorway. "It won't be long now, Daddy. I just want to go out and have another look at the kid. We sewed him up and left him with his mother."

"Better bury that dog first thing in the mornin'!" her father said. "If you don't, we'll have every buzzard in the County on the place!"

Sue motioned to Roy, handing him the lantern, and the two slipped out of the house, to the barn. They approached the stall and, as Roy held the lantern high, both looked in.

The little kid was lying cuddled against his mother's side. It raised its head and blinked its eyes toward them.

"M-a-a-a-a-a!" it said.

"Hear that?" exclaimed Sue, happily. "He's going to be all right!"

"Good gosh!" said Roy, shaking his head. "The things you have to do on a farm!"

They left the barn for the night and stopped to look out over the woods which now formed a black fringe against the darkened sky. It was cold and clear and, as they gazed upward, more and more stars became visible.

Roy stood, entranced. "You could count to *a billion* and not even be started!" he said. "I never saw such a stretch of sky before. It makes you feel quite small, doesn't it?"

They were standing, their shoulders brushing each other.

"Not me," said Sue. "I always come out here under the stars when I'm troubled about something, and they seem to talk to me. They tell me how wonderful the world is, despite everything, and I feel all right again."

Roy set the lantern down on the ground and moved away from its illumination.

"Come over here," he invited. "You can see much better in the dark!"

Sue joined him. The boy from the city seemed strangely moved as he said, impulsively: "It's peaceful here with you. Gives me a different feeling than I've ever had before. Maybe, if I'd something like this a few years ago, I wouldn't have done what I did."

Sue looked toward him, sympathetically. His face was masked by the darkness but she could sense the struggle going on within him. She didn't know what to say so she just stood quietly, awaiting further expression from him.

"That little kid," said Roy, finally. "After what it went through tonight—happy and contented there with its mother.

"No one ever cared what happened to me. My mother died when I was two years old and Dad married again when I was five, and my stepmother hated and beat me. I couldn't do anything to please her, so I ran away from home and got mixed up with the wrong crowd and got in trouble . . . and then *more* trouble . . . and then, when I was twelve, they sent me to the reformatory . . ."

Roy suddenly reached out and touched Sue's arm. "Oh!" he exclaimed. "Did you see that? *A shooting star!*"

"Yes," said Sue. "I was looking right at it."

"So was I! That was a thrill!" Roy was silent for a moment, as his thoughts returned to himself, and Sue was about to start for the house when he spoke again. "The reform school didn't help me any. I came out worse than when I went in . . . Dad didn't know what to do with me and I stayed away from home as much as I could . . . sleeping in the parks . . . being chased by the police . . . hiding out with wrong guys. Despite all this, I managed to get through high school.

"When I got my diploma I thought, 'Well, Roy Willard, maybe here's where your luck changes. Maybe you can go out now and get a job and make something of yourself . . .'"

Roy laughed, bitterly. "Fat chance! My record was too bad. Nobody would give me a break. Dad and my stepmother were getting ready to split up . . . she was blaming me . . . and Dad took to blaming me, too. That was the pay-off.

"I joined a gang of fellows and we stuck up the manager of a filling station, one night, in South Chicago. I had a gun. He shot at us and I shot back. He fell and we beat it but someone had seen us and called the police. They cornered us before we'd gone a block in a car that one of the boys had stolen . . . We were all sent to jail for from one to five years. The guy I shot recovered or we'd have been sent to the chair.

"I got out after eight months on good behavior—but there was a robbery in our block which I didn't do. The police picked me up, just the same, and hung it on me. They brought me before Judge Braude, of Boys' Court. He took a look at me and said, 'Roy, I'm getting tired of seeing you up here and sending you away. I'm going to hold your case over and have a talk with your father. If he can find some place for you to go in the country, where you can get away from the old crowd in Chicago, I'd be in favor of putting you on probation and giving you a chance to straighten yourself out.'

"I told the Judge that I'd rather go back to the 'pen' than be farmed out some place—but he knew me better than I knew myself. He called Dad in and Dad wrote your father—and here I am!"

"And you really like it here?" asked Sue, deeply touched by his recital.

"It's the most wonderful place I've ever been," he said, huskily.

"You mean that—with all the things you've seen?"

Roy looked up at the stars and pointed. "That's worth more to me than all Chicago. Of course, there's the same sky there but you can't see it on account of the lights and buildings—and it doesn't *get* you like it does out here."

A shrill whistle suddenly screeched. Roy started.

"What's that?" he asked.

"That's Daddy," said Sue. "He's getting impatient. He wants his supper."

Roy picked up the lantern and they started toward the house.

"I'm trying to get used to your father," he said. "I've never run into anyone quite like him before."

Sue's reply was cautiously reserved. "I think Daddy would have been different if he hadn't been sick for so long."

"Maybe he would," said Roy, "but, just the same *I* wouldn't let him order me around the way he does *you*. Looks to me like you don't have a thought or a moment of your own."

"Daddy means all right," Sue defended.

"But he can't live your life for you and his, too," said Roy. "That's what my step-mother tried to do to me—and it won't work. You'll blow up, sooner or later . . . or walk out, like *I* did . . . or go to pieces. Something's bound to happen!"

Sue's hand was on the kitchen door. "I hope not," she said, fearsomely. "Daddy just couldn't get along without me."

Roy's reply was pointed with frankness. "Then he'd better get wise to himself—and start treating you *decently!*"

Chapter VI

THE HIDDEN VALLEY News Weekly was published each Friday. It was widely read by the farmer folk in Rock County for Editor Herb Bevins wisely kept its editorial style of news reporting true to the color and atmosphere of the back hills. He loaded it with personals, choice little morsels of news which home folks loved to chew over, such as:

> Si Willis came to town last week to have a tooth pulled.
>
> Mr. and Mrs. Ira Dailey had two things happen to them last week. One was good and the other bad. They welcomed a fine baby boy, born the 19th, and lost their home by fire on the 20th. We all congratulate them on the arrival of their son and sympathize with them on the loss of their home.
>
> Henry Cody, wife and eight children attended a family reunion in Okemah, Oklahoma, last week.
>
> Percy Evans of the Buffalo River country, north of here, has sold out and moved to Marked Tree, Poinsett County. Sorry to lose you, Percy.
>
> Guy Halsted, who bought the Percy Evans place, was in town yesterday. Welcome to this region, Guy!
>
> Sam Farris is erecting a new barn on his farm four miles east of here. He is going in for livestock raising.
>
> Ray Mackey, who fell off a truck and broke his arm in two places when it hit a boulder on Stony Creek Route, is mending nicely. Tough luck, Ray.

But the feature story of this week's paper concerned the formation of the Hidden Valley 4-H Club. Reporter Porky O'Connor had furnished Editor Bevins with a first-hand account of what had taken place at the organization meeting, held in the home of Fred and Anna Dodds. County Agent, Big Jim Watson, had supplied additional information. The aims and purposes of

75

the boys' and girls' farm group were outlined and this event became the leading topic of discussion in town and county.

Dave Carson, 4-H President, coming into Hidden Valley for a conference with the County Agent on club plans, suddenly thought of Mayor Ed Brannigan's invitation to drop in and see him. The Mayor's office was on the first floor of the Court House and Dave marched in. He caught the town's most prominent citizen, seated at his desk with Hidden Valley's News Weekly spread out before him.

As Mayor Brannigan looked up and saw Dave, his mouth fell open.

"Well!" he exclaimed, recovering his composure. "Come in, my boy, and have a chair! I was just reading about you. Quite a story! I see they made you President!"

Dave smiled as he shook hands. "Yes," he said. "I have *you* to thank for that. In fact, I have you to thank for this *whole thing!*"

"*Me?*" said the Mayor, staring hard at Dave. "Why, how's that?"

"What you said at my home-coming," explained Hidden Valley's returned war hero. As Mayor Brannigan looked a bit taken aback, he hastened to add: "You are absolutely right! I was trying to cover too much territory but I'll never forget your advice—that there were enough problems to solve right in this very community—and if I *really* wanted to do something, I could start right here at *home!*"

"Did I say that?" said Mayor Brannigan.

"Those were almost your exact words," said Dave, somewhat surprised.

Mayor Brannigan cleared his throat, uncomfortably.

"Well, I didn't mean for you to take me too . . . er . . . literally. I . . . er . . . a . . . just meant that every community has its problems . . . and . . . well—taking it all in all—we have a mighty good little town here. Most everyone's happy and contented . . ."

"Yes," said Dave, with rising zeal, "but there's lots of things that need to be done to make this a *better* town—and you probably read that the motto of 4-H is 'To Make the Best Better'!"

Mayor Brannigan's face sobered. "That's a great motto," he said, "if it's not carried too far. You young people aren't so much interested in improving the town, I take it, as you are in improving things on the farm. You've got enough right there to keep you busy!"

Dave nodded. "That may be true," he admitted. "But we consider Hidden Valley *our* town, too, since it's the County Seat and most of us do our trading here and go to school. For that very reason, we figure we ought to have better roads leading into Hidden Valley and the Public Square around the Court House should certainly have been paved long before this.

"On a windy day, I don't see how you merchants stand it, let alone the people on the streets. There're such clouds of dust flying, you have to close all the windows and doors, and folks from out in the country don't feel like standing around and talking or doing any extra shopping. These conditions mean less business and I know lots of farmers are driving thirty miles to Batesville, even though the roads are bad, so they can enjoy themselves in an up-to-date town, with modern conveniences, once they get there!"

Mayor Brannigan had leaned back in his chair and taken off his glasses. His heavy eyebrows were bunched in a disturbed scowl.

"Are you making a complaint or is this a threat of some kind?" he demanded.

Dave looked at him in astonishment. "Why, I'm just telling you how most of the people in Rock County feel about some things," he said, simply. "The only trouble is, they haven't been able to do anything about it before. But with this 4-H set-up, we can at last join with you city folks, Mr. Brannigan, and really fix up this town!"

For once in his public career, the biggest man in Hidden Valley was flabbergasted. Just how to diplomatically deal with this determined young man who had come back from war in a crusading spirit was the Mayor's "$64 question." He hoped he could answer it in a soothing and satisfactory manner because it was plain to him now that the younger generation of Rock County was on the move.

"If you'll allow me to say so," Ed Brannigan ventured, eyeing Dave Carson, carefully, "I think you're still trying to cover too much territory. Your 4-H Club organization is a fine thing if it's kept in the right and proper channels. But if you're going to mix your Club into town affairs which are, frankly, none of its business, then I can tell you, right now, that you're going to be in for trouble!"

Dave looked at the Mayor of Hidden Valley and shook his head, unbelievingly.

"Do you mean, Mr. Brannigan, that you and the citizens of this town aren't interested in co-operating with us to make this a better place to live in and to shop in? Do you mean you don't care if this town never has a sewage disposal system or any sanitary public toilets? Or paved highways leading into it?"

Mayor Brannigan was starting to rise from his chair but Dave was fired now and he kept going.

"Do you mean you don't care how long most of the people of Rock County have to do without electricity and telephones? And having their children miss school because the highways are so bad?"

Ed Brannigan had reached his feet by this time and was banging both fists on his desk.

"I mean, young man," he shouted, "that you're not only impertinent but a confounded meddler! I've done more for this town than any ten men in the County—yes, any *fifty* men! And you have the unadulterated nerve to come into my office and insinuate that I don't give a hoot about the town, the county and the people in it!"

Mayor Brannigan's voice took on a hurt quality. "Why, my boy," he said, "I was *born* in this great state. My father moved here to Hidden Valley when I was just a lad. He was one of this town's pioneers. He built the Brannigan Lumber Mills . . . !"

"Yes!" broke in Dave, "and he bought up all the first growth timber for miles around and cut it off without any thought of conservation—and *you* haven't done any better!"

"See here!" protested Ed Brannigan. "That's going too far!"

"No!" cried Dave, "I might as well go the *whole* way and get it out of my system! I can see right now why you don't want any improvements around this town. It doesn't cost you much to make donations to charity and throw home-coming celebrations. You charge that off to advertising. But when it comes to improving Hidden Valley and Rock County, that would mean raising taxes and with all the property *you* own in these parts, you'd have to shell out *real dough!*"

Ed Brannigan's face was on fire. He was so mad he was speechless.

"Why . . . you . . . you . . . !" he finally gasped. "I don't know why I ever welcomed *you* home! You're a bad influence in this community. You've gotten a little taste of the outside world and you've come back here sewing seeds of discontent from the moment you got off the train. That's a fine way to pay the community back for all it's done for you!

"I was the best friend you had in this town up to a few minutes ago. I would have done anything for you—*anything!* But I'm going on record as saying, here and now, that I won't do a thing for you or your 4-H bunch as long as you're President! They're under the wrong leadership and the sooner they realize it, the better for them. They won't get any support in this town as long as I'm Mayor!"

Dave stood up under this withering blast without blinking an eye. He was even grinning at the finish.

"Mr. Brannigan," he said. "What you've just said doesn't faze me a bit. I've had stiffer dressing downs from top sergeants!"

With that, Hidden Valley's returned war hero stamped out of the Mayor's office.

County Agent, Big Jim Watson, listened gravely to the 4-H President's recital of his run-in with the town's most prominent citizen.

"That's very unfortunate," he said. "This being a backward

county, with many poor farmers in it who possess little or no
political influence, it's been hard to get the politicians to make
needed improvements and repairs. Now, with Mayor Brannigan
against you, hardly anyone will dare to come right out in the
open and give you 4-H'ers real assistance."

"Then we'll get along, somehow, by ourselves!" declared Dave.

Big Jim shook his head. "4-H doesn't thrive on opposition,"
he said, "it thrives on *co-operation*. It's our job to make friends
and not enemies. You didn't step on Ed Brannigan's toes, a
few minutes ago—you jumped on both his feet. That hurt
because everything you told him was true and perhaps it's a
good thing, in the long run, that he heard it from somebody—but
when you're bucking Mayor Brannigan, you're just about bucking the whole town. I'm not even sure your 4-H Club can keep
going without his support."

Dave paced back and forth in the County Agent's office. "I
guess I'll have to learn to control my tongue," he said, regret-
fully. "This is the second time I've sounded off. But what's
our younger generation going to do? Bow and scrape to influential persons like Mr. Brannigan, as our parents are doing,
and put up with rotten conditions all *our* lives, too?"

Big Jim looked at Dave, admiringly. "I can't answer that.
I just know the forces you're up against, that's all. But since
you've declared war on the *home front,* all I can do, having
warned you, is to join the fight with you."

He extended his hand to Dave, who gave a smile of relief.

"That's swell, Mr. Watson," said Dave. "If you'll stick to me,
we'll get around Mr. Brannigan, somehow. If we could only
find some public-spirited citizen who wouldn't be afraid to
oppose him and who'd champion our club! Do you know any
such possibility?"

Big Jim nodded. "I was just coming to that. There's a new
man in town. His name's Sam Jordan. He's bought the Freeley
property, kitty-corner across the Square from Brannigan's General Store. He's going to raze the old frame building and put up
a modern stone, two-story, fire-proof structure."

"He *is!*" exclaimed Dave, interested. "What's he putting in there?"

"An up-to-date drug store," said Big Jim. "With the first and only soda fountain in Hidden Valley."

Dave's eyes gleamed. "Oh, brother—will *that* do business! He'll give Mr. Brannigan real competition!"

Big Jim nodded in agreement. "He most certainly will—and competition is something Mr. Brannigan doesn't like."

"It sounds to me as though Mr. Jordan could be our man," said Dave. "Have you met him?"

"Yes," said Big Jim. "Just this morning. County Judge, George Middleton, introduced me. I ran into them as they were coming into the Court House."

"Where do you suppose Mr. Jordan is now?" asked Dave.

"He's probably over at his property or at Brannigan's Dew Drop Inn," said Big Jim.

"Then what are we waiting for?" cried Dave. "Let's hit him right away! Lead me to him!"

Sam Jordan, the little man with big ideas, was poring over blueprints and discussing building operations with Sidney Pell, the town's leading architect and builder, when Dave and Big Jim located him back of the old Freeley store.

"I don't suppose you recall who I am," said Big Jim. "George Middleton introduced us this morning."

The bright-eyed, dynamic, bushy-haired Mr. Jordan gave his caller a quick, appraising look. "Oh, yes!" he recognized. "You're the County Agent! But your name *does* slip me. I'm not so good on names, anyway."

Big Jim smiled as the two shook hands again.

"My name's Watson. And I want you to meet the President of the new 4-H Club which was just organized. Dave Carson!"

The energetic Mr. Jordan turned to Dave, putting out his hand. "How do you do, Mr. Carson! Are you the young man I've been reading about in your town paper? Just back from the Service?"

"That's me," said Dave, quietly.

Mr. Jordan looked about for a place to talk. They were standing on the loading platform of the old store building which was covered with debris. The inside of the structure was a confusion of half-ripped out walls and sagging floors.

"I'd ask you folks in but everything around here's a mess," he apologized. "We're just starting to tear this flimsy old fire-trap down. Then we're going to lay a concrete foundation and put up the best stone structure in Hidden Valley."

"Yes, that's what Mr. Watson's been telling me," said Dave. "I think that's swell. The city council ought to pass a law, requiring every merchant who puts up a new building to build it out of stone. Our public square certainly looks unsightly with all those old wooden store fronts."

Mr. Jordan nodded. "You've got the right idea, Mr. Carson. It would improve the appearance of this town a great deal. But I've learned from past experience that changes like this take time. Lots of small town business men, especially, can't see any profit putting their money into a good building and equipment. I've found, however, that it pays. I've seen people come into towns like this before—and build attractive stores and take most of the business away from the old line merchants." He chuckled. "If you want to know the truth—that's what *I* intend to do *here!*"

All laughed, and lanky, sandy-haired builder Sidney Pell, stuffing blueprints in his pocket, said: "I guess a little competition won't hurt this town any. In fact," he winked, broadly, "it might do Hidden Valley a lot of good. I wouldn't want any of you gentlemen to quote me but I'm after thinkin' that Ed Brannigan's had things his own way around here about long enough!"

Mr. Jordan smiled. "Well, I can assure you of one thing," he predicted. "I'm going to give your Mr. Brannigan a run for his money!"

Dave's eyes glowed as he nudged Big Jim Watson.

"I'm glad to hear you say that, Mr. Jordan," he cried, impulsively. "That's what we . . . I mean . . ." as Big Jim punched him in the ribs, "That's what *I* came to see you about!"

The eyebrows of Hidden Valley's new business man raised with interest.

"It that so?" he said. Then, as he saw Dave hesitate, with a glance toward Builder Pell, who was looking on, curiously, he said: "I guess that covers everything, Sidney, for now. You go ahead with your wrecking crew and get this building down as soon as you can. I want to have Jordan's Drug Store up and ready for business by July Fourth!"

Builder Pell grinned and nodded. "You'll have it," he assured, "the best drug store in town."

"In *town!*" scoffed Mr. Jordan. "The best drug store in all of Rock County! As good as any you'll find in Batesville!" Then with a proud wave of the hand, "Yes—or even in *Little Rock!*" he concluded.

Builder Pell, laughing, took his departure. Sam Jordan, all five feet, six of him, sat himself down on the edge of the platform, after dusting it off with the top of a paper carton.

"Sit down here, men," he invited. "In a few months, I'll be entertaining you inside and we'll be seated in comfortable chairs at a little table, eating a chocolate sundae or sipping a soda!"

"I can hardly wait," said Dave.

Mr. Jordan eyed him, pleasantly. "All right, Mr. Carson, since you favor my giving your town's biggest man a run for his money, what have you come here to propose?"

Dave was about to let out a torrent of words, then bit his tongue and looked appealingly toward the County Agent.

"Perhaps *I* can explain what Mr. Carson has in mind," Big Jim volunteered. "He's come back from the Service, eager to do something for his home community. He's seen the advantages that other people have and he wants to get the same advantages for the folks here. That's why he's organized this 4-H Club, with my help, but a group like this needs the guidance and support of the business men as well as farmers in this region.

"Unfortunately, some of the improvements Dave would like his 4-H members to go to work on, don't meet with Mayor Brannigan's approval. Mr. Carson found that out a short time

ago, when he told the Mayor what he had in mind and Ed
Brannigan told Dave, in no uncertain terms, that he would have
nothing to do with the 4-H'ers and their projects!"

Sam Jordan slid down off the platform, his bright eyes popping. He looked like a little Napoleon.

"Oh, he *did,* did he?" he said, excitedly. "Well, that's just
fine! I've had *my* run-in with your Mayor, too—and I'm ready to
state to you that anything *he's* against—*I'm* FOR!"

Dave could not control an exultant exclamation. "That's great,
Mr. Jordan!" he cried. "Simply great! Then you mean you'll
help us?"

"You bet I'll help!" declared the fiery little business man.
"Anything you want in time, money, merchandise! When I
get my store built, you can make your headquarters in the front
rooms above—write your own ticket! This town's going to be
my home and I want to do everything I can to help improve it!"

Dave's joy was unbounded. He grabbed Mr. Jordan's hand and
shook it. "Can we make a public announcement of your support?" he asked.

"I should say you can!" said Sam Jordan. "I'll take an ad in
the paper, myself, extending my congratulations and best wishes
to you 4-H young people. Anything I can do, just call on me."
He reached in an inside pocket and drew out a checkbook.
"Here," he said. "I'll start you out with a contribution. You
can't do anything worthwhile without a little money behind it."

He produced a ball-point pen and wrote out a check, handing
it to Dave. "Take this over to Mr. Brannigan's bank and open
a special account in the name of your Hidden Valley 4-H Club
for 'Civic Improvements.' You might even call this little deposit
to his attention—and give him my compliments!"

Dave glanced unbelievingly at the check. It was made out
for *five hundred dollars!*

"This is going to make Mr. Brannigan awfully mad!" he said.

Sam Jordan laughed, imperturbed. "The madder he gets, the
better I'll like it," he said.

"I don't know how to thank you," stammered Dave.

Hidden Valley's new business man gave another wave of his hand. "Don't try. If Mr. Brannigan considers it good advertising to give you a home-coming celebration, it's certainly good public relations for *me* to back your 4-H Club. I know something about this 4-H work. If you young folks get off to the right start, you can turn this community upside down!"

"This is mighty fine of you," said County Agent Jim Watson. "It's too bad that a man as influential as Mr. Brannigan should be so short-sighted. It's going to mean a great deal to the town of Hidden Valley to have a public-spirited citizen like you and it's going to mean even *more* to these fine farm boys and girls of Rock County."

He took Dave's arm and led the dazed President of the 4-H Club from the presence of the littlest business man in Hidden Valley who now, in Dave's eyes and estimation, had become the *biggest*.

Chapter VII

THERE WERE FAMILY conferences in many homes in that section of Rock County which surrounded Hidden Valley as boy and girl 4-H Club members discussed with their parents what projects they would elect to work on. It was a question of importance out-weighing all others which must be decided as quickly as possible so that youthful enthusiasm could begin expressing itself.

Lyle "Porky" O'Connor had quite a time convincing his father that raising pigs the 4-H way would produce better hogs than the methods his parent had been using for years.

"A hog's a hog," said Farmer Alf O'Connor, "'n' y'cain't teach him any diff'rent. Y'mean to tell me y'want t' pick one o' my best sows 'n' take her litter when she farrows 'n' feed 'em all by theirselves? What're y' gonna try t' do—learn 'em table manners?"

"No, Pop," laughed Porky. "I'm going to try to fatten them up by modern, scientific methods."

Farmer O'Connor guffawed. "Son, yer fixin' t' waste yerself an awful pack o' time. These County agent fellers kin think o' more ways fer t' keep a farmer busy when he ain't got 'nough hours in the day now. But if'n y'want to be nurse-maid to a bunch o' pigs, I reckon y'kin go ahead."

"That's swell, Pop," said Porky. "I want to build myself my own hog-house and have my own pasture. I'd like to plow up that land across the road from where your hogs are now and plant it to oats and get it ready for the pigs to run on. Let me mix my own slop and feed my pigs, after they get weaned, according to my own ideas—and we'll see who has the best hogs by fall!"

Farmer Alf O'Connor gave a snort of amusement. "Go to it, son! I'm not a stoppin' y' but I'm raisin' hogs t' sell t' market 'n' t' make money, not t' put in a side-show!"

"Okay, Pop," grinned Porky, good-naturedly. "You raise your

hogs like you've always done and I'll raise mine like the Extension Service tells me to—and I'll bet you I'll have fatter hogs and more money when we get through."

Farmer O'Connor's laugh was derisive. "I'm not bettin' y', son, becuz y'd *lose!*"

In the Hilton home, three attractive daughters barricaded their parents in the kitchen after supper and wouldn't let them go until they had agreed to co-operate on their chosen projects.

Carolyn wanted to work at becoming an "All-Around" homemaker, and trying to win the 4-H Girls Record Contest. Eleanor had chosen "Home Grounds Beautification" as her project, while it was Doris' desire to take up canning. All three sisters wished to learn more about making their own clothing and possibly competing in the Dress Revue. They kept up a running fire of cross comment which soon had their parents "on the ropes" and begging for mercy.

"All right! All right!" said John Hilton, raising hands above his head. "We'll do anything you say, only please keep still! I don't know what I've ever done to have the Lord treat me this way. On a farm where a man needs hired hands, I prayed for three boys and got three girls. After that I was afraid to pray any more!"

The girls screamed with laughter and Mrs. Hilton, coming to their defense, said: "Now, John, you've said yourself they've done almost as much work in the field as most men and you're glad the Lord disappointed you!"

Farmer Hilton grinned, sheepishly. "Well, a man's got to put up with whatever he gets in this life. If you girls keep on growing up, maybe I won't have to wait much longer to get some boys, after all!"

Mrs. Hilton smiled. "I think that would be just as nice," she said, "to be called 'Mother' by the boys you girls marry."

"And to be called 'Grandmother', too," suggested her husband, "that's a nicer part yet!"

Eyes were suddenly misty as all laughed softly together, and the girls blushed prettily. There was affection in the Hilton family that ran deep and fresh and strong, like the pure well water under their place.

"Say, Carolyn," spoke up Eleanor. "Not wanting to get off our projects, but what's the matter with Dave? He's been home over a week and hasn't been out to see you."

"You don't have to remind me," said the oldest of the Hilton sisters, "I guess he's just been too busy. At least, I hope that's the reason!"

"Dave's a fine young man," said Mrs. Hilton. "Of course, not seeing him for around two years, I wouldn't know how much he might be changed, but I've always been glad he seemed to be interested in you."

"So have *I,*" said Carolyn, frankly. "And he wrote me such wonderful letters . . ."

John Hilton interposed a thought. "You don't suppose there's been any feeling on the Carsons' part because we didn't get in to the home-coming and weren't able to go with you girls to the 4-H meeting, do you?"

The three sisters exchanged consulting glances.

"I wouldn't think so," said Carolyn.

"If Aunt Ella hadn't been so ill all week," said Mrs. Hilton. "But I think we know the Carsons too well for them to be upset by not seeing us."

"Dave couldn't have been nicer to us," recalled Doris. "Of course there wasn't any chance for him to really see Carolyn, either time."

"But he *did* manage to tell me," reported Carolyn, "that he hoped to be seeing me soon."

John Hilton scratched a favorite place behind his left ear. "Well, if that's the case, I wouldn't worry too much. He's gotten mixed up in this 4-H business . . ." He gave a sidewise glance at his daughters. "And you girls have, too, for that matter," he added. "Then he's probably had lots of folks to see and maybe some relatives at the house, all of which is tolerably discouraging to romance."

"That sounds logical," considered Carolyn, somewhat relieved. "I confess, I'd begun to wonder . . ."

Eleanor and Doris laughed. "We only wish we had someone
as promising as Dave to wonder about," said Eleanor.

"She's right about *that!*" seconded Doris. "They just don't
come by the door, every day, like Dave."

All three girls heard the sound of the motor at the same time.
A car was turning in at their drive and making the climb up
the hill.

"Speak of the devil . . .!" cried Eleanor and Doris.

"That's the Carson car, all right," identified John Hilton.
"You see, Carolyn, I told you not to worry."

Carolyn leaped to her feet, eyes dilated with excitement. "But
I *am* worrying! Just look at my hair—my dress—I'm a sight!
Girls, come on upstairs and help me! Dad—Mother—you en-
tertain Dave till I get ready!"

The three sisters flew out of the room and up the stairs with
Carolyn in the lead. John and Myrtle Hilton sat, momentarily,
at the supper table, looking at one another. He reached across
and patted her hand.

"I'd pray for another daughter," he said, "if I thought I could
stand it!"

She raised his calloused hand to her lips and kissed it.

There was the sound of a car door slamming, then footsteps
on the front porch which had been only too familiar, more than
two years ago.

"It seems like it was just yesterday," said Father Hilton, getting up from his chair and starting toward the living room.
"Come on, Mother—let's go to the door together."

Dave Carson's old-time rap sounded: *ta—ta-ta-ra-ta—ta-ta!*

The parents of Carolyn Hilton swung open the door. They
beheld an older, more mature young man but with the same
infectious smile and the same blue serge suit, now tight-fitting,
which he used to wear when he had come calling before the war.
He was carrying a small package, wrapped in green paper, which
looked suspiciously like a box of candy.

"Say, you folks haven't changed a bit!" he greeted, as he came in. "It certainly seems good to see you again! I must apologize for not getting up here sooner. I've intended doing it every night but things kept coming up. Is Carolyn home?"

"Yes, she's home!" called Eleanor, from the head of the stairs. "And so are Doris and I! Did you bring a couple of extra fellows with you?"

"Not tonight," Dave answered.

"That's too bad," replied Doris, "then Carolyn will have to share you with *us!*"

"You girls hush up!" laughed Mrs. Hilton. "Come on in by the fireplace, Dave—and sit down."

Dave dropped in his usual place on the over-stuffed sofa, nearest the fire.

"This room hasn't changed any, either," he said, in a pleased voice, looking around. "I like places and people, that I'm fond of, to stay the same—or, at least, so I can recognize them!"

John Hilton laughed. "I didn't think, from reports the girls have brought us, that you wanted *any*thing to stay the same. Seems to me you've started right in to change the town and county and all the people in it!"

"Well . . . a . . . not exactly!" said Dave, a trifle embarrassed.

"You've already upset the routine of this household," continued Carolyn's father, enjoying Dave's discomfiture. "If you keep on and my daughters get much more involved in 4-H work, I'm apt to have to give up farming and devote my full time to helping them on their projects!"

Dave laughed. "I thought, for a moment, you were serious. I know a lot of parents aren't sure how this new activity's going to work out. I'm hearing that some of them think it's a lot of nonsense and others don't think we can get anywhere, even if we try."

"We don't think that," said Mrs. Hilton. "We know you young people can do big things when you get underway."

"Don't get me started on this subject," warned Dave. "Dad says that's one of my faults—once I get going on something, I never let up!"

"That's a pretty good fault, sometimes," said John Hilton. "The world owes a great deal to men who persisted with good ideas until they put them over."

Dave's enthusiasm began to rise within him. "Mr. Hilton," he said, "before we're through, we're going to get electricity out here and a telephone and a paved road. You'll be able to live just as well as people do in the city. And, as for the town of Hidden Valley . . . !" He broke off abruptly and stood up as he glimpsed a golden-haired vision coming down the stairs. "Here's Carolyn!" he announced, "I'll have to tell you about this later. I promised my folks I wouldn't fill you up on 4-H, anyway!"

The girl he was calling on swept prettily into the room. She was wearing a bright red dress of her own making. It was cut on the simplest lines but its very simplicity accentuated her blonde beauty.

"Good evening, Mr. Carson!" she said, and laughed.

Their eyes met and held each other, for a moment.

"Well, *hello!*" said Dave, when he had located his voice.

They shook hands a bit self-consciously and Father Hilton, clearing his throat, motioned to his wife.

"Chores aren't quite done," he said. "Glad you're back, Dave. You must come over often."

Dave had eyes only for Carolyn. "Yes," he said, with genuine fervor, as he looked at her, "I certainly *must!*"

The older folks slipped from the room and then, for the seemingly longest moment, there was no voice or sound but the occasional snap and crack of the blaze in the fireplace. Carolyn's lips were trembling and her eyes were moist, as though a wisp of smoke from the open hearth had touched them.

"I've missed you, Dave," she whispered, as she placed a hand upon his arm. "I've missed you terribly!"

Dave closed his strong hand over hers and drew her gently toward him. "I've missed you, too," he said.

He had her in his arms and their lips joined in a kiss which spoke more eloquently of the feeling each had for the other than words could ever convey. The glow from the fireplace projected their blended forms like a magic lantern on the living room wall. The sharp pistol-like report of a burning log brought them back to this world.

Dave did not want to let her go but she would not let him kiss her again, just then. Instead, she led him to the sofa and was about to sit down, when he cried: "Hey, wait a minute!"

As she looked at him in wonderment, he reached around behind her and rescued the box wrapped in green paper.

"Here's a little something I brought all the way from New York. It doesn't amount to so much but you can't get any decent brands like this around here."

Carolyn unwrapped the package, tossing the paper and string in the fire. It burst into flame immediately and the light shone on the golden box in her hand.

"Schrafft's!" she exclaimed. "Oh, Dave— I've seen this advertised so much and I've never had a piece of this candy in my life!"

She lifted off the lid with an expression of delighted anticipation.

"Have one, kind sir!" she offered.

"After you," he smiled, and leaned forward and kissed her cheek. "You're sweeter than any candy—sweeter than any girl I ever knew!"

"I think I'll take this one," said Carolyn, her head bent purposely low over the box.

"I picked that color box because I thought it matched your hair," said Dave. "It almost does, too. It's *beautiful!*"

"The box—or my hair?" laughed Carolyn.

"You know which!" said Dave, and tried to kiss her, but she pressed a chocolate between his lips.

"That's not the *kind* of sweets I want!" he protested.

"I think they're very nice," fenced Carolyn.

They were seated on the sofa now with the box of candy between them. Dave subsided, momentarily.

"I thought you were *never* going to get around to seeing me," she said, after a minute of munching.

"I certainly came home all wound up," Dave admitted. "But

I guess I've come down to earth now. I've been doing a lot of thinking since I've been away. I made up my mind what I wanted in life, if I got back home safe." He eyed her, testily. "And the first and most important thing was—*you*."

Carolyn's face had sobered. She reached down and slipped the cover on the box of candy.

"I brought something else from New York for you," Dave continued, sliding his hand in a side pocket. "I went into a store on Fifth Avenue and I told the clerk who waited on me that I wasn't any millionaire but I'd been saving up my Service pay for a girl back home who was worth more to me than all the money in the world—and I wanted him to sell me the best diamond ring my dollars could buy!"

Dave produced an exquisite little jewel box and handed it to Carolyn. She took it in trembling fingers and fumbled a moment before she could open it. The brightest sparkle in the room was no longer in the fireplace. It came from a tiny stone set in a golden band against a velvety purple cushion.

"Oh, Dave!" she cried, and smothered a happy sob. "From *Tiffany's!* Oh, it's just too, *too* beautiful!"

"The man said, if you didn't like it, I could send it back," said Dave.

Carolyn looked up at him, smiling through her tears. "I'm afraid," she said, "that he's never going to see this again!" She took it from the little case and held it out to him. "Would you put it on for me?" she whispered, softly.

Dave's own hand was none too steady as he took the ring. "Let's see," he said, "which hand—I mean—which *finger* does this go on?"

Carolyn, eyes fixed upon Dave, held out the fourth finger of her left hand. He took it, a trifle clumsily, and both held their breaths as he slid on the ring.

"It fits!" she cried, joyfully.

And Dave, before she could draw her hand away, bent forward and kissed the ring and finger.

Carolyn gave him her lips and when they felt like talking

after that, Dave said: "I'm not ready to be married quite yet and I don't suppose you are, either—but it means everything just to know that we're going to belong to each other. Dad said he'd give me some of his five hundred acres and a pure bred beef herd of my own, when we're ready. But I want to build us a home and building materials and supplies and labor are not only still scarce but practically out of sight as to price. The government says it's going to do something about housing for ex-G.I.'s—and perhaps, if we wait a few months . . . !"

Carolyn gave his hand a squeeze. "Of course we'll wait," she said. "I want to get a little better prepared to make you a good wife."

"I'm not worrying about that," assured Dave.

"No," laughed Carolyn, "but *I* am."

Dave stood up, suddenly, eyes lighting with the force of an idea. "Say, Carolyn!" he cried, excitedly. "It just occurs to me —I don't know why I didn't think of this before! Tom Dodds has all the materials for a home stored in his father's barn, ready for building. Remember—they even put in the foundation back on the place! But now that he and Sue aren't going to be married, maybe he'd sell that house to *us!*"

Carolyn's excitement matched Dave's. "If he only *would!*" she exclaimed.

"I'll see him about this, first chance I get," Dave promised. "Of course we'd have to follow their house plans as the lumber and everything's all made to fit, but I don't think you'd object to that so much. I saw the blueprints, once, and I think it would make us a cozy little home!"

Carolyn's eyes were dancing. "Oh, Dave, it all sounds *wonderful!* I just hope Tom *will* sell! I don't see any reason why he shouldn't!"

"I don't, either," said Dave. "In fact, I've a hunch, under the circumstances, he'll really be glad to get rid of it!"

They kissed each other joyously and then became conscious of a stir in the room which was not the fire. They looked up to see Eleanor and Doris, standing in the doorway.

"We thought we'd given you enough time," said Eleanor.

"Shall we go back and try again?" asked Doris.

Dave and Carolyn slipped their arms about one another.

"No," said Dave, no longer embarrassed. "Come in and be the first to congratulate me!"

The two younger sisters of the Hilton trio registered mock surprise.

"Oh, Dave! . . . Carolyn! . . . Not *really* . . . !"

Then, as if by pre-arranged design, they raced, not toward Dave, but toward the kitchen, crying: "Mother! . . . Father! . . . Come in here, quick! . . . She GOT him!"

Chapter VIII

It was Saturday morning of the day the Hidden Valley 4-H Club was to have its second meeting at the Dodds' home when Frank Carson, Local Leader, had a visitor. She arrived on foot, having walked three miles further out on the Stony Creek Route from her own place, to see him.

The air was raw with clouds spitting a varying mixture of snow and rain. Dave's father had just returned to the house from the barn where he had been inspecting some of his five-month-old beef calves. He stood on the front porch and watched the black-haired young woman as she turned in at the gate and swung up the path toward him.

"Well!" he greeted. "Quite a trip up here! Bad weather, too! Hope you didn't come to see Dave as he's not at home."

"No, Mr. Carson," said Sue Kendall, soberly. "I came to see *you.*"

"Fine! Then, come right in!" He opened the door and gestured inside. "You look like you're chilled through. Get in there next to the fire."

Sue hesitated. "I—I'd like to see you *alone,*" she said. "It's something extremely personal."

Frank Carson nodded. "We've got the whole house to ourselves," he said. "Mrs. Carson's gone over to be with Dave's Aunt Ella. She's been pretty sick."

"Oh, I'm sorry to hear that," said Sue.

She went into the spacious living room which radiated a cheery warmth.

Frank Carson could see that she was under tension of some kind so he poked up the fire and said nothing as Sue rubbed stiff hands and stamped her feet.

"Guess I got a little colder than I thought."

Her 4-H Leader smiled. "You'll warm up quickly enough in here. Just let me slip off your coat."

Sue switched her curly dark hair to one side as the coat came off. Then she sat in a straight chair close to the fire.

"That's not very comfortable," said Frank Carson. "Wouldn't you rather sit over here?" He pointed to his overstuffed easy chair.

But Sue shook her head. "No, thanks. I'd get lost in it and I'd have a hard time getting out. This is all right."

Dave's father slid into the chair himself and took out his favorite pipe, spanking it on the palm of his hand. Then he drew on it as he eyed Sue, waiting for her to disclose the reason for her visit.

Matt Kendall's daughter made a pretense of warming her hands longer than was needed. Her Leader was just in the act of lighting his pipe when Sue finally turned and, with tears in her eyes, suddenly blurted out: "Mr. Carson, I can't belong to the Club! My father's against it!"

"Well," said Frank Carson, easily, "that's not so unusual, Sue. Lots of folks have been against 4-H in the beginning. They were against County Agents, too, and specialists in the Extension Service and the Department of Agriculture . . . and scientists and professors who've tried to show them better and more profitable ways to do things. But most folks, in time, though they took a lot of convincing, changed their minds. When your father finds out a little more about the work, he may change *his* mind, too."

Sue regarded him doubtfully. "You don't know my Daddy," she said. "He's awfully set in his ways." She hesitated, and then went on: "But I didn't come to see you about myself, Mr. Carson. I wanted to talk to you about the boy who's come to live on our place."

"Oh, yes!" said her Leader, concealing his quickening interest. "Dave's told me a little about him. Came from Chicago, didn't he?"

Sue nodded. "Yes, sir. His father wasn't happily married and he didn't get along well with his stepmother. Mr. Willard and my Daddy were boyhood friends and Roy's father sent him out here to us. He was resentful, naturally, and didn't like it at first, but he's gotten interested now and I think he needs . . . well, he's not a farm boy, of course—but since he's going to stay here . . . I was wondering if he couldn't join the 4-H . . . and work with you and everybody . . . I think it would help him a lot . . ."

Frank Carson exhaled a puff of smoke and watched it rise toward the ceiling. He chewed thoughtfully at the end of his pipe and looked at Sue who was eyeing him, hopefully.

"What do you think he might be interested in doing?" he asked.

Sue's eyes glowed. "Anything with animals!" she said. "He just loves them, Mr. Carson. Why, one of our little kids got badly torn by a dog some days ago, and Roy helped me sew it up, and ever since he's been hanging around the stall where I've been keeping the kid with the mother, doing what he could for it.

"He gets awfully melancholy, though, thinking of his past . . . I mean . . ." She caught herself, "all his unhappiness at home. He doesn't feel that he *belongs* anywhere . . . and it seemed to me, if he could be invited to take part in a project . . . that he'd get a new hold on himself."

"Could be," said her Leader, reflectively. "I'd have to see the boy first and have a talk with him. Have you discussed 4-H with him?"

"Well, yes," said Sue, "I've told him about it and he knows Daddy's against my belonging. But he's in a different position. If he wanted to join, I don't see how Daddy could stop him. Roy's got quite a mind of his own," she added, half in explanation. "Besides, as much as I'd love the work, he needs it more than I do."

Frank Carson stood up and reached for Sue's coat which he had thrown over the back of another chair.

"Come on," he said. "I'll drive you home. I want to have a talk with your father and Roy."

A flash of fear and apprehension shot into Sue's face. "Oh, I don't know, Mr. Carson—if that would be the way to do it.

I guess I'll have to tell you—my Daddy doesn't think so much of you. He says you and Dave are trying to run this community. He doesn't know I've come to see you. He'd be terribly angry with me if he did. Can't you work it out some other way?"

Her 4-H Leader nodded, understandingly. "I've got to go in town, anyway. I'll drop you off at your road and let you go home alone. Then I'll run in for a visit with your father on the way back. The going may be a little rough but don't you worry, Sue. I'll do what I can for this boy—and for you, too!"

"I'd appreciate it ever so much," said Matt Kendall's daughter, as they left the house and went toward the car, parked in the driveway. "But don't mind me, I'll get along, somehow."

Matt Kendall heard the sound of a car approaching on his steep, rocky road. He pressed the field glasses between his mis-shapen hands and lifted them to his eyes. What he saw, surprised and irritated him.

"It's Frank Carson a-comin'!" he called to Sue. "Now what in tarnation is *he* up to? He ain't been around in *months!*"

It was shortly after the noon meal and within an hour of the time for the 4-H meeting at Dodds'.

"If he's a-comin' up here to try to git me to let you go to them doin's, he's a-wearin' out tires and burnin' up gasoline for nothin'!"

Sue, having finished washing the dishes, carried the pan of soapy water to the back door, and emptied it.

"Sue!" her father called. "I'm a-talkin' to you! Do you know what Frank Carson's comin' here for?"

Sue hung the dishpan on the kitchen wall and untied her apron, draping it on a nearby hook.

"How should I know?" she answered, nervously.

The car had reached the rough turn-around beside the house and was coming to a stop. Frank Carson's figure slid out from behind the wheel and walked toward the front door. He was momentarily lost to sight but Matt Kendall was following the footsteps as they crunched on the gravel—the firm, steady strides of a positive, determined individual.

There was a solid rap on the door. Sue started across the living room to answer it but her father snapped: "You stay out. I may want to give Frank Carson a piece of my mind and it might not be pretty for you to hear."

"But, Daddy!" protested Sue, in a low voice. "That's no way to act. Mr. Carson's just trying to be friendly . . . !"

"How do *you* know what he's a-tryin' to be?" ranted Matt Kendall. Then, with a canny glance at her, he fired: "Have you been a-talkin' to him? Is that where you was this mornin'? . . . You turned up that way on the road . . . !"

Sue, startled, could not conceal a trapped expression. "No!" she cried, involuntarily.

Her father's gnarled hand tapped agitatedly on the table top. "That's it!" he deduced. "This here's a *put-up job!*"

The solid rap was repeated.

Matt Kendall raised a bony finger and shook it at his daughter. "You git out o' this room and git, quick! You two ain't goin' to work on me. I'll have words with you later!"

Sue, in tears, retreated into the kitchen and closed the door.

"Come in!" barked the chronic invalid.

The door knob turned under the firm hand of one of Rock County's most progressive farmers. A smiling Frank Carson stood in the doorway.

"Hello, Matt!" he greeted, stepping in and shutting the door behind him. "I thought it was about time I risked my life and my car on your hill and came up to see you."

"I don't know as I'm a-thankin' you for doin' it!" glowered the semi-helpless man in the chair. "Never mind inquirin' after my health, Frank Carson. You just be a-statin' your business!"

Dave's father tossed his hat on a chair and threw open his coat. "All right," he said, accepting the challenge, "I've come here to see you about two matters. One is your daughter—and the other is the boy you've got staying with you."

Matt Kendall sucked in the corners of his mouth so that the scant flesh pulled tight over his cheek bones.

"What about 'em?" he demanded.

"I want them both in my 4-H Club," said Frank Carson. "You probably know I'm the Local Leader."

"Yes, I know that—and I know all I want to know about the whole business!" exploded Matt Kendall.

His unwelcome visitor pulled up a chair and sat down, directly facing him.

"That's your trouble, Matt. You don't know enough about what's going on outside any more to really know anything! You've been tied down to that chair and you've let it tie your mind down, too. Things are happening out in the world. Young people are going places—and you can't stop your daughter or this boy from going places, either. If you try, you'll only hurt yourself."

Matt Kendall moistened dry, thin lips with his tongue. "Came up here to preach to me, did you? I ain't asked for any help from this community. I ain't even asked for sympathy. I just want to be let alone."

"Most folks are letting you alone," said Frank Carson. "If you keep on, you won't have a friend left in the County. But you've got a wonderful daughter, and if you don't care for yourself, you might think of her and her future!"

"She's doin' all right here with me!" rejoined Sue's father. "I ain't heard her complain."

"She's not the sort who complains—but you've no right, Matt, to keep her from enjoying the friendship and the satisfaction of working with young people her own age—doing things worthwhile."

"I know what's best for her," declared Matt Kendall. "And, as for the boy, you ain't goin' to touch him, either! He's under my care and I'm responsible for him."

Frank Carson surveyed the emaciated figure, propped in the easy chair.

"I've just barely met the boy," he said, "We gave him and Sue a lift from town, the day Dave arrived. Sue tells me he's a fine fellow."

"When did she tell you that?" Matt Kendall's eyes were boring.

"It doesn't matter *when*," side-stepped the 4-H Club Leader. "But if Roy Willard is going to make his home with you, we want him as a member of our Club. He'll get a training there, in a few months, that will make him much more valuable to you—and to himself."

Sue's father, face twitching, looked out the window. Then, his eyes came back to rivet upon his caller.

"How much has Sue been after tellin' you about this boy?" he asked.

"Not much, except that he came from an unhappy home and that he likes it here in the country. That's enough for me."

Matt Kendall gave vent to a dry, cackling laugh.

"You won't be so anxious to be doin' somethin' for this boy when *I* git through tellin' you about him. You didn't know that he's got a prison record, I reckon—and that he's just out on probation! That kinda changes things, don't it? . . . You won't want him to be mixin' with the *nice* boys and girls of Rock County . . ."

Frank Carson had risen from his seat and Matt Kendall laughed again, that shrill, hollow sound in his throat.

"I thought so! . . . You're only interested in *pure bred stock*. You and your bunch o' 4-H *reformers!* . . . You won't be wantin' my daughter any more, either—seein' as how she's livin' under the same roof with an *ex-convict!* . . . Well, you got your own ideas of how to do things—and I got mine—but how many of you'uns would even take a no-good boy in like I've done . . .? Answer me *that*, Frank Carson!"

Matt Kendall had taken extreme relish in turning the tables. His visitor was in full retreat now, toward the door. This exposure of Roy's real background had changed the whole picture. Now, maybe "better-than-thou" people like Frank Carson would let him alone; stop getting Sue all excited about outside activities and interests!

His visitor was turning at the door, hand on the knob.

"Where is Roy Willard now?" he was asking.

Matt Kendall sat upright, body straining.

"He's out in the barn. Why?"

"I'm going out to see him," said the 4-H Local Leader of Hidden Valley. Then, in a surprisingly kindly and respectful tone, he added: "I've changed my opinion of you considerably, Matt Kendall . . . You're a *real human being,* after all . . . But I'm not going to let you help this boy all alone—you just can't do for him all that needs to be done. You've got to let me do *my* bit, too!"

"You stay away from him!" raged Sue's father.

Frank Carson smiled. "Stop shouting, Matt. I don't scare that easy. After what I know now, you couldn't keep me away from this boy with a branding iron!"

The crippled form of Matt Kendall subsided, fuming but exhausted, in his easy chair.

The boy from the city was wearing a pair of Matt Kendall's long unused overalls and an old shirt and sweater of his own, when Frank Carson came upon him. He had just finished cleaning out the barn and was leaning over the stall bar, talking to the little kid which Sue still kept confined.

"You're almost as good as new, Cutie," he was saying, unaware of anyone near. "That was some repair job she performed on you. If it wasn't for those little pieces of thread sticking out, I couldn't even see where you were sewed up . . . !"

"M-a-a-a-a-a-a!" cried the kid.

"That's a fact," laughed Roy. "I know you're lonely in there all by yourself, but you'll have your mother back tonight, and tomorrow you can run with the herd again!"

Tomorrow not being today, the little kid cried some more. Roy slid down from his perch on the stall and started as he saw a man standing quietly by.

"Oh! Mr. Carson!" he recognized. "How long have you been here?"

"Not long," smiled Dave's father. "I didn't want to break in on an important conversation."

Roy laughed a bit sheepishly. "I don't think he understands

me very well but, somehow, the little thing seems almost human to me. You just feel like talking to him."

"I know," agreed Frank Carson. "Lots of folks don't realize it but a person can get mighty attached to a goat." Then, eyeing Roy closely, he asked: "You're pretty fond of animals, anyway, aren't you?"

The boy from the city nodded. "I guess I am," he said. "I didn't realize it until I got out here. This little kid was hurt and . . ."

"Yes, Sue's been telling me," cut in Mr. Carson. Then, pointedly: "Roy, I've come to have a talk with you. As Leader of this new 4-H Club, I want our young people to make as good a showing as possible. We're going to need all the help we can get on our projects. Will you join up and work with us?"

The unexpectedness of the proposal left Roy momentarily speechless. "You don't want me," he said, finally. "I don't know anything about farming."

"No, but you have a real interest in animals," said the best beef breeder in Rock County. "And if you really wanted, you could learn to raise a beef calf."

"Yeah!" grinned Roy, "but I'd have to *have* the calf first!"

"That part could be arranged," Frank Carson assured. "You've got good pasture land for an animal up here. Of course, if a professional started out with a five-months-old beef calf to raise a champion, the calf would be kept on milk for awhile—but it's not the most economical method of feeding. How many cows does Mr. Kendall have?"

"Only one," said Roy, ruefully, "and that's twice too many for me. I've been trying to milk her but I haven't got the hang of it yet and every time she sees me coming, she tries to break out of the stall!"

Dave's father grinned. "My son had the same experience some years ago. He didn't think he'd ever learn how—but now he can milk with the best of them." Frank Carson looked about the barn. "Do you have a place where you could keep a beef calf?"

"Oh, there's room, all right," said Roy, "but how am I going to get a calf? I haven't any money, and besides, Mr. Kendall wouldn't . . . !"

"Yes, he will!" insisted Frank Carson, quietly. "I've just been talking with him. You let *me* handle him. The main question is—do you think you'd like to tackle something like this?"

Roy hesitated. "Well, I don't know. I might not be here too long . . . and Mr. Kendall's been keeping me so busy, I don't think I'd have the time."

"I tell you what you do," proposed Frank Carson. "You come with me to the house and slip into some other clothes, and let me take you to the 4-H meeting, with Sue. You can meet the other girls and fellows there and learn about the projects they're going to work on—and make up your mind later."

Roy's eyes widened. "I thought Mr. Kendall wasn't going to let Sue belong to that Club," he said. "And *me*—I'm really an *outsider* . . . !"

Frank Carson took him by the arm. "Oh, no, you're not," he smiled. "I've seen enough of you, right now, to know that you're *one* of us! Come along!"

Sue Kendall was surprised that her father did not call her in immediately after Frank Carson left. She remained in the kitchen with the door closed, and saw her 4-H Leader go around the house to the barn.

She almost wished, now, that she hadn't acted on impulse and gone to him about Roy. She might have known this would only cause more trouble and heartache. Her father had an uncanny way of finding out her every thought and action. He was probably boiling now at discovery that she had defied him. Especially since she had appealed to a man whom he detested, to do something for this boy from the city. This was quite evident from the angry voices which she had overheard.

The stillness from the other room frightened her. Could her parent have died from a stroke? . . . Sue softly opened the kitchen door and looked in. Matt Kendall was lying back in his chair, eyes fixed on the ceiling. He began to mutter to himself.

"Breakin' up my home—that's what he's a-doin'! Turnin' my daughter and the boy a'gin me! I won't stand for it, I tell you—I won't stand for it!"

Sue closed the door again, somewhat relieved. Thank heaven, nothing had happened—nothing physical, that is. But why her parent had not taken his temper out on her, as yet, she couldn't understand. Usually, when things upset him, he could hardly wait to unleash the full violence of his feelings. Perhaps it was because he knew that Frank Carson was still on the premises.

And there he was now, stepping out of the barn with Roy! Her 4-H Leader had his hand on the younger man's shoulder and they were talking earnestly as they walked up the path toward the rear of the house. Sue realized with a start, that they were coming in the kitchen door.

But still no word from her father! She had never known him to remain so long subdued. Or was he, like an apparently quiet volcano, actually seething inside, in danger of an outbreak at any moment?

The men reached the porch and Roy, opening the kitchen door, looked in.

"Hello, Sue," he said, in a low voice. "Mr. Carson wants to talk to you."

Dave's father stepped in behind the boy from the city. "Get ready," he smiled. "We've just time to get to the 4-H meeting. Roy's going with us."

Sue stared at her 4-H Leader in amazement. "Did Daddy say we could?" she asked.

"He didn't say you *couldn't*," said Frank Carson. "So get dressed, both of you, while I go in and have a few more words with him."

Sue and Roy hesitated, exchanging glances.

"You really want to go?" asked Sue.

"Sure!" grinned Roy, "don't you?"

She nodded, then glanced toward the living room.

"But Daddy said . . . !"

Frank Carson took her gently by the arm. "Come on in with me." He crossed with her to the closed kitchen door and Roy hurried to his own little room.

"Won't take me long to get ready," he said.

Matt Kendall heard the kitchen door open, and Frank Carson's step on the threshold. His body stiffened but he did not turn his head. It was only when his daughter and the man he had despised stood before him, that he looked at them.

"Well," he said, in a bitter, weary voice, "what is it now?"

"I'm taking the young people to the 4-H meeting," announced Frank Carson.

The eyes of the chronic invalid centered upon Sue. Her own eyes wavered and filled with tears.

"You're a-goin' whether I say 'no' or not?" he demanded.

Sue shook her head. "No, Daddy," she said, in a choked voice. "If you say 'no', I'm staying here."

There was a moment of heart-tearing silence. Frank Carson was standing, gazing out the window which overlooked the Dodds' place.

"Quite a lot of folks there already," he remarked, in an effort to break the tension.

A sudden flame leaped into Matt Kendall's eyes.

"All right," he cried, hoarsely. "Get going! . . . Get out of here! The whole pack of you! You're all ag'in me!" He almost raised himself off his chair as he brandished a bony fist. *"Get out!"* he shouted.

Sue, at first unbelieving, had stood motionless. Then, under the whip lash of her father's tongue, she broke and ran to the bedroom.

Frank Carson turned his back to the window and smiled at the emotionally exhausted figure in the chair.

"You'll never regret this, Matt," he said.

There was no answer, but a groan of deep-seated anguish escaped the tight-set lips of the chronic invalid.

Sue came out, struggling with her coat. She took several nervous dabs at her hair and glanced at her 4-H Leader.

"I guess I'm ready," she said.

"That's fine," said Frank Carson. Then, lifting his voice, he called: "Roy, we're going now. Are *you* ready?"

The boy from the city appeared in the kitchen doorway, wearing the one good suit he had to his name, the one in which he had arrived. His dark hair was neatly combed but his four-in-hand tie was slightly askew from the haste of dressing.

"I'm ready," he announced, and crossed the living room to the door.

Sue hesitated, looking toward her father. Matt Kendall's eyes were closed. His gnarled hands were lying resignedly in his lap. There were wet spots on his cheek bones.

Sue, with a little cry, ran to him, bent over and kissed the gaunt face.

"Goodbye, Daddy," she said, in a quavering whisper. "And, thanks . . . !"

There was no response from the form in the chair and Sue, rejoining Roy and her 4-H Leader at the door, slipped out of the house. Their feet crunched on the gravel as they hurried, unspeaking, out to the car. A door slammed and the car motor started. Its tires bruised themselves on the rocks as it turned around and started down the hill.

Matt Kendall opened his eyes and reached out, shakily, for his field glasses—then changed his mind and dropped his head back, as a great sob shook his slight frame.

Chapter IX

THERE WAS THE hum of tremendous excitement at the second meeting of the Hidden Valley 4-H Club. Almost everyone wanted to talk at once and tell of plans completed for projects or present new ideas for Club activities. President Dave Carson had a difficult time holding to the Roberts' rules of order. He finally, laughingly, called on his father.

"Dad," he appealed, "this thing is getting out of hand. You'd better take over."

The Club's 4-H Local Leader stood up, greatly amused, and walked to the front of the room.

"Well," he said, "you young folks have covered a lot of ground this afternoon. Practically all of you now know what you want to work at. You've got your projects pretty well lined up, and you'll be started on them this week. I'm glad to see we've added seven new members and I'm especially glad to welcome Roy Willard, because he's a boy from the city who wants to learn how we do things on the farm."

All eyes turned in the direction of the youth mentioned who was seated in the back row beside Sue Kendall.

"Roy just told me a moment ago," Mr. Carson continued, "that he's decided he'd like to tackle a beef raising project. I'm arranging to let him pick one of my beef calves on Monday and take it up to the Kendall farm where he lives. The calf will really be old enough to wean but I think it would do better if he was still kept on milk for awhile. I understand, though, that Kendalls' only have one milk cow and I don't suppose they'd want to use her for that purpose. I was wondering if any of you Club members might have a nurse cow that Roy could borrow? It would help him a great deal on his project."

Several hands shot up, among them the thin hand of Tom Dodds. Frank Carson smiled. "Well, that's fine!" He looked over the hands and nodded toward the young man in the blue

109

bathrobe. "All right, Tom!" he recognized.

The bosom pal of Dave Carson raised himself on an elbow.

"If Mr. Willard will see me after the meeting," he said, looking in Roy's direction, "I'll fix it so he can have one of our cows. We have more milk than we need now and since we're his nearest neighbor . . .!"

"There you are, Roy!" beamed Frank Carson. "You see how we do things in the country!"

The boy from the city grinned. "That's swell!" he said. "With all this help, raising a beef calf ought to be a cinch!"

There was a howl of laughter from the wiser members of the Club and Roy looked puzzled. "Did I say the wrong thing?" he asked.

"You'll find out how much of a cinch it is," said his 4-H Leader, "before you get through with your project!"

It had been electrifying news to the Club members that Hidden Valley's new business man, Sam Jordan had proffered his whole-hearted support and backed it up with a five hundred dollar contribution to start a "Civic Improvements" Fund, to which other merchants and public-spirited citizens could also subscribe. Dave Carson had frankly told them of his run-in with Mayor Brannigan and the obstacles they would have to face in trying to do things for their town and county.

"We'll start on our farm and home projects, first," he had concluded, "And work these civic projects in, as we can. There's not so much that any of you can individually do, at present. I'll have to do some scouting around, myself, as your President. But when I find some real place to strike, we'll hit it hard!"

The 4-H Club meeting was climaxed with several song numbers by the Hilton sisters, after which Song Leader Carolyn introduced her fellow members to group singing. There was a spirited response as voices were raised in "A Song of the Open Country":

"A song of the open country, that we love so well,
Where freedom of outdoor living holds us in its spell,

The splendor of skies and dawning; the golden sunset's glow—
Our hopes arise 'neath starlit skies, all nature helps us grow..."

At the finish, just before adjournment, President Dave Carson
stood up beside Carolyn, slipped an arm about the blushing song
leader, and said: "And now I have a special announcement to
make. Carolyn and I are *engaged!*"

There was a gasp of pleased surprise, followed by cries of
congratulation, cheers and applause.

"Quick!" said Dave, turning to Carolyn, "make it official!
Put your ring on!"

Carolyn fumbled happily with a slender ribbon which had
been dropped inside the neck of her blouse, and detached the
gold band with the sparkling stone, just getting it on the proper
finger as well-wishers crowded around.

She and Dave found themselves, eventually, in the company of
the fellow in the blue bathrobe. He held out hands to them both.

"You know what I wish for you," he said. "All that I could
ever have wished for myself," he added, brokenly.

The engaged couple nodded with expressions of sympathy
and understanding. Dave looked about him. There was a buzz
of conversation in the room. Refreshments were being served.
Roy Willard was being greeted by Club members and Sue was
standing by him to make personal introductions. This might be as
good a moment as any to speak to Tom about a certain matter.

Dave nudged Carolyn and they both sat down on cushions
beside his chair, near the fireplace.

"By the way, Tom," Dave began, "Carolyn and I have been wondering . . . building costs being so high and material so scarce . . .
You still have all the supplies on hand for *your* house, don't you?"

The question seemed to hit Tom with unusual impact. His
eyes had strayed away from them and had fixed upon Sue who
was still standing beside the good-looking boy from the city.

"Yes," he said, in a distant voice, "I have . . ."

"Well," continued Dave, "we'd like to build as soon as possible. Would you consider selling your house to us?"

The body of the young man in the blue bathrobe appeared to grow tense. He gripped the chair with his long, slender fingers and looked off into space.

"If I would ever sell to anybody," he said, slowly, "I'd sell to you—but I've never even considered selling. I'd like to think it over for awhile—do you mind?"

Dave and Carolyn exchanged sober glances.

"Why, no, of course not," assured Dave. "Take your time, Tom . . . I only thought—you know—all that material not being used . . ." He was embarrassed that he had even brought the subject up.

Tom's eyes were following Sue everywhere. She had moved from one group to the other with Roy who was an easy conversationalist and handled himself well in meeting people. He was wise-cracking now and had some of the 4-H Club members laughing. Sue's face was bright and relaxed as Tom had not seen it for a long, long time.

Sensing that Dave and Carolyn knew where his thoughts were, he turned to them and said: "Doesn't Sue look wonderful, today? I was afraid her father wouldn't let her come back. How did your Dad ever manage it?"

Dave grinned and shook his head. "I don't know—but Dad has a mighty persuasive way about him. He surprised me, though —lining Roy up for a beef project. That's a tough assignment, even for a fellow who knows something about it."

Tom nodded, thoughtfully. "If your father's done that," he said, "he must think Roy's got something to him. That's one reason I want to help him all I can."

Sue suddenly turned and looked toward Tom. Their eyes met and she touched Roy's arm. "I think we can see Tom now," she said.

Porky O'Connor had a toe-hold on the boy from the city which was hard to break.

"I don't know anythin' about the raisin' of beef," he was saying, "but if you ever take to raisin' pigs, I'm your man. I've got a litter of eleven right now—the rootin'est little devils you ever saw! My old man thinks I'm crazy, the care I'm takin' of 'em—but I'm doin' everythin' the County Agent tells me—and I'm gonna have the best hogs in this part of the state or know the reason why. You should see the hog-house I've built . . .!"

Porky paused to draw breath and Sue cut in with: "That's wonderful, Porky—but Roy's got to see Tom now about that milk cow for his beef calf!"

The fattest boy in the 4-H Club gave Sue and Roy a good-natured push. "All right, go ahead! I'm so full of hogs, I'm commencin' to look like one!"

Sue and Roy laughed as they turned toward the fireplace and the fellow in the blue bathrobe.

"Tom," said Sue, "I guess you haven't really met Roy Willard yet. Roy—this is Tom Dodds."

The boy from the city held out his hand and took Tom's thin fingers in his. "I'm glad to meet you," he said. "That was darn nice of you—offering me the loan of that cow."

Sue's former fiance gave a slow smile. "You'll be doing us a favor taking it," he said. "Dad just happens to have a few too many at present and if you feed her and care for her, along with your beef calf, that'll pay for the loan."

Roy grinned. "I'll do the best I can," he promised. "But some of you folks had better give me the 'know how' pretty soon, to go along with these projects, or I'll be a nervous wreck before the first week's over!"

All laughed and Dave said: "Don't worry—we're all in these projects together and what one doesn't know, someone else usually does. But I warn you, Roy—*I'm* taking a beef project myself and I've had quite a few years experience. If you're figuring on trying for a contest winner, you're going to get all the competition I can give you!"

There was a friendly gleam of rivalry in the eyes of the boy from the city. "I don't expect to beat anybody my first time out," he said. "But if I can even give you a close battle with a beef calf from the same herd, I'll be satisfied."

"Well, if I know Dad," said Dave, "he'll give you as much

help as he does me—maybe more. So good luck to us both!"

Tom, with a sigh of fatigue, motioned to Dave. "I'm sorry, folks," he apologized. "I've been down here long enough. Dave, if you'll just give me a lift upstairs again . . ."

"Sure thing!" said his bosom pal, and knelt down, ready to make the carry.

"Sue," directed Tom, "take Roy to my Dad. I guess he's in the other room helping Mother with refreshments. Ask him to go out to the barn with Roy and show him the cow he can have."

Sue nodded and smiled her appreciation. "Thanks, Tom," she said, "thanks, awfully much."

Their eyes met once more, held for an instant, then wavered and broke.

Sue led Roy away and Dave, lifting Tom in his arms, said to Carolyn: "I'll be down in a few minutes. I want to see you before you go."

As he mounted the stairs, Dave said to his chum of many years, "you're looking lots better today, Tom—no kidding—there's been a big change in two weeks' time!"

"I was hoping you would say something like that," said the fellow in the blue bathrobe, as Dave pushed in the bedroom door with his foot. "I've started on my biggest project," Tom continued, "getting back my health!"

"Good boy!" said Dave. On entering the room, he stopped short, still holding Tom, and looked up at the ceiling over his pal's bed. "Holy smoke!" he exclaimed. "What's that?"

"It's an exerciser I invented," Tom explained, enjoying Dave's surprise. "Put me down and I'll show you how it works."

Dave placed him on the bed and helped slip off his bathrobe. Tom was dressed as before, in pants, shirt and tie. He reached up toward the harness which hung from the ceiling on a pulley arrangement, and fastened a belt about his waist. Then, taking hold of straps with each hand, he pulled, and body and arms were stretched with muscles flexing and unflexing.

"Please fasten those straps on my feet," Tom commanded.

Dave complied and the infantile paralysis victim began to

work his pathetic appearing legs back and forth while lying in a face upwards position. By manipulating the various ingeniously strung ropes and leather straps, Tom was able to activate every vital muscle in his body.

"That's wonderful!" Dave declared, delighted. "Who made that for you?"

"My Dad," smiled Tom, "according to my specifications. I dreamed it up, Dave, after you left. I figured I needed something like that to help develop the strength to stand on my feet and maybe, some day, walk with crutches. It really works swell and I can feel my circulation improving in my legs and arms already."

Dave eyed his bosom pal, admiringly. "Now you're back on the beam, Tom. You've got the old fight you used to have. It's only a matter of time till . . ."

Tom held up his hand. "Don't say it. I couldn't stand it to be disappointed. If I don't make it, I don't want anybody but you and my folks to know what I've been trying to do. Promise?"

Dave nodded. "Sure," he said.

For some reason, a big lump was rising in his throat and, so that Tom wouldn't see how he really felt, he gave him a quick pat on the shoulder and turned and left the room.

Chapter X

THE BOY FROM the city arrived at the Carson farm at ten o'clock Monday morning, by appointment, to claim the beef calf which had been promised him. He was wearing overalls and denim work jacket, reinforced underneath by two sweaters, for the wind was biting and he had walked all the way.

He had helped Sue with the regular routine chores and had slipped off, by arrangement with her, while she was attending her father. The two of them had decided, since Matt Kendall had not forbidden their joining the 4-H Club, that they would go about their work in it as quietly as possible without making an issue of requesting permission to do this or that, just so they performed the duties he assigned to them. This new technique of not crossing his authority more than they could help had seemed successful, thus far, although Sue still lived in apprehension that they would overplay their hand and be called severely to account any moment.

Both Dave and his father were waiting for Roy and took him at once to the large stock barn where Mr. Carson's famed purebred Aberdeen Angus herd was kept.

"Have you got the stall ready for your animal?" Mr. Carson asked, as they entered the barn.

"Yes," said Roy, feeling a tremor of excitement run through him. "Sue and I worked at it yesterday. She helped me scrub it." He grinned. "It's clean enough for *me* to sleep in."

"That's a good start," approved Rock County's best beef breeder. Then, chuckling, he added: "I guess Dave's already told you that he's going in for a meat animal project, too?"

Roy nodded, and glanced aside at Dave. "Yeah, he did!"

"Well," said Mr. Carson, "I've decided to let you two men select your calves at the same time."

Roy laughed. "You'd better pick my calf for me, Mr. Carson. I wouldn't know one calf from another."

They were reaching the section of the barn now, where the five-months-old beef calves were quartered. The Carsons' old hired hand, Jud Emery, was awaiting them. He lifted his lanky frame from a stool where he had been sitting and pulled at the leathery skin of his chin as he sized up the strange young man.

"Hello, son," he said, when introduced. "You're the luckiest boy in the County to be gettin' one of these here beef calves. They'd bring at least a hundred an' twenty-five at market right now—an' Mr. Carson might not even sell 'em for that."

Roy turned to Rock County's finest beef raiser. "I'm glad he mentioned that, Mr. Carson," he said, "because I don't want anything for nothing. I've been asking some questions around and I've found out that I can pay for my own calf if I can borrow some money at the bank. I don't know what you had in mind but I just couldn't let you *give* me an animal, Mr. Carson. That wouldn't be right."

His 4-H Leader smiled. "I was going to give him to you," he said, "on condition you would pay me back out of the money you will get for him in the fall. But if you'd rather borrow what you'll need to buy and feed the calf, I'll take you in to the Hidden Valley bank and have you meet Mr. Brannigan and put through a loan."

"That's what I'd like," said Roy. "That makes me feel better right off. How much do you think I'd need?"

"Three hundred dollars should be ample," said his 4-H Leader. "I'll make you a price of one hundred on whatever calf you take."

Roy glanced at the hired man and then back at Mr. Carson. "Didn't *he* say you could get a hundred and twenty-five or more right now?" he asked. "I'd rather pay the *regular* price. I don't want to start off with any favors."

There was an air of independence about Roy which his 4-H Leader liked.

"All right," he smiled. "then that's the price—but you'll have to watch your expenses and keep a careful record to make out even by fall."

Jud Emery had divided the beef calves on Frank Carson's orders, into two groups. These two separate herds had been run out into the feed lot behind the barn and were now ready for inspection. The hired hand, long entrusted to the grooming of this livestock, was proud of his job.

"You're really goin' to see somethin', Mr. Willard," he said, as he slid open the rear door and they stepped out to a point where they could overlook the feed lot. "Just cast your eyes over these calves! Aren't they a bunch of black beauties?"

The boy from the city stood leaning with his arms against the stout enclosure, an expression of interest on his face.

"I went through the Chicago stockyards once," he recalled to Mr. Carson, "but I never saw any calves as nice looking as these. What have you got them separated for?"

Frank Carson smiled and nodded at his son. "You tell him, Dave," he said.

"It's simple," Dave explained, "when you know. These calves on your left, Dad's going to hold for breeders. The others, on your right, he's going to fatten for meat animals. They've already been castrated. We've got to pick our steers out of this bunch. You take your pick first."

Roy Willard hesitated. "They all look just about alike," he said. "I'll take whichever one you give me."

Frank Carson shook his head. "No, Roy, I won't sell him to you that way. You've got to make your own choice. These animals may look alike but they're all different. Each has a different temperament, disposition, and individuality—just the same as humans. Remember—you're looking at purebreds. Each one of those baby beeves has a pedigree and a good one. But that doesn't mean they'll all react the same under your handling, any more than you can expect different children, from the same father and mother, to turn out exactly alike."

Roy's eyes were widening. "No kidding!" he said. "Is that the truth?"

Frank Carson nodded, soberly. "These calves will respond, under proper kind and intelligent handling, just as a boy and girl will develop under the right direction of their parents. You'll practically have to live with your beef calf and gain a real understanding of him and see to it that he understands you—if you want to produce a winner."

Roy's eyes had been examining the splendid specimens before him which, in turn, seemed to be critically examining *him*. He noted this and remarked, with a laugh: "I'm commencing to get what you mean. Right now I have a feeling those animals understand *me* better than *I* understand them. They're probably saying to themselves: 'Oh, Brother—I hope I don't have to go home with *that* guy!'"

Dave and his father laughed.

"I'll tell you what to look for in a beef calf," said Mr. Carson. "A good beef animal should be blocky in appearance. It should have straight top and bottom lines—a broad back, loins and rump. The body should be deep and wide, and the legs short. You should look for an animal with a short full neck which blends solidly into the shoulders—and the shoulders should be smooth and well covered. Those are some of the main points to keep in mind when judging beef animals. Oh, yes . . . you should always be sure that the hindquarters are full, deep and thick!"

Roy had been listening intently and trying to apply some of Frank Carson's points to the animals in front of him.

"I can follow you on some of that," he said, "but how in Sam Hill is a fellow going to tell a calf's disposition or quality?"

"That's harder," admitted Rock County's best beef breeder. "But quality in a beef animal is shown in the head, bone, hide and hair. By 'quality', I mean refinement. Some breeders can tell by a study of the head alone. A clean-cut head usually indicates what one may expect in the rest of the body. This calls for the exercise of intuition as well as judgment. If an animal you are considering seems to add up in every other respect, and his head looks good, and you get the *feeling* that you and this animal can hit it off all right together—then that's the animal for *you!*"

Roy suddenly pointed to a beef calf which had been edging along the corral. "There's an animal I like," he declared.

"He's yours if you want him," said Frank Carson, but Roy shook his head.

"No, I can see now—according to what you've told me—that calf's legs aren't short enough. Also, his neck is too long . . ."

Jud Emery, who was in the enclosure with the animals, glanced at the boy from the city and grinned, as he said to Mr. Carson: "He catches on quick, don't he?"

Dave and his father exchanged pleased glances as they watched Roy sizing up one animal after another.

"There's *my* meat!" he cried, pointing to a beef calf in the middle of the herd. "Maybe I'm wrong but it looks to me like that animal has *everything*. I think I'll go for *that* one!"

"All right, Jud!" called Frank Carson. "Rope him and lead him out of the lot." Then, to Roy: "For your information, you made a fine selection. I couldn't have done better myself and if Dave does as well, he'll be lucky."

This praise from Rock County's finest breeder of Aberdeen Angus herds, was immensely heartening to the boy from the city. He was keeping his eyes on his animal as the hired hand adroitly roped it and brought it toward him.

"You hold him," he said, and passed the rope end over to Roy who reached a hand down to pet his choice on the head. The calf jumped back and reared, almost pulling Roy over the fence.

"Whoa, bossy!" he called. "Nice bossy!"

Jud Emery howled. "You're goin' to make that calf mighty mad callin' him *that!*" he said.

Roy's face reddened. The animal was tugging hard on the rope but he took a half hitch on the fence post and quieted the baby steer down.

"You ought to name your steer," suggested Frank Carson. "It will help you identify him. And if he's ever shown, anywhere— he'll go by that name."

Roy considered for a moment, as he studied the animal. "You say he's from royal blood," he reflected. "How about 'Your Majesty'?"

"Very good," approved Frank Carson. " 'Your Majesty', it is!" He glanced toward his son. "All right, Dave. Have you found the animal *you* want?"

Dave nodded. "Yes, I'll take the one standing next to the calf Roy turned down. I was afraid he'd pick that animal himself. He's got a little shorter neck than Roy's selection and I believe his legs are a trifle shorter, too. He ought to fatten into a real blocky beef by fall. I think I'll call him 'Carson's Pride'."

Jud Emery roped this steer and pushed it toward the barn.

"That's a good choice, too," said Dave's father. "But which calf turns out to be the best all-around meat animal will be determined, largely, by which one of you gives your steer the best care. You've made your choices now—and may the best man win."

He turned and shook hands with them both.

Matt Kendall was half dozing when he heard the labored coughing of a truck motor on his road. He twisted his body, painfully, and reached for his ever-present field glasses.

"Sue!" he called.

"Yes, Daddy!" She came from the kitchen where she was preparing the noon-day meal.

"Whose truck is that—and what's it comin' up here for?"

"Why, I—I think that's Mr. Carson's," said Sue.

"You don't think—you *know!*" barked her father. "Now what's he up to?"

"You'll see in just a minute," said Sue. "It's a . . . it's a surprise!"

"*Surprise!*" bellowed Matt Kendall. "I don't like surprises!" He kept the glasses to his eyes, arms trembling. "Why, dammit-all if there ain't a beef calf and a cow in that truck! And there's Roy! So that's where he's been! . . . Open that window, girl—I want to give Frank Carson a piece of my mind . . ."

"But, Daddy—it's cold out and you might . . . !"

"Don't care if it is—open that window!"

Sue thrust the window up just as the truck made the turn to go around the house toward the barn. She waved and Frank

Carson, driving, stopped in full view, leaned out and called: "Hello, Sue! . . . Hello, Matt—I'm bringing you a little *company!*"

"*Company!*" shouted the chronic invalid from his chair. "That's not funny, Frank Carson—not funny a bit! We ain't fixed to take in any more animals. You turn that truck of yours around and get off my hill! Roy, come in here. I want to talk to you! . . . Get off, now, Frank! I mean it!"

"Got to unload, first!" replied the man Matt Kendall despised.

The truck started up and passed from sight, reappearing on the other side of the house where Sue's father could watch it all the way to the barn.

"Where'd that cow come from?" demanded Matt Kendall. "It's a Shorthorn and Frank don't have one to his name."

"It's one of Dodds', Daddy," informed Sue, nervously. "Tom's loaned her to Roy as a nurse cow till it's time to wean the calf . . ."

"Great saints and sinners!" swore Matt Kendall. "We can't afford to raise no beef calf . . . they cost money for feed and care . . . I'll get the law after Frank Carson . . . I got *some* rights! . . . He can't come onto my place and run it like this!"

"It won't cost you anything, Daddy," said Sue. "Roy said he wouldn't take the calf unless he could pay for it."

"How's he goin' to pay? The boy doesn't have a penny."

"He intends to borrow the money—at the bank."

"Go in debt, eh!" raged Matt Kendall. "This is gettin' worse and worse! . . . Close that window! That air's knifin' the back of my neck!"

Sue, in the excitement, had forgotten the window entirely. She slid it down with a bang.

"Oh!" Her father pressed hands against his ears. "Leave the pane in the sash!" He looked toward the barn and groaned, helplessly. "They've got the cow out now . . . and there goes the calf!" He squinted. "Not a bad lookin' animal. Bet it's got a fancy price, too! . . . Nice scheme for Frank Carson to sell a lot of his baby beeves . . . to you 4-H kids. How many more is he startin' on a beef project . . . ?"

"Roy's the only one I know of," said Sue.

Matt Kendall nodded and ground hard on his teeth.

"Takin' advantage of him because he comes from the city! Roy can't no more raise a beef calf than I can fly to the moon."

"He can learn!" Sue persisted, surprised at the growing courage with which she could face her parent.

"There they go—in the barn!" Matt Kendall reported. "You see—Roy's havin' trouble with the calf! It's balkin' on him. Bad disposition! It needs a little kick in the rear!"

Sue, looking on, as her father spoke, saw Frank Carson lead the cow in the barn but Roy couldn't get the calf to budge.

"I'll go out and help!" she volunteered.

"You're stayin' right here!" commanded Matt Kendall. "If Roy thinks he wants to raise a beef calf—he might as well get his fill of it—right now!"

The chronic invalid's face took on a look of sardonic enjoyment.

"I'd break that calf if *I* had him!" he muttered, as he watched Roy's struggle. "You've got to show an animal who's master. If they once find they can run you—you're finished. Clip him over the ears with the end of your rope! Smack him in the ribs! Don't let him hold back on you that way! . . . You'll never make a beef handler! . . . Look at him—pettin' the animal! He'll be *kissin'* him next! . . ." Matt Kendall growled his disgust, then leaned forward in amazement. "Well, I'll be dogged—he got the calf to *move!*"

"It's in the barn, Daddy!" cried Sue, her eyes moist. "Roy got it in—all by himself—and he never lifted a hand to it!"

Mayor Ed Brannigan, as Hidden Valley's most prominent and also busiest business man, was apt to be found at any one of a number of different offices, at any time of the day or night. He traveled, as occasion demanded, from the Mayor's office to his office in the Bank, to Brannigan's General Store, to the Feed and Seed Store, or the Drug Store, or Dew Drop Inn,—or the Brannigan Lumber Mills.

But it so happened that Ed Brannigan was in the bank when

Rock County's finest beef breeder dropped in with a strange young man and asked to see him.

"Come in!" waved the Bank President, from his private office. Then, seeing the unfamiliar youth with him, he said: "Oh, I thought, for a moment, that was your boy!"

"No," smiled Frank Carson. "This is Roy Willard. He's a newcomer to our region from Chicago. You may have heard— he's staying with the Kendalls."

"Oh, yes!" recalled President Brannigan. "Seems like I *did* hear some talk about him!" He stuck out his big hand. "How are you, young man?"

"I'm all right," answered Roy, shaking hands.

"I've brought Mr. Willard in to arrange a little loan for him," explained Mr. Carson. "He's joined the 4-H Club and I've interested him in raising a beef calf as his project."

President Brannigan gave Roy an appraising glance. "Breeding or meat animal?" he asked.

"Meat animal," said Roy.

"How much do you want?"

Roy looked questioningly at his 4-H Leader. "Why, Mr. Carson thinks I need . . ." he started.

"Make him out a note for three hundred, with your usual rate of interest," interposed Dave's father. "Payable on December fifteenth. He should have his money out of the animal by then."

President Brannigan paused. "Has the boy ever had any experience raising beef before?" he demanded.

"No, sir," said Roy, frankly. "I'd never even been on a farm before, till I came here, a few weeks ago."

The biggest business man in Hidden Valley stared hard at Rock County's finest beef breeder. "Looks to me like there's quite a little risk attached to this."

Frank Carson smiled. "Not for the bank," he said. "I'm signing this note with Roy."

President Brannigan drummed his fingers on the desk. "Are you insuring the animal?"

He was gazing at Roy. This was a new thought.

The boy from the city turned to Frank Carson. *"Are* we?" he asked.

"We *are!"* said his 4-H Leader, emphatically.

President Brannigan pressed one of a number of buttons on his desk. He was proud of this installation. It was the only one in town—in fact there wasn't a service like this nearer than Memphis or Little Rock. A buzzer sounded in the Cashier's cage and a bespectacled little man left a depositor standing at the window and ran down the hallway to the President's private office.

"Yes, Mr. Brannigan!" he said.

"Mr. Jessup," said the President. "This Mr. Willard, here, wants to open an account with us on a loan of three hundred dollars. Frank Carson's going on his note. Fix up the papers. Make out a check and supply this young man with a check-book. He's going to begin spending his money right away."

"Yes, Mr. Brannigan!" bowed Mr. Jessup. "I'll attend to it. Glad to meet you, Mr. Willard! Glad to welcome you as a new depositor!"

He backed out, bowing, and disappeared down the hallway.

President Brannigan turned to Frank Carson. "Don't be in a hurry. I've been wanting to have a little talk with you," he said, a bit lamely. "It seems that your boy and I had a slight misunderstanding a few weeks ago. He came to me about this 4-H business and began telling me about all the changes he thought ought to be done in this town. I got a trifle hot under the collar and perhaps I said a few things . . . well, I didn't mean I wouldn't do anything for your 4-H Club—if it stayed on the farm where it belongs!"

Frank Carson nodded. "Yes, I know. Dave reported his conversation with you."

President Brannigan's irritation rose to the surface. "I suppose, Frank, I may as well come right out with it. I think your boy had one hell of a nerve, after all I've done for him, going to Sam Jordan and getting him to put up money for a 'Civic Improvements' fund. That blow was aimed right at me—and me only. This man, Jordan, is just intending to use your 4-H Club to feather his own nest. That donation was a grandstand play to make *me* look bad—and I resent it!"

Frank Carson leaned back and crossed his legs. He reached for his pipe and emptied it in the palm of his hand.

"Well," he said, "what's done is done. As I understand it, Ed, you had first chance to co-operate with Dave and the 4-H Club. He went direct to you. If you weren't in favor of some of the improvements he had in mind, you haven't anyone to blame but yourself."

Frank Carson stood up and walked over and dropped a palm full of ashes in the President's waste basket.

President Brannigan produced his latest copy of the Hidden Valley News Weekly and opened it to a large ad on page 3.

"You've seen this, of course?" he raged.

Frank Carson looked down at the copy, and read:

CONGRATULATIONS!

to

HIDDEN VALLEY'S NEWLY FORMED 4-H CLUB!

from

JORDAN'S NEW AND BETTER DRUG STORE

(Due to Open for Business—July 4th!)

We take pride in having made the first contribution of $500.00 to HIDDEN VALLEY'S CIVIC IMPROVEMENTS FUND which is to be administered by the HIDDEN VALLEY 4-H CLUB!

We cordially invite ALL PUBLIC-SPIRITED MERCHANTS and CITIZENS interested in BETTERING their Town and County, to make THEIR DONATIONS to this Fund, direct to the HIDDEN VALLEY BANK.

A LIST OF DONORS AND AMOUNTS CONTRIBUTED will be published each week in this paper.

SUPPORT YOUR 4-H CLUB BOYS AND GIRLS AND LET THEM HELP YOU BUILD A FINER COMMUNITY IN WHICH TO LIVE!

"I don't see anything wrong with that ad," said Frank Carson. "I think it's pretty fine of a new man in town to be showing such a genuine interest in our affairs!"

President Ed Brannigan folded up the paper, shoved it in the drawer of his desk, and slammed the drawer shut.

"It's blackmail—that's what it is!" he stormed. "Your boy's trying to publicly embarrass me and force me into line. He probably figures I'll have to make a *bigger* contribution than this fellow Jordan or lose face around here. But I don't donate to anything when someone puts a gun against my back!"

"That's your privilege," smiled Frank Carson. "I doubt, with contributions coming in like they are, that your financial help will be necessary, anyway."

"That's another thing!" exploded President Brannigan. "Why does this ad refer everyone to the Bank? Why didn't your boy have checks made payable to him or the 4-H Club and then turn them over to the Fund? Why should we have to handle these details? That's what I call—rubbing it in!"

Rock County's finest beef breeder was amused. "Ed," he said, "I've known you a good many years. You've never been *for* anything you haven't started yourself. You're not so much peeved at my boy—you're peeved that a band wagon is starting to roll that you didn't help push. You had your opportunity and if you don't want to climb on the band wagon now—you'll have to listen to the music, whether you like it or not!"

President Brannigan's face was charged with conflicting emotions. He took out a cigar, tore open the cellophane wrapping and savagely bit off the end. He struck a match so hard that the head flew off.

"Damn!" he said. "Nothing works right around here!"

Roy, who had been studying the various framed tributes paid to Ed Brannigan—Mayor of Hidden Valley, the Town's Number One Citizen, the Leading Merchant, the Outstanding Philanthropist, the Head of the Scrap Drive, the Director of the Red Cross, the County's Champion War Bond Salesman—and other citations which covered all one side of the wall, had all he could do to keep from laughing outright. He was thinking that big men in small towns were little different from big men in big cities—or, rather, men who *thought* they were big. Roy's admiration, however, for Dave's father, had been growing with association.

The bespectacled Mr. Jessup appeared in the doorway, with the necessary papers.

"I have everything prepared," he announced, as he caught the President's eye.

Ed Brannigan finally managed to get his cigar lighted but missed the waste basket with the still blazing match.

"Well, bring it in!" he ordered, "and have Mr. Willard and Mr. Carson sign up."

"Yes, Mr. Brannigan," said Mr. Jessup. He crossed dutifully to the desk and laid out the note, ready for signatures. Then, handing a pen to Roy, he requested, in a thin, nervous voice: "Will you put your name here, please, Mr. Willard?"

As Roy signed, President Brannigan, looking on, blew out a great cloud of smoke and said: "This ought to prove to you, Frank, that I'm always willing to help the 4-H Club with its farm projects. This bank is here to be of service to the entire community and if you have any other members who need a little financing and would like the loan of some money . . . !"

"I'll bring them in," assured Rock County's finest beef breeder, as he affixed his name to the note underneath Roy's. "Provided of course," he added, pointedly, "they can furnish ample security or get somebody acceptable to go on their notes with them!"

The President of the Hidden Valley Bank choked—but it was not on his cigar.

Chapter XI

FEBRUARY had slipped into March without being aware of it and March was now about to make a lamb-like change into April. Things were starting to grow in Arkansas, on the hoof and in the ground. Growing, too, were the projects of 4-H Club members, all now launched and under way.

On the Dodds' farm it was time for spring planting of corn. Fred Dodds had his best team hitched, ready for plowing, when his wife came hurrying out to the barn.

"Oh, Fred!" she cried, "I'm glad you haven't gone yet. Tom wants to see you."

"What about?" asked her husband. "Can't he wait till lunch time?"

"No. He said he wanted to be sure to see you right away."

Farmer Fred Dodds tied his team to the nearest fence post and started toward the house. "I wonder what's up?" he said.

"Don't know!" called Anna, after him. "But he seems quite excited about something!"

Tom Dodds *was* excited. He was seated on the side of his bed, blue bathrobe on, and crutches under his arm pits, with their rubber tipped ends resting on the floor.

"Dad!" he cried, elatedly. "I've done it! I've walked across the room on these things!"

Fred Dodds stood in the doorway, surprised and overjoyed. "You don't say!" he exclaimed.

Tom's eyes were alight with a fire his father had not seen in all the time since he had been stricken.

"Of course," he went on, "I can't hope to walk very far for some while but I think, in a few weeks, I can get out and around a little on the place . . . and I was wondering . . . you know how I used to like to help you raise corn . . . Now that I'm a member of 4-H—well, no one really expects me to tackle a project this year . . . just the same, I'd like to do something . . ."

Tom hesitated, a trifle embarrassed and self-conscious. Then, gaining courage, he continued: "Dad, I sent for you to ask if, when you're breaking ground for yourself, would you mind plowing up a couple of acres for me?"

Two unbidden tears coursed their way down the tributary wrinkles of Fred Dodds' face. "Sure, son," he said, huskily. "I'll plow up the two richest acres in our bottom land, right next the creek. It's fairly level there and you might be able to get about some."

"That's swell, Dad!" cried Tom. "I've got what I want to do all figured out. I'd like to run an experiment. When it's time to plant, I want to put in an acre of some pure variety—I guess 'Paymaster's' as good as any. Then I intend to plant a good Hybrid on the other acre—and tend them both the same—and see which yields the best. I'll keep a careful record of cost and time and labor, and follow all of the methods, as recommended by the Extension Service."

"Go to it, Tom," encouraged his father, "I'll help you all I can."

Tom shook his head. "No, Dad," he said. "Don't you do anything on my project unless I tell you. I'm permitted to hire all the work done, if need be, just so I supervise it, but I don't want any favors. I'm counting on being out there with you when it comes time to plant, even if you have to carry me."

Farmer Dodds nodded, not trusting himself to speak, and left the room. On returning to the barn, he found his wife standing by the horses.

"Well?" she asked, anxiously. "Was everything all right?"

"*All right?*" repeated Tom's father, untying the horses and climbing up on the plow seat, "They're *better* than all right! They're wonderful, Mother! *Simply wonderful!* . . . I'm breaking ground for our son!"

He cracked the reins against the horses' flanks and the team moved off.

Mother Dodds looked at him incredulously. "What's that, Fred?" she cried after him. "What did you say?"

"The boy's walking!" he called back. "He's using his crutches! . . . *He wants to plant corn!*"

Sue Kendall was burning her Aladdin lamp in the bedroom later than was customary. She could hear her father, who had retired for the night, stirring restlessly in the living room. But, still, she was reluctant to give up what she was doing.

Finally, as she had anticipated, a voice called out.

"*Sue!*"

"Yes, Daddy?"

"What in tarnation are you doin' in there?"

"Oh, just a little sewing."

"*Sewing?* . . . What's so important to be mendin' this time of night?"

"I'm not mending, Daddy—I'm making me a new dress."

There was a snort of impatience from the living room. "*A new dress!* . . . What you makin' that for?"

A moment of prickling silence followed, and then she replied: "For the 4-H Dress Revue."

"*Dress Revue!*" fairly bellowed Matt Kendall. "And what might *that* be?"

Sue appeared in the doorway. "It's just a contest, Daddy, where all the girls in our Club, who want to make dresses, put them on and show them off before some judges—and the one who wins first prize gets a free trip to the 4-H State Camp at Fayette-ville, in August."

"Well, this just about beats me!" ranted her father. "I've put up with an awful lot since you and Roy joined 4-H. All the care he's been givin' that beef calf . . . and your crazy ideas about cleanin' up and beautifyin' the place . . . and now you're goin' in for makin' dresses and makin' a show of yourself! That's just too much!"

"But, Daddy," protested Sue. "The others girls . . . !"

"I don't care about them!" raved Matt Kendall. "I've got to draw the line some time. I've been noticin' your fussin' around a lot lately with your hair . . . and reddenin' up your lips . . . and

I just been a-waitin' to see how far you was a-goin' to go!"

"What's wrong about it?" asked Sue. "I'm old enough now to be fixing myself up. You don't get out and around, Daddy. You don't know how the other girls look. But they all . . ."

"Your mother never did it!" said her father. "Who's been a-teachin' you these things?"

"Our Home Demonstration Agent," said Sue.

"Who's *she?*" demanded Matt Kendall.

"Miss Millie Logan," Sue answered.

"Millie Logan!" derided the chronic invalid. *"That* fat old maid! What's *she* know about clothes or good looks—or anythin'?"

Sue stood her ground. "She may be fat, Daddy . . . and she may be an old maid. . . . but she's a wonderful person and she knows an awful lot about sewing . . . and how a girl can make herself more attractive . . . and save money doing it!"

"Save money!" repeated Matt Kendall. "You can't do that and make new dresses! How much did you pay for the cloth you're usin' right now?"

"Not a cent!" said Sue, defiantly.

"You can't tell me that. Bring that dress out here and let me see it!"

Sue left the doorway and returned, carrying an armful of brown material and the Aladdin lamp which she set down on the table before stepping to the side of her father's bed.

"Here's what I'm using," she said.

Matt Kendall reached out gnarled hands to examine the cloth.

"This looks like you ripped it up from somethin'," he observed. "Where'd it come from?"

Sue's eyes filled with tears. "Can't you tell?" she asked.

Her father shook his head. "How should *I* know?" he demanded.

"It was the store dress Mother sent away for," said Sue. "The one she had her heart set on, out of that catalogue. But she never had a chance to wear it. It got here the day after she died."

Matt Kendall handed the material back to Sue.

"Yes," he said, hoarsely. "I remember now. Better put it up for tonight and get to bed." Then, in a tone of voice, almost tender, he added: "And, after this, do more of your sewin' in the daytime."

The Hiltons were one of few families out Stony Creek way who owned a sewing machine. Largely for this reason, the 4-H girls, with sewing projects, were meeting at their home. Millie Logan, Home Demonstration Agent, was on hand to give instruction and encouragement where needed.

"I want you girls to understand right at the start," she said, "that there's no reason why you can't be as well dressed as any girls in the city. Of course you all have better figures to begin with, than I had. I was pleasingly plump in the wrong places . . . I still am for that matter!" She laughed and the girls laughed with her. "They used to say that about the only thing that would fit me was a feed sack. I got mad one day, took a sack, added a little style, and it really turned into the most becoming dress I ever had. It started me on my sewing career."

Miss Logan paused and surveyed the eager group in front of her.

"Some of you girls, I see, are getting old enough to want to look nice so you can catch a man. I, personally, have never met a man whom I felt was good enough for me . . . at least, that's the best excuse I can think of . . . !"

The girls looked at one another, amused, and Eleanor Hilton spoke up.

"Carolyn's already got *her* man," she said, impishly, "Do you think it was the dress she was wearing that did it? If it was, maybe *I'd* better start wearing it from now on!"

This comment brought shrieks as Millie Logan replied: "I'm afraid, Eleanor, that what worked for your sister, won't work for *you*. Most young men don't know or care how clothes are made but they can tell when a girl *looks* pretty. Each one of you has a different problem to solve in finding the type of dress best suited to you.

"And you're going to find that looking pretty depends not only on how good a dressmaker you are, but how well you wear your dress, how much poise you have, how good your posture is, how attractively you fix your hair and all the other little beauty aids to appearance and personality which go to make up the complete impression you give to others."

"Is *that* all!" exclaimed Sally Eiker, fifteen, blonde and freckled, who lived on State Highway Nine, out of Hidden Valley. "I guess I'd better stop trying now!"

Miss Logan chuckled. "I know that sounds like a rather big order but few girls are born perfect beauties. They have to develop their attractive features and learn how to overcome their weak points. It's a life-time project—I'm still working on mine!"

There was a burst of merriment.

"Now, girls," said their Home Demonstration Agent, becoming serious. "Let's get down to business. I want to check what each of you is working on and see whether I think it's practical, considering how much sewing experience you've had."

She went the rounds, discussing their individual problems and then gave a demonstration on the sewing machine for those who had never seen or operated one.

"The first things you beginners must learn is how to use a thimble and sew a straight seam." She watched Sue Kendall as she ran her brown material through the machine. "Now, there's a good example," she pointed out. "You see how Sue's doing it. She sews like a veteran. But you don't have a machine at home, do you, Sue? Where did you learn?"

Sue's fingers followed the material. "At the Dodds'," she said. "I used to go down there lots. Seems mightly nice to be using a machine again."

The inexperienced girls gathered around with expressions of admiration at the ease with which she stitched her garment.

"That's beautiful cloth," said Miss Logan, examining it. "One doesn't find material like this now-a-days. What's it been taken from?"

"From a dress of my mother's," said Sue, eyes intent on her work.

Miss Logan looked at the pattern. "You've selected a good style for you," she approved. "This should make up into something very attractive."

"Thanks," said Sue, pleased. "I was hoping it would." She finished her seam and pulled out the bastings. "I love to sew," she said, a bit self-consciously, with her fellow members looking on. "I think it's fun to make things." She glanced about, catching sight of the dress in Carolyn's lap. "My, that's pretty!" she exclaimed. "What's that going to be?"

Carolyn held up the dress. Its soft, filmy gathers fell in graceful folds.

"An evening dress," smiled Carolyn, and added, with a joyful note, "But, maybe with a *veil* . . . !" Her face colored, prettily.

Eleanor and Doris took the cue and hummed a strain of Lohengrin's Wedding March. Other Club members joined in, amid laughter.

All but Sue.

To the amazement of those present, she burst suddenly into tears, picked up her sewing, and ran from the room. Then, as she had done once before at the first meeting of the 4-H Club, she snatched up her coat, evaded Carolyn who sought to restrain her, and hastened from the house.

The boy from the city was spending every spare moment with his beef calf. He had been studying all available literature on the raising of meat animals and consulting with his Local Leader, Frank Carson, who had dropped by, on occasion, to check on how things were going.

One of Roy's greatest troubles was the training of his calf to lead well and stand properly. He might never be a good enough animal to show but he had become increasingly attached to it and wanted the calf to look its best at all times. This meant daily cleaning and grooming. He worried a great deal over the right feeding, just how much grain and roughages to add to his steer's ration.

Roy treated his calf gently. He took care not to make any quick movements which might frighten it, and avoided any loud talking in his presence. He accustomed the steer to the feel of his hands, in petting and scratching it. To keep his calf contented was Roy's daily aim in life.

Now, as he was about to turn his steer out to pasture for the night, he said: "I'm proud of you, Your Majesty! You're coming along fine. That's the right stand to take! . . . Feet squarely under you—and head up! . . . Now, don't forget that. And hold that position till I want you to break!"

Sue suddenly appeared in the barn doorway. The steer blinked but did not move. Roy looked around and grinned, happily: "See that!" he said, softly. "He's getting better control. I'll have him leading perfectly in a little while. And how do you like that *stand?*"

Sue advanced toward Roy and his calf. "It's wonderful," she said. "My, Roy—he's commencing to fill out. I can see a change every day. Look at his under-pinning!"

Roy nodded, pleased. "Yeah," he said. "Those legs begin to look like they could carry the load of beef I want to put on him!" He looked at Sue and, noting a strange expression on her face, asked abruptly: "What's the matter? Something gone wrong? . . . Did your old man—I mean—your father . . . ?"

Sue shook her head. "No, it's not Daddy this time. It's just . . . well, I don't think I'll go on with my 4-H project . . ."

Roy turned to his calf, removed its halter, let down the bars and sent his steer through the gate to pasture. Then, wheeling about to Sue, he caught her arm as she lowered her head, and demanded: "Come on—give out! You've been working your head off on that dress. *I* think it's going to be a knock-out!"

"That's what I thought, too," said Sue, brokenly. "But there's so many things . . . I don't think I could ever get up before people and model my own dress. I might break down and make a fool of myself in public."

She was still looking down at her feet, her head bent forward so that all Roy could see was her wild tumble of black hair.

"Here, here! What kind of talk is that?" he said to her. "Did you get cold feet when you saw what some of the other girls were making?"

Sue nodded, and tear drops spotted her dusty shoes. "I guess so," she admitted. "Especially when Carolyn showed me her dress . . . it's going to be beautiful . . . it's for evening wear and she intends to make it into her *wedding* gown."

"So *what!*" said Roy. "Why should that bother *you?*"

"When folks talk about weddings, I just go to pieces."

Roy put a calloused hand under her chin and forced her to look up at him. "I've got my steer about trained and I see I'll have to start in on you!"

The boy from the city eyed her, questioningly. "You still love Tom Dodds?" he asked, point blank.

"Then you've got to forget it," declared Roy. "*I* was in love with a girl once—or thought I was—and when she turned me down, I felt like I couldn't live. It took me quite a while to find out that there were other swell girls in the world.

"There's no use making yourself miserable over something that's past. I know it's tough having the fellow you've loved get in the shape Tom's in—but if I was in his condition, I wouldn't want a girl I cared for to be tied up to me, either. I don't know Tom very well. I think he's a nice guy and all that—but you need to stop kidding yourself. You can't ever marry *him!*"

Sue dried her tears with a wadded up handkerchief. "I know," she whispered, resignedly. "I've got to get over this, somehow."

She turned toward the house but Roy put a restraining hand on her shoulder.

"And you've got to keep up with your project," he commanded. "I've been in nightclubs and I've seen beauty shows and how girls show off clothes . . . and when you get your dress finished, I will be your audience—and you're going to model for *me!*"

"Oh, Roy!" exclaimed Sue. "I couldn't do that!"

"Oh, yes you can!" he insisted. "And when I get through with you, you're going to be able to go out on any stage in this country—and knock 'em dead!"

Sue stared at him, incredulously. "Not me," she said, "Not in a million years!"

"No," grinned Roy, "in just a couple of months from now!"

Chapter XII

It was a warm early morning in late April when Fred Dodds rapped and looked in at his son's door.

"Good morning, Tom," he greeted. "I'm starting to seed my Lower Twenty today. Looks like it might blow up a good rain by tonight. Would you like to get *your* two in?"

Tom reached for an overhead strap and pulled himself up to a sitting position.

"I sure would," he said.

His father hesitated. "If you'll tell me how you want it done . . ." he proposed. "I don't want you running any risk . . ."

Tom shook his head, determinedly. "No, Dad, I said when it came time to plant, I was going to be down there with you, if you had to carry me—and I meant it. Please get my overalls and blue shirt and work shoes for me."

Fred Dodds crossed to the closet and rummaged around.

"They don't seem to be here," he said, a little awkwardly. "I guess your mother put them away for safe-keeping." He went out the door, saying with a tremor of excitement in his voice: "I'll go hunt them up."

Anna Dodds was in the kitchen, getting breakfast. Her son's tray was on the table, ready for serving.

"Oh, Fred," she said, as he entered. "Just a minute and I'll send you up with Tom's bacon and eggs. How is he this morning?"

"He's fine," said her husband. "Put that tray away. He's coming downstairs to eat."

"He *is!*" Anna Dodds almost dropped the coffee pot.

"Yes, Mother," said Fred Dodds, lowering his voice. "He's going out planting with me and he wants to get dressed. But where have you put his work clothes? They're not in his room and I . . ."

Tom's mother pressed the corner of an apron to her eyes.

"Why, I thought he'd never . . ." she said. "They're in that old trunk in the store-room." She started out of the kitchen. "I'll get them—I'll get them right away!"

She came back almost immediately with the bundle of clothes and the shoes wrapped inside.

"I came near giving these away a few weeks ago," she said, tremulously. "I'm glad now I didn't." Then, catching her husband's arm as he took the clothes and headed for the stairs, "But, Fred—isn't Tom attempting too much?"

"He may be," said her husband. "But we've got to let him try it. Dave's done what the doctors couldn't do. He's restored the boy's spirit—and we mustn't do anything to kill it."

It was a spindly looking young man who permitted his father to carry him down to the breakfast table. His overalls and shirt hung loosely on him and the shoes were now too large.

"I want to take the crutches with me," he said. "I'd like to try standing up outside."

His mother did not try to conceal her joy at seeing him seated in his accustomed place and in his old familiar clothes. They had been bringing him down for evening meals since the day Dave Carson had first carried him to the living room for the 4-H meeting, but this was a first time for breakfast.

"We'll use the two horses and our two row planter," said his father. "I've got the 'Paymaster' and Hybrid seeds for you. I guess there's not much choice between the two acres. They're both right along the creek."

"Doesn't make any difference," said Tom, "which one we plant to Purebred or Hybrid." He lifted the cup of coffee to his lips with a hand which still trembled slightly. "See, Mother," he said. "I'm getting more strength in my arms. Don't worry about me. I've been hanging on to those straps upstairs. I'll be able to hold the reins all right."

Mrs. Dodds gasped. "You mean—you're not going to do the planting *yourself?*"

Tom nodded with a smile which stretched the thin flesh tight against his cheek-bones. "I sure am," he declared. "Part of it, anyway."

Farmer Dodds rode the back of his bay horse and his son sat strapped to the seat of the two row, horse-drawn planter as they went down over the hill toward the bottom lands, with Mother Dodds waving them out of sight.

The smell of fresh, fertile soil was in Tom's nostrils and familiar scenes were returning to his gaze. His heart and mind and body drank them in and he gulped hard several times as his father turned, happily, to point out old landmarks.

"Remember that young oak tree that had the top blown off in the windstorm?" he called. "We both thought it would die—but there it is. You'll have to look close to see its scars now."

Tom gazed at the twisted limbs, now covered with new foliage.

"You can't beat an oak," he said. "They'll stand up under most anything."

Reaching the river bottom and the place where Fred Dodds had staked off his son's two acres, the father dismounted.

"All right, Tom," he said. "How wide apart are you going to make your rows?"

"About three and a half feet," Tom answered. "Forty-two inches."

"You must be expecting a mighty good yield!"

"I am!" grinned Fred Dodds' son. "Guess I'll put the open-pollinated corn in first."

His father poured the seed in the containers, ready for planting.

"If you get too tired, son—let me take over!"

Tom nodded, and spoke to the horses. They started off along the bank of Stony Creek.

Farmer Dodds stood looking after the swaying, thin figure in the faded blue shirt, then chewed hard on the roughened knuckles of one hand.

"Thank you, God," he said.

There were three great events scheduled to take place on Independence Day, July 4th, in the town of Hidden Valley, and none of them involved fireworks. The first had to do with the announced opening of Jordan's New Drug Store; the second concerned the opening of the 4-H Club rooms on the upper floor of the same drug store, and the third noteworthy occurrence was to be the holding of Rock County's 4-H Dress Revue in the spacious rooms of that same club in that same building!

When Mayor Ed Brannigan heard of these three events, he provided the loudest pre-holiday explosion. His blasts of rage were aimed in the direction of two people mainly—one, a newcomer to the town by the name of Sam Jordan, and the other, the young man he had welcomed so vociferously but a few months ago, Hidden Valley's returned war hero, Dave Carson.

"They can't *do* this to me!" he raved.

But it was being done, nevertheless. All of the power and influence Ed Brannigan had in the community couldn't stop it. It couldn't even keep Sam Jordan from placing a full page ad in the Hidden Valley News Weekly advertising the Grand Opening of his store, "containing the only soda fountain in town," and announcing his building as the "Headquarters for the livest organization in the County—the young men and women comprising Hidden Valley's 4-H Club!"

It was a new experience for Mayor Brannigan to be left on the sidelines, and he didn't like it. Dave Carson had not been near him since their heated interview. He had seen Dave's father on several occasions about town, but Frank Carson, himself, had appeared cold and distant.

To make matters more embarrassing, everybody seemed to be talking about the 4-H'ers and the fine work many of them were doing on their farm projects. Meanwhile, the Civic Improvements Fund had been steadily growing at the bank, although there had been no announced plan of Community Betterment. It had been rumored, however, that 4-H President Dave Carson was quietly exploring ways and means of securing rural electrification and starting a program for better roads in the County.

This common talk was all very disturbing to Mayor Brannigan. Things were going on which he couldn't help and which, worse still, he couldn't fight. Townspeople were looking less and less to him and more and more to this newly developing younger leadership. As for his new business rival, Sam Jordan, he could cheerfully see him hanged from a lamp post in the public square. This energetic little man had been buzzing in and out around town, always ending up like a gnat in Ed Brannigan's hair. It required no prophet to predict that the man who had been Hidden Valley's most prominent citizen would have little to celebrate this July Fourth.

The Mayor was in his office in one of his bluest moods, the day before the holiday, when he saw the two men he most detested standing in his doorway. Sam Jordan and Dave Carson came in together.

"How do you do, Mister Mayor!" greeted his new competitor. "How are you?"

He extended his hand which Ed Brannigan disregarded.

"Hello, gentlemen," he replied, eyeing them coldly. "What brings *you* here?"

Dave Carson smiled. "Just a friendly visit, sir. Mr. Jordan and I wanted to invite you to attend the 4-H Dress Revue and to award the prizes to the winning girls."

Ed Brannigan scowled, cleared his throat, set his teeth, and said nothing.

"I've been too busy to be sociable, Mister Mayor," addressed Sam Jordan, "but I hope to have more time from now on. I'd like, after you've attended the 4-H show, to take you through my drug store. I'm catering to a different kind of business . . ."

Ed Brannigan's big fist hit the desk. "You mean," he roared, "you've been up to *monkey business!* I don't mind fair and above-board competition but when a man like you comes to town and influences one of the leading young men in this County against his own fellow citizens—people like myself who've been his best friends—you've got a lot of brass coming in here and offering any olive branches to me!"

Sam Jordan opened his mouth but Mayor Brannigan closed it with another bang on his desk.

"My answer to your invitation is 'no'! . . . As for you, Dave Carson, if that Dress Revue was being held anywhere else but in his building, I'd be honored to accept. However, I don't intend to advertise his business by making a personal appearance in his establishment. You 4-H'ers have made your bed with him and now you've got to lie with him. Good luck, my boy—and *good day!*"

Another bang on the desk almost blew the town's new drugstore proprietor and 4-H President out of the room.

Out on the Kendall farm, a nervous young woman was surveying herself before a half-broken mirror which hung on the wall of her bedroom. She was wearing a new brown dress, now completely finished, and holding a pouch handbag, made of the same material. Fitting snugly to her head was a little brown hat, also created from this same cloth. The whole effect was smart looking, enhancing the natural beauty of her face and figure.

Sue Kendall, in the months since February, relieved of some of her heavier farm duties, had filled out becomingly. She was wondering now if she had touched up her lips too brightly, but wondering even more what her father would say when he saw her.

Roy, too, had been waiting for this moment, which should have taken place several weeks before. But Sue had not been satisfied with the dress, when first completed, and had altered part of its design. This had taken extra time and consultations with her Home Demonstration Agent, Millie Logan. Then, too, there had been accessories to make, something she hadn't originally counted on and this, in turn, had led to the necessity of buying some new hose and a pair of brown shoes—both outrageous luxuries, in the opinion of Matt Kendall. But, in a moment of unexpected generosity, he had thrown a bill at her and snapped: "Well, you've gone *this* far—might as well go the rest of the way—but see to it, young lady, you don't get mixed up in anythin' like this again!"

Sue, now, was suffering an attack of stage-fright. She hated the thought of posing before her father's severe and critical gaze —and she feared what Roy, himself, might say and think. At the end of this long, hard road on her project, she was fighting the panicky urge to take off her dress, hang it up, and abandon the intention of competing in the Dress Revue.

She had never really seen herself dressed up before, and she wasn't any judge as to whether she looked all right or not. But one thing she *could* detect—all adolescent qualities were gone. She had been but a girl when she and Tom had been on the verge of marriage. Today, two years later, as she stood before the mirror, she saw a fully developed, vibrant young woman.

It was mid-afternoon and the sun's light would be flooding the front porch. It would also be streaming through the west windows of the living room. This was as good a time as any for her to exhibit herself if she were going to. She heard the kitchen door open and close and knew that Roy had come in from tending his beef calf. Her audience of two was on hand!

Sue drew a deep breath, took one last glance in the mirror, tucked an unruly wisp of black hair under her hat, and stepped through her bedroom doorway, just as Roy entered from the kitchen. He was in his work clothes and was rolling up his sleeves, ready to wash.

She saw his eyes behold her, widening as they did so, in frank amazement and admiration. Then both looked quickly toward the form in the chair.

Matt Kendall was dozing.

Roy beckoned to her and she tip-toed after him, into the kitchen. They stepped out together onto the back porch where Roy, plunging his hands and face into a basin of water, grabbed up a towel and said, between vigorous rubbings: "Sue, you're absolutely beautiful! I *mean* it! You're stunning! . . . I've always thought you were pretty—but I had no idea—well, I haven't seen the other girls, of course . . . but they'll have to go some to top *this!*"

Sue's lips quivered. "Oh, Roy, please don't! You're just doing this to build me up. Don't be afraid—tell me the truth!"

"I am!" Roy insisted. Then, directing her: "Turn around . . . let me get the whole picture . . . Now, walk away from me . . . now, turn again . . . sidewise . . . give me your profile . . .

that's it! Now, walk some more . . . come toward me . . . back away . . . Turn all the way around . . . relax a little—you're too stiff. Don't give me that frozen look—*smile!* Let's see those nice white teeth! . . . You've got lots of charm—don't be afraid to turn it on!"

Sue stopped, laughing self-consciously. "Roy, quit it! You've got me all confused!"

"But these are things you've got to know how to do," he persisted. "And you've got to do them gracefully, too, or you won't make a good impression on the judges. I've seen girls in beauty contests who weren't nearly as pretty as some of their rivals— but they knew how to show what they had. I'm about as graceful as a duck but stand over here and watch me a minute!"

Sue went to a corner of the porch and Roy took on the pose of a beauty contestant, imitating her entrance on stage, her half turns and pirouettes, down to the final bow and walk-off.

"Do you get it?" he said, at the finish. "Now let's see *you* run through that routine!"

Sue complied, repeating it until he was satisfied.

"Now you haven't a thing to worry about," he assured. Oh, yes there's one other suggestion I'd make. I think you could still do things with your hair. Do you have a comb in your purse?"

She nodded, hesitantly. "Yes," she said, "But what . . .?"

Roy stepped over to her. "I'm no technician on hair-does," he said. "But I've seen quite a few glamour girls in Chicago—and I think you'd look much smarter if you turned your hair in this way—page boy fashion." He took hold of the thick masses of hair at the sides and rolled them under. Then, turning Sue's head so she could look in the small mirror which hung over the wash basin, he said: "You see what a pretty effect you get? You could easily train it to stay that way."

Sue's eyes brightened with eager interest. She opened her handbag and took out a little comb, then removed her hat and handed it to Roy.

"Hold this a moment," she said.

Going to the basin, Matt Kendall's daughter poured some water in it, moistened her comb and ran it through strands of her hair, turning them under as she did so.

Roy, watching, directed as she went along. "Not too much . . . that's just right . . . whoa—hold it! . . . Now the other side, the same way . . . Get what I mean? . . . That's wonderful! . . You've got a natural wave there. It'll stay in place, too, after you do it a couple of times . . ."

Roy's mounting enthusiasm threw him into city jargon. "Baby!" he cried, as Sue replaced her chic little brown hat, "you're a hot number! I mean—you're *plenty okay!*"

He seized her suddenly, on impulse, and kissed her full on the lips.

She pushed him from her, startled and indignant.

"Roy Willard! Don't you ever do that again!"

"I'm sorry!" he apologized. "But you looked so darn wonderful, I just couldn't help it!"

The raised voices brought a call from the living room. "Sue! Roy! . . . Where are you? . . . Come in here!"

Matt Kendall's daughter and the boy from the city exchanged concerned glances. There was no delaying from such a summons. They entered the living room with self-conscious expressions of guilt. But the quick eye of the chronic invalid discovered something else. He pointed at Roy.

"What are those red marks at the side of your mouth?" He darted a glance at Sue. "Has he been kissin' you?" he demanded.

Sue did not reply, but Roy spoke up.

"Yes, I have!" he said, defiantly.

"So that's what happens when a girl gets dressed up!" said Matt Kendall. "I've been ag'in too much of this thing from the start!" He turned back to Roy. "If I catch you up to any more of this business, I'll give you a bad report to the Judge!"

"It won't happen again," promised the boy from the city.

Chapter XIII

ALL ROADS in Rock County, on July 4th, whether in good condition or not, led to Hidden Valley and Jordan's New Drug Store. The long deferred thirst of the natives of that region for an ice cream soda was at last about to be satisfied. Heretofore, it had required a trip to Batesville, in the adjoining county, thirty miles distant, over a rough and rocky highway. Now, while the roads were not any better in and around their own County seat, the trip to a soda fountain was much shorter.

Sam Jordan had supplied an equally good mouse-trap, closer to home, and appreciative folks in the County were beating a path to his door.

The Grand Opening was a grand success!

But the magnet which brought the throng in on the Nation's Holiday was the Jordan's Drug Store offer of three cash prizes of one hundred, fifty and twenty-five dollars to the first day customers who held the lucky coupon at a drawing to take place in front of the establishment immediately after the 4-H Dress Revue.

Sam Jordan was a merchant showman who believed in spending money to get money. This was a radically new procedure in Hidden Valley where the business philosophy had been to compel people to trade at home by opposing construction of good roads which might enable them to trade elsewhere. Under the compulsion theory and Ed Brannigan's influential example, the town's business men had not considered it necessary to keep their stores up to date, to carry a complete line of stock, or to make improvements around the Square. Why go to this expense? The people would *have* to trade there, anyway.

Today, in Hidden Valley, Jordan's Drug Store was the only business that was open but, to look around the Square, one would have thought it a busy Saturday afternoon. Cars and trucks of all makes were parked thick about the Court House

147

and people stood in line awaiting their turn to meet the industrious Sam Jordan and buy themselves a treat at his soda fountain and get a chance on the winning of the cash prize.

Mayor Ed Brannigan could see this throng from his home on the heights and it upset him more than a cannon cracker some boys next door exploded beneath his front porch.

Rivalling the drug store as an attraction were the new club rooms of the Hidden Valley 4-H Club, occupying the entire second floor. They were reached by a separate outside stairway and an attractive white placard over the stair doorway, bore the words, printed in green:

HEADQUARTERS
HIDDEN VALLEY
4-H CLUB

There was a constant line of curious and interested visitors going up and down these stairs to look in on the club rooms and be welcomed by the proud and happy 4-H members who were holding Open House.

President Dave Carson had donated the combination phonograph and radio set he had been given as Hidden Valley's outstanding war hero, and the music of selected records added to the warm and inviting atmosphere.

The rooms were attractively decorated with streamers of green and white, the 4-H colors, while banners and pennants containing large reproductions of the Four-Leaf-Clover hung from the walls.

The patriotic touch was supplied by the red, white and blue of a beautiful silken American flag which draped gracefully from its standard at the side of the stage in a cheerfully appointed little auditorium with a seating capacity approximating three hundred persons. There were dressing rooms back stage for boys and girls who might be participating in playlets or ceremonies or, as in the case of this afternoon, the all-girls' event known as the 4-H Dress Revue.

Along one side of this auditorium was located a kitchen and serving bar, so that refreshments or meals might be prepared.

The remaining rooms, situated up front, consisted of a simple but charmingly furnished reception and reading room with a boys' and girls' cloak room opening off it. All ordinary club meetings, exclusive of special affairs or community gatherings, could be held here.

It was evident to the over-awed and admiring country and townspeople that Sam Jordan, Hidden Valley's new business man, had made a magnificent contribution to the youth of Rock County. He was made the recipient of spontaneous praise and acclaim.

"Think nothing of it," he kept happily repeating. "I was glad to do it. Proud to have the young people meeting here. . . . If we don't do something for our boys and girls, how're we going to keep 'em with us? . . . I believe in the younger generation. Give 'em a chance and they'll make this a better town and county!"

The 4-H Dress Revue was scheduled for two in the afternoon. The first eight rows of seats were reserved for parents and friends and members of the 4-H Club which was a fortunate precaution because the auditorium was jammed with all standing room taken.

This being the first event of its kind in Rock County, there were only eleven entrants in the contest. Home Demonstration Agent Millie Logan assigned five of these girls to one dressing room and six to the other, that they might change from street clothes to the garments they were modelling.

There was a surprising feeling of excitement and suspense experienced by the audience as the three judges took their seats in the front row next the stage. These judges were the wife of County Agent Jim Watson, who had formerly been a dressmaker in a fashionable shop in St. Louis; Editor Herb Bevins, of the Hidden Valley News Weekly, who was called in to judge everything from pig contests to horse-shoe pitching; and Mrs. Vera Courtland, proprietress of the only Ladies' Dress Shop in town, who knew as much about styles as any one in the County.

Sue Kendall found herself in the dressing room with the

naturally glamorous Hilton sisters and the freckle-faced Sally Eiker.

"I don't know what you and I are doing in this contest," Sally said to Sue, as they dressed. "The three winners are right here in the room with us!"

Her remarks were directed purposely so that the Hilton sisters would hear, and Carolyn, already attired in her white evening gown, and standing before a full length mirror loaned for the occasion by Mrs. Courtland, smilingly replied: "I wouldn't be too sure about that."

But Sally was positive. "With all the stage presence you girls have got," she rejoined, "why, just the thought of walking up there on the stage before all those people makes my knees wobbly!"

"Mine, too," confessed Sue. She had slipped the brown dress on and was standing nervously by, waiting for Carolyn to finish before the mirror. "You look lovely," she said, to Dave Carson's fiancee, "I don't think I've ever seen a prettier dress!"

"So glad you like it," said Carolyn. Then, eyeing Sue: "Your dress is pretty, too. I like those unpressed pleats."

Eleanor and Doris voiced their own admiration as Carolyn stepped away from the mirror and Sue surveyed herself for the first time before a full length looking glass. Her hair was somewhat blown out by the trip in and needed re-doing. She must give it just the touches Roy had suggested. He had said that he would be out there in the audience, as close to the stage as possible, on her left hand side, and that she should look toward him and forget everybody else when she made her entrance.

The girls had drawn for places in the Revue, upon arrival, and the luck of the draw put Carolyn third from last, Sally Eiker next, and made Sue the final participant. She had hoped that she would be first and thus get the suspense over but waiting this thing out would be an ordeal.

Millie Logan stuck her cheery head in the door.

"Well, girls—are you all ready?" she queried. Then, before they could answer, she observed: "Yes, you're far enough along.

We're starting the show now. Remember your order and what you're each supposed to do. Advance toward the center of the stage, bow to the audience, state your name and tell the folks, in your own words, about your dress, then do a complete turn, or whatever you think displays your dress to best advantage, and walk off the other side. We're playing background music for you on the phonograph. Now don't any of you be nervous. Just relax and don't forget to smile. I'll be out front watching. Good luck to each of you!"

She disappeared and Sue turned back to the mirror, applying comb and brush to her curly mass of black hair. As she created the effect she wanted, Sally Eiker exclaimed: "Gee, Sue—what a hair-do! Where'd you learn that?"

The daughter of Matt Kendall blushed. "I'm not telling," she said.

The Hilton sisters looked on, admiringly. "It's stunning," said Eleanor. "Becomes you very much!"

"It sure does!" said Doris. "I think *I'll* try that some time."

Sue smiled, uneasily, and sat down in a corner of the dressing room.

Outside the girls could hear applause and then the voice of President Dave Carson, addressing the audience.

"We, the members of the Hidden Valley 4-H Club, are happy to welcome you to this, our first public event. We wish to thank Mr. Sam Jordan again, for these wonderful club rooms and we will do everything in our power to be worthy of his faith in us. We 4-H'ers realize that we cannot accomplish everything that we want to do for the town and county in a day—and we can't do *anything* really, without your help and co-operation. But, if every individual was as public-spirited as Mr. Jordan, we'd have the finest county in the state in no time!"

This remark brought vigorous applause.

"I think you've all met the gentleman I'm speaking of by now," smiled Dave. "But, anyhow, I'd like Mr. Jordan to get up and take a bow."

The owner and proprietor of Jordan's Drug Store stood up in

the next to the last row and held clasped hands over his head, shaking them in a friendly gesture as he beamed at the assembled people of Hidden Valley and Rock County. There was more applause.

"And now," continued the 4-H President, "the event you are all waiting for! I wish to present Miss Millie Logan, our Home Demonstration Agent, who is in charge of this Dress Revue. Miss Logan!"

Her plump, jovial figure appeared on the stage and was cordially greeted.

"A Style Show for Rock County is something new," she said. "But I've long believed that some of our girls are just as beautiful and have just as much talent as girls anywhere in Arkansas —in the whole United States, for that matter!"

This remark produced laughter and a round of hand-clapping.

"Dress making, developing the skill and knowledge necessary to plan, select, construct, assemble and care for suitable costumes for work and social occasions is one of the most important projects 4-H girls can undertake," said Miss Logan. "These contestants you are about to see, have had to choose the style of dress which they feel best suited to them and most expressive of their personalities. They will be judged not only upon their sewing ability and appropriateness of garment for their own use and type, but upon their demonstrated grace, poise, posture and evidence of good grooming. I am going to call upon the contestants by number and they will introduce themselves. Are the judges ready?"

She called attention to the three judges seated in the front row, with score sheets and pencils.

"We *are!*" announced Editor Herb Bevins, in his most professional tone.

"All right," said Miss Logan. She turned toward the wings and called: *"Number One!"*

Dave Carson, at the phonograph, placed needle to record, and the musical accompaniment began. Its strains reached into the dressing room and brought nervous shudders from Sue Kendall.

Sally Eiker gave a jittery giggle. "What am *I* worrying about?" she said. "I haven't a chance, anyway. I might as well go out there and enjoy myself! If I fall flat on my face, it won't make any difference!"

Her remark helped to break the tension for Sue, but the Hilton sisters, unaffected through years of experience in public appearances, were relaxed and ready for their calls.

Bursts of applause greeted each contestant as she came and went off stage. The tension commenced to build up again in the little dressing room as the competition simmered down to the last four and Sue realized her big moment would soon be at hand.

"Number nine!" sounded Miss Logan's voice, and Carolyn got up to go. Her two sisters, Eleanor and Doris, had already returned from their turns and were sitting back awaiting completion of the Revue.

"Good luck!" called Sue. "You're beautiful, Carolyn—I'm sure you'll win!"

The fiancee of Dave Carson did make a glamorous picture in the long, full, white evening dress, with its tight-fitting bodice. It was touched off by an exquisite necklace of white pearls, with ear rings to match. Her golden hair was combed in a long, lustrous wave. She smiled and curtsied to Sue.

"You're very nice," she said. Then, gathering her gown in one hand, she stepped gracefully from the room and, a moment later, a burst of applause told those waiting that she, by audience acclaim, was the favorite thus far.

She returned a minute later, face happily flushed, crying: "That Dave Carson! Wait till I get him alone! He blew a kiss at me from the audience and everyone saw it—and it almost broke me up on stage!"

"Number ten!" called Miss Logan.

Sally Eiker stood up. "Goodbye, girls!" she said. "Here goes *nothing!*"

Every freckle seemed to glow as she smiled, infectiously, and tripped out of the room. She was wearing a simple but fetching sun suit which she had made from a feed sack. It was pink in color and of flowered design.

Sue, heart pounding so she could see it through the bosom of her dress, heard a great roar of laughter as the contestant just ahead of her made her appearance.

The Hilton sisters smiled. "Sally's a great sport," complimented Carolyn. Then, noticing Sue's drawn face and fingers which trembled as she smoothed out the folds in her dress, Carolyn patted her shoulder, sympathetically: "Don't tighten up that way. Just take a deep breath and let go. I get a funny feeling in my stomach, even yet, just before I have to go on—but the deep breath does it for me."

There was more laughter and applause and the sound of Sally running off stage to the dressing room. She came in, grinning, and let herself drop in a chair.

"Well, would you believe it?" she exclaimed. "I *did* fall flat on my face! Tripped over the carpet just as I was coming on. But I got the biggest hand of the afternoon. Listen to them— they're still laughing. I may be no model—but maybe I'm a *comedienne!*"

"Number *eleven!*" Miss Logan was calling.

The crowd was still in such a good-natured uproar that she had to speak twice.

Sue stood up, fright in her eyes. She moistened her lips, started toward the door, then ran back for a last nervous look at herself in the mirror.

"Here, Sue!" said Carolyn, "you forgot your bag." She handed her the brown pouch which had been lying on a chair. Sue took it with a little nod of thanks and hastened from the room.

Her Home Demonstration Agent was standing in the wings as she approached the stage.

"How do I look, Miss Logan?" she asked, shakily. "Is everything all right?"

"Yes, yes. You look fine," said Miss Logan. "But be careful, Dear—don't trip over that mat like Sally did!"

This warning served to take Sue's mind off herself for the

instant as she stepped on stage. Then a barrage of sound greeted her and she stopped, facing the audience, fighting a panicky urge to break and run off. Her eyes sought out the familiar face of Roy as he had instructed, seated somewhere down front, on her left. She couldn't see him and Roy, detecting that she was badly confused and nettled, raised his hand, flashing her a reassuring smile.

The effect on Sue was hypnotic. She smiled in return, recovering her composure and starting her walk to center stage where she turned and said, in a voice so under control that it amazed her: "My name is Sue Kendall. This dress did not cost me anything to make because I made it out of a dress my mother bought but never had a chance to wear. This purse and hat were made from the same material."

So saying, she did a complete turn-about, then backed away slightly and stood, for a moment, to give the audience a little side view. As she did so, she was turned away from Roy and another face came within her range of vision. The unexpected sight of this face almost unnerved her. Its owner was sitting in an aisle seat toward the back, with crutches lying on the floor beside him. As their glances met, his face lighted in a smile and he raised his thin hands to start the applause which accompanied her wavering footsteps off stage.

The three judges conferred by comparing notes and holding whispered discussions in their front row seats, as the packed auditorium buzzed with the expressed opinions of all present.

Dave Carson kept the audience entertained with light orchestral selections as anxious minutes for the contestants ticked away.

Sue, rejoining her 4-H rivals in the dressing room, replied in answer to questionings: "It wasn't as bad as I thought it was going to be." Then, added feelingly: "But it was bad enough!"

At last, the great moment arrived. County Agent Big Jim Watson had been delegated to secure the verdict of the judges. He was handed the fateful slip of paper by Editor Herb Bevins, and immediately went into a huddle with Miss Logan over the choices revealed.

"I'll get the girls on stage," said his Home Demonstration Agent.

She crossed excitedly to the dressing room on her right, and rapped on the door. Five girls straightened tensely, awaiting a possible summons.

"It's a funny thing," smiled Miss Logan, as she opened the door, "but all the winners are in this room . . ."

"What did I tell you!" cried Sally, grinning at the Hilton sisters. "Congratulations, you three! Go out and take your bows!"

"Hold on! Not so fast!" said Miss Logan. "The judges and you don't quite agree. I want Carolyn, Sue and you to come with me!"

"*Me!*" squeaked Sally. "What am *I* going to get—a Red Cross medal for falling down?"

Miss Logan laughed. "Hurry up, don't keep the crowd waiting! It's getting impatient."

The three girls named accompanied their plump Home Demonstration Agent, with Eleanor and Doris Hilton following after, to witness the awards.

"Well, *one* of us placed, anyway," said Doris.

"Yes," smiled Eleanor, "but *where* . . .?"

As the three winners walked on stage—Carolyn leading, then Sue, and finally Sally, who stepped elaborately over the edge of the carpet, a great blast of applause and laughter greeted them.

County Agent Jim Watson with first, second and third place 4-H medals in hand, met the three Dress Revue models at center stage, as they stood, side by side.

"The First Place Award," announced Big Jim, "Judged on the basis of the costume itself—its individuality, style, suitability and construction; then, the girl—her posture and poise; then the costume on the girl—its adaptability to her figure and personality; and, finally—its general effect and completeness—for top score in all these features—the silver medal and a free trip to the State 4-H Camp at Fayetteville in August, goes to Miss . . .!"

As he was about to speak the name, an uncontrollable tickling in his throat caused Big Jim to cough. The three prospective winners eyed each other, wonderingly, as the crowd laughed. Then it roared as Sally, reaching around behind Sue, gave Carolyn a little push forward.

"I beg your pardon," gasped Big Jim, catching his breath. "The first place winner is—Miss Sue Kendall . . . !"

There was a murmur of pleased surprise—then applause.

"Yea, Sue!" Everyone looking in that direction saw the boy from the city standing on his chair, waving and shouting.

But he was not the only young man standing up. There was another, in the center aisle, who leaned on crutches and applauded as he cried: "Bravo, Sue! . . . Bravo!"

Matt Kendall's daughter, stepping forward to receive the medal from Big Jim, was almost overcome. She took the silver award in her hand and gazed at it, shaking her head, unbelievingly.

"Second place goes to Miss Carolyn Hilton."

And now it was Dave Carson's turn to lead in the cheering!

"Third place—goes, after some deliberation and special credit for originality—to Miss Sally Eiker," Big Jim announced.

As Sally started forward, she almost stumbled over her own feet—she brought the house down.

When quiet could be restored, Home Demonstration Agent Millie Logan said: "I'd just like to say, before the first 4-H Dress Revue becomes history, that Miss Sue Kendall will compete at the State Camp for a chance to represent Arkansas at the National 4-H Club Congress held in Chicago, in December. I'm sure we'll be rooting for her to go on to greater honors."

The loudest applause of the afternoon followed.

Then Carolyn, turning to Sue, threw her arms about her and kissed her on the cheek as she said: "I tried my best to win— but I'm glad, if I couldn't, that *you* should be the one!"

"Thanks," smiled Sue. "I really didn't think I . . ."

"Neither did I!" cut in Sally. "I've been picking wrong all afternoon. I don't know how *I* ever won anything . . . unless they counted my freckles and added them to the score!"

Chapter XIV

Sᴜᴇ ʜᴀᴅ just finished slipping off her prize winning dress and placing it lovingly in a box, together with her new hat, handbag, hosiery and shoes, when there was a rap on the dressing room door. Since she was the last remaining person in the room, she called out: "Just a minute, please. I'm not dressed!"

There was a laugh and a voice said: "That's okay. It's only me!"

The doorknob rattled and Sue shrieked: "Roy Willard—you stay out!"

The door did not open.

Sue hurried into her street dress and loafers. She could not resist the quick luxury of a last look at herself in the full length mirror. What a change! Cinderella was the princess no longer. The clock had struck twelve and now she was being called back to every day life, to the humdrum of pots and pans and menial barnyard chores. But it had been fun and exciting while it lasted. She literally had to *pinch* herself to realize that she had won the first award and a trip to the State Camp at Fayette-ville! This would mean the first journey out of the County for her—if her father would permit it and she could get away the required four days.

Her hair needed a few new touches with the comb . . . better leave it just the way Roy had suggested . . . ! She turned toward the door.

"You can come in now!"

The boy from the city entered. He was still exultant over what had happened.

"I promised I wouldn't kiss you again," he cried, "but, by thunder, I'm going to *hug* you!"

He grabbed her in his arms and did as announced, lifting her off the floor.

"Roy!" she protested. "Put me down!"

"Baby, you were terrific!" said Roy. "I thought, for a second, you were going to freeze out there—but you got hold of yourself and went through like a trouper . . . all except your exit—it was pretty ragged. We'll have to work on that for the State. What happened?"

"I don't think I'll be upset again," said Sue "Going through it once before an audience did something inside. I've got confidence in myself now—but what threw me was seeing Tom out there. Did you know he was here?"

"Not till it was all over," said Roy. "But why should *he* throw you?"

"I don't know. I guess it's just that I realized this was the first time he's been away from home since his illness . . . "

"Well," said Roy, "you've got to get so that *nothing* affects you up there. If you'd seen him a little bit sooner, you might have fizzled out and lost the contest. Are you ready to go?"

"Yes, we'll have to be getting back as quickly as we can."

Roy took Sue's dress box under his arm and they left the dressing room, and went out into the deserted auditorium.

"Where *is* everybody?" asked Sue.

"They're all outside at the drawing," laughed Roy. "We'd better hurry. Maybe you'll win that, too!"

They descended the stairs and encountered a crowd which filled the public square on the Jordan Drug Store side. The drawings had just been concluded and Sam Jordan, in front of his store, was paying off the prize coupon holders. As the crowd started to disperse, one of the winners turned in the direction of Sue and Roy and they saw who it was. His face lighted up as he glimpsed them.

"Hi, folks!" he cried, and waved his hundred dollar bill. "This is something I'm not going to feed my pigs!"

"*Porky O'Connor!*" exclaimed Sue. "Are *you* lucky!"

"What do you mean—'am I lucky'!" retorted the fattest member of the 4-H Club. "I *worked* for this! I had ten chances in that draw. I had to down three malted milks, five sodas and two root beers to get them!"

Sue and Roy laughed. "What're you going to do with all that money?"

"I'm turning it over to Pop," said Porky. "He wants to build himself a new hog-house and buy some pure breds. My pig project is showing his hogs up so bad that he's going to follow my system!"

Porky started off, looking for new friends to greet, then suddenly thought and whirled about.

"Say!" he cried, eyeing Sue. *"You* didn't do so bad today *yourself!* Boy, were you beautiful! . . . I mean—you still *are*—but that dress was a *honey! . . .* Come over and do some sewing for *me* some time. I need a new patch on my overalls!"

Sue laughed. "That will cost you a *hundred dollars,"* she said.

Porky stuck the century note in his pocket and backed away. "That's too high for me," he said, "I guess I'll just have to die of *exposure!"*

Sue and Roy looked about them as Porky lost himself in the crowd.

"Well," said Sue, "now we've got to find someone who's going our way, to give us a lift."

She had hardly spoken than an older man touched her elbow.

"Congratulations!" he said. "Tom wants to know if you and Roy won't ride home with us?"

Sue turned to face Fred Dodds. "Why, we'd be glad to," she accepted.

Tom's father smiled. "That's fine. Our car's parked down here just off the Square, across from Brannigan's General Store. Follow me!"

There were still quite a few people on the street, and Jordan's Drug Store was doing a thriving business as they left.

Mrs. Dodds and Tom were seated in the car, awaiting them.

"Oh, Sue, we're so happy for you!" beamed his mother. "You and Roy get in the back seat with Tom. I remember so well, Sue," she continued, "your Mother sending for that dress. She showed me its picture in the catalogue and said she'd always loved that shade of brown. It looked lovely on you. You must have been inspired to use that material!"

Sue, slipping into the back seat beside Tom, with Roy following, replied: "Yes, it really worked out quite well."

Tom's slender fingers gripped her hand. "Just kick those crutches out of your way," he said, "and make room for your feet." Then, looking at her with eyes not so deep sunken now, he said: "Sue, you gave me one of the biggest thrills of my life today. I know what it meant, doing what you did, and I think it's wonderful!"

"Thank you," whispered Sue, and looked away.

Fred Dodds was behind the wheel and the car was slowly feeling its way through traffic toward the Stony Creek Route.

Tom glanced across at the boy from the city. "Roy, how's your beef calf coming?" he asked.

"Seems to be all right. It's been so hot lately, the pasture's kind of drying up. I hope he's getting enough feed."

Tom nodded. "Yeah, this weather's pretty hard on my corn, too. It could stand a little rain at this stage. The leaves are commencing to curl in some places."

"Guess we'll all have to start praying for rain," said Sue.

Tom smiled. "I'm already praying," he said.

"How high *is* your corn now?" Sue asked, their eyes meeting again.

"It's up to my waist," Tom replied.

"You mean—you're getting right out in it?" asked Roy.

"I sure am," responded the fellow who had so recently been flat on his back. "Of course, I have to use these things." He pointed down at his crutches. "But the ground's fairly level and I . . . well, maybe some day . . ." He broke off and stared out the car window.

"You're looking fine," said Sue, softly. "You've got a swell tan."

Tom did not reply but Fred Dodds, overhearing the remark, called from the front seat: "He should have. He's spending three to four hours in his corn patch every day!"

Tom laughed, drily. "Well, it gives me a change of scene, anyway," he said. Then, directly to Sue: "I'm really proud of that

corn, though. If you get time, why don't you run down and
have a look at it? I'm usually there in the mornings."

Sue smiled. "I'd love to," she said. "Maybe I can do it some
time this next week."

They were nearing the turn in to the Dodds' home.

"Won't you and Roy come in for a few minutes?" invited
Mother Dodds.

Sue shook her head. "I'm sorry, we can't. You know how it
is." Then, to Tom's father, "You don't need to drive us on down
to our road. Roy and I can walk."

"It's no trouble," Fred Dodds protested.

"But it's so dusty," insisted Sue, "and everyone who lives out
this way is on the road now. Just look behind at what's coming.
Whew! I'll bet you'll be glad when this route is fixed up!"

Fred Dodds turned into his drive and stopped. "I hardly expect that any more in my life-time," he said, with a half laugh.
"That is, not unless you 4-H'ers get it done for us!"

Roy, sliding out of the car with Sue's dress box, extended her
a helping hand.

"Goodbye, Tom," she said. "It was nice seeing you . . . and
I'll be seeing your corn pretty soon, too. So long till then."

"Thanks for the lift," called Roy.

"Don't mention it," said Tom, reaching down for his crutches.

He shot a last lingering glance at Sue as she and Roy started
off down the road and the Dodds' car moved slowly up the drive.

Nothing could take place within the range of Matt Kendall's
vision without his being aware of it. His field glasses now
brought him the images of two young people trudging up his hill.

"Not a bad lookin' couple," he said aloud. "That boy's done
all right around here. Better than I expected. He gets along well
with Sue, too. She's brighter these days than she's been since
Tom took sick . . . and with Roy here, she's been takin' better
care of *me* . . . I'd hate to see this boy leave . . . I wonder if
anythin's developin' between 'em? . . . Can't tell nothin' from
Sue—she's bottled her feelin's all up inside . . . But if she still

cares for Tom, she's got to git that notion out of her head . . . It's bad enough to have a cripple for a father . . ."

Sue and Roy were now close enough so they could see Matt Kendall looking out at them. They lifted their arms and waved. He lowered his glasses and raised a gnarled hand in response.

They came in the front door, Sue first, and Roy following with the dress box which he put down on a chair.

"Well," snapped Matt Kendall, "How'd you make out?"

"I won, Daddy," said Sue, quietly.

A look of stunned incredulity crossed her father's face. "You *won!*" he repeated. "You won—*what?*"

"This silver medal," she said, opening up her hand and going over to him.

He had no grip in his fingers, but by pressing them together on both sides of the medal, he was able to lift it from her palm. He examined it critically and then exclaimed: *"First* prize!" He glanced up at her, a flash of pride in his embittered features. "Well, your mother's dress came to some good, after all!"

"Yes," said Sue, lips trembling. "A great deal of good, Daddy . . . more good than you'll ever know."

He held out the medal to her between his twisted fingers. "What kind of talk is that?"

Sue shook her head. "I can't explain it so you'd understand." She took the medal, closing her hand about it, tenderly, and turned to pick up her dress box. "There's lots to be done. I'll get to work right away."

She hurried into the bedroom and closed the door.

Roy had been standing, eyeing Sue's father with growing feelings of resentment. "She looked beautiful, Mr. Kendall," he said. "I wish you could have seen her."

"I've seen her," said Matt Kendall, grudgingly. "I see her every day. I know how my daughter looks."

"Not like she looked on the stage," said the boy from the city. "She was different . . . There was something in her face I haven't seen around here."

The canny eyes of Matt Kendall darted from Roy to the bedroom door, and back again. "Just what are you drivin' at?" he demanded.

"That's for you to figure out," said Roy, and left the room.

It was a hot, baking morning in the second week of July that a dark-haired girl dropped in at the Dodds' home. She was wearing blue denims over a red figured cotton blouse she had made from a feed sack.

"Sue Kendall!" cried Mother Dodds, happily. "So glad to see you! How well you look in that outfit!"

Sue smiled. "It's nothing much. Is Tom here? I promised him I'd take a look at his corn . . ."

"No. He's already down in the field," said Mother Dodds. "Isn't it good to have him getting up and around again?"

Sue nodded. "Yes, it is," she said, restrainedly.

"Of course we don't know that he'll ever walk again," Mrs. Dodds added, "But Tom's showing such a fine interest in things . . . we're naturally hoping . . ." She left the thought unfinished and then, as Sue found nothing to say, she changed the subject by asking: "Tell me, how's your father?"

The light faded from Sue's face. "He doesn't change," she said. Then, as though afraid to commit herself further, she backed away. "I can't stay long. I'll just run down and look in on Tom for a few minutes."

"I'm just about to take some bread out of the oven," Mother Dodds proposed, "and we have some nice, fresh butter. Won't you wait and sample a slice?"

"Sorry," Sue declined. "I really haven't time. Thanks just the same."

She left the house and started running down the hill and through the fields toward the creek bottom.

Mother Dodds stood in the doorway, watching her disappearing figure and pressing her lips tight to hold back her emotions.

"She's a wonderful girl," she said to herself. "And I'm sure our Tom still loves her . . ."

The waist high corn was waving and crackling in the dry-as-dust breeze which was blowing in from the south. There was no evidence of a human in sight as Sue reached the bottom lands and approached Tom's two acres along Stony Creek. She could detect a difference in quality from the nearby corn of Fred Dodds' planting. It was several inches shorter and did not appear to possess quite the vitality of the stalks in Tom's project.

As she cut through the rows to get to Tom's plot, she saw patches of weeds which needed chopping. These ragweeds and cockleburr and pig weeds and crab grass seemed to be everywhere. You could pull them up and turn your back and they'd almost be starting up again.

The soil was baked hard in spots despite the cultivation. Tom was right—the corn needed rain. She hadn't kept track but it must have been fifteen or twenty days since they'd had any wet weather at all . . . She was on one of Tom's acres now.

This looked like Hybrid corn—a good, hardy grade . . . Strange how pure bred corn was less resistant to dry spells and disease than when you crossed two pure lines and made a hybrid. Nature seemed to thrive on crossing breeds. She'd always heard that Hybrid corn had stronger root systems, too . . . This would be a good experiment, seeing just how much hot weather this corn could stand in its present stage of growth.

But where was Tom? . . . She must be half through this acre now . . . There was Stony Creek not far ahead . . .

Sue stumbled over some pieces of wood in the middle of a row. She started as she saw what they were—*a pair of crutches!*

Tom couldn't be far from there . . . And then she caught sight of him. He was perhaps a hundred feet away, his back turned to her, dressed in overalls and open neck shirt, down on his hands and knees, crawling through the corn and weeding it by hand, as he went.

Sue stood, silently, watching, and tears mingled with the perspiration on her face. Tom, unmindful of her presence, continued to drag his semi-useless legs after him as he pulled himself along, leaving neat piles of weeds behind. It was evident to Sue that he was reveling in his work.

She regained control of her emotions and stepped out of sight beyond the next row, then called: "Tom! . . . Oh, Tom!"

There was an instant, joyous answer. "Hi, Sue! . . . Right over here!"

She strode into view and Tom, sitting up on the ground, lifted a slender arm in greeting.

"It's swell of you to come," he called, as she neared him. "Doesn't it beat all how these weeds grow, even in dry weather? Sometimes I think we ought to cross corn with one of the hardiest weeds and see what we get!" He gazed up at her as she smiled down at him. "How do you think my corn looks?"

"Not bad," said Sue, "What I've seen of it. Most of it's a nice dark green . . . but some of it's beginning to turn pale green, almost yellow . . ."

Tom nodded. "That's what worries me," he replied. "And there isn't anything that can cure that—except *rain.*" He scanned the sky and pointed to a patch of fluffy clouds. "Do you think they may have any water in them?"

Sue studied the heavens. "I'm afraid not," she said.

"If we don't get rain in the next three or four days," said Tom, "my corn is really going to be hard hit. My Hybrid's holding up fairly well—but the Paymaster is commencing to curl. If this drought is broken, though, I've got a chance to get a swell yield off both my acres."

Sue examined the hybrid stalk and leaves. "This will be over your head in another month, with any kind of luck," she observed.

An especially high gust of wind whipped the corn and set it waving. Little eddies of dust whirled through the rows. In several spots it looked like dust funnels were trying to form in the air.

"Could I trouble you to bring me my crutches?" Roy asked. "They're back up the row somewhere."

Sue, pretending she had not seen them, retraced her steps and came upon them. Tom had quite a struggle to get the crutches under his arm pits and raise himself to his feet but Sue knew better than to offer any assistance.

"Let's go down to the big willow by the creek," he proposed. "I'm not as tough as this corn. I could stand a little shade."

He swung himself along with difficulty as the rubber tipped ends of his crutches sank in the soft earth or broke through the dried crust. But they finally made it and sat on the old bench there.

It was a spot they had often been before, when both were aglow with vibrant health and high hopes. They could see, from this vantage point, the hill upon which they had planned to build their home. A cluster of pine trees seemed to be beckoning to them. For quite some time neither spoke, being concerned with their own private thoughts.

"It's always so peaceful and nice here," Sue said, finally.

Tom was sitting, watching little minnows sporting about in a shallow, sheltered portion of the creek, near the bank. Both of them could see their reflections in the water, two suddenly solemn figures, shimmering on the surface. Now that they were together, a strange gulf of restraint had welled up between them. More clouds rolled up in the sky and embraced each other—but Tom and Sue sat carefully apart on the bench.

Sue finally stirred. "I've got to be getting back," she announced. "There's always so much to do on our place and you know how Daddy is about my being away any time for long."

Tom nodded. Her comments seemed to release something in him.

"I'll say I know," he assured. "I've often wondered how you stood it. But since I've been laid up, I appreciate more how your father feels, too. It's not exactly a bed of roses to be wanting to be out and doing things and not be able to." He stood up with Sue, balancing himself on his crutches. "Thanks for coming down," he added. "It means a lot to me."

"I wanted to come," said Sue. "Maybe I can come down again and see it when it's full grown."

Tom's eyes lighted. "I wish you would," he said, with spirit.

"If we only get some rain, I'll show you some real corn by then!"

Sue turned to leave. "Well, goodbye," she said.

She was standing close to him. He could have leaned on his crutches and reached out an arm and put around her, and perhaps she might have let him kiss her. But whatever his own inner feelings, he didn't do it, and she moved away.

"Oh, Sue," he said, as though it were an after thought. "I've meant to ask—how's Roy making out on your place?"

Sue turned back toward him. Their eyes met.

"Just fine," she said, without a waver. "He's done wonderfully well for a fellow who didn't know anything about country life."

"It's probably none of my business," said Tom, hesitantly, "but knowing your father as I do, how is Roy getting along with him?"

"He does his work and that's all Daddy asks of him," Sue gave short answer.

"Good—I'm glad to hear it," said Tom, sincerely. "It must be much easier for you—and that's what counts with me."

"It *is* easier," Sue admitted, and then, in a burst of feeling, "I wish you'd stop worrying about me, Tom Dodds! I wish, since you wanted it that way, that you'd forget me entirely. I'm going now. Goodbye!"

She wheeled about and ran down the row, then cut through the corn and was lost to sight.

He saw her again as she reached high ground and he hoped she would turn and wave.

"Sue!" he cried, and his voice echoed back to him in the hot morning air from which the breeze had died. "Sue!" he shouted once more, but she did not look back.

Tom's chin sank against his chest. He stabbed a crutch futilely into the ground. A crow cawed raucously nearby and a mountainous thunderhead cast a shadow over the earth.

Chapter XV

THREE NIGHTS LATER, shortly after sunset, there was lightning all around the horizon. A humid, deathly stillness hung over the dry landscape. Roy and Sue stood in the back barnyard, studying the sky.

"Looks like we're going to catch it tonight," said Sue. She glanced down the hill toward the Dodds' place. "I hope it comes in time to save Tom's corn. He's worked so hard at it."

Roy chuckled. "I'm glad my beef calf doesn't depend on rain," he said. "But the pasture's pretty badly burned out at that. Do you think it's safe for me to leave him out tonight?"

"Oh, I think so," said Sue. "A little water isn't going to hurt him." She gasped as she saw a particularly vivid streak of lightning. "My, did you see that! It went straight down! That hit something!"

"I just caught it out of the corner of my eye," said Roy. "Pretty far away, though. No thunder yet."

They waited, and after what seemed more than a minute, there was a long, faint, ominous rumble.

"There it is," said Sue, "that *was* a long way away!"

An ugly cloud bank began to poke its head up in the west. Red tongues of lightning licked along its top. A light wind sprang up and dry dust peppered their faces.

"Look!" said Roy, pointing above them. "The stars look like they're covered with dust, too!"

"We may get quite a blow out of this when it comes," Sue speculated. "We haven't had a real storm this summer."

"We'd better fasten everything down good, then," said Roy. "Don't they have cyclones out in this country?"

"Once in awhile," said Sue. "But we've never had one right through here. Don't you love to watch lightning? *I* do!"

"If it doesn't get too close," said the boy from the city. "I was playing ball once in the school yard when it struck a flag pole and knocked out two of my chums. That wasn't funny."

They stood for awhile, unspeaking, as the rumble of thunder drew closer. The lightning was almost continuous along the sky line.

"Guess we might as well turn in," Sue suggested. "The storm may not break for some time yet."

Roy held the screen door to the back porch open for her, latched it on the inside, and closed the inner door. Matt Kendall heard them coming in and called: "What do you think—is it going to rain?"

"In a little while, Daddy," Sue answered. "We're getting ready for it, so we won't have much to close up after we go to bed."

"That's good. My arthritis is painin' me pretty bad. That's a sure sign we're goin' to have a big change in the weather."

In the Dodds' home, Tom's father had just come in from locking up the barn. His son called down to him.

"Looks like it's really coming this time!"

"It's coming all right," said Fred Dodds, grimly. "Maybe too much of it. That's the trouble with weather like this—we either get a feast or a famine. A heavy wind and rain would do us plenty of damage."

"Oh, pshaw!" said Mrs. Dodds. "Stop borrowing trouble. This may all blow around us."

"What did you say, Mother?" called Tom.

"I said—'it may blow around'," she repeated, raising her voice.

"Don't wish us anything like that. I'd rather take our chances. We've got to have rain or we're finished!"

A scurry of wind rattled the shutters. It had come chasing down the hill from the Kendalls' place. Far off, a lonely dog howled. There was a disturbed flutter in the chicken house. A lightning flash photographed the countryside. The bombardment of thunder was now almost constant. It rolled like a thousand distant kettle drums, from west to east.

"Here it comes!" cried Fred Dodds, closing all remaining windows.

It struck the Kendall place first—a shattering blast of wind which shrieked and ripped at the old frame house, and banged it with loose stones and sticks. Then the first close stab of lightning crackled through the air, followed almost instantaneously by what sounded like a mile-long string of box-cars crashing together.

Roy and Sue had just gotten ready for bed and all lights were out except a kerosene lamp which burned all night in the kitchen.

Matt Kendall lay on his cot in the living room with electric needles of lightning tracing a weird tattoo on his face. His quick eyes were blinking as he tried to keep them open against the brilliance of the flashes.

"Sue! . . . Roy! . . . Get up!" he ordered. "Can't tell what this storm's goin' to do! It's a *ripper!*"

Matt Kendall's daughter and the boy from the city leaped from their beds and fumbled into their clothes. They dressed by nature's illumination.

There was a screeching sound, far off at first, like a company front of locomotives with their whistles tied down. It increased in volume as Sue and Roy raced from their rooms and gazed, white-faced, at one another in the flickering glare of the kitchen lamp.

Terror wrote its signature on Matt Kendall's face.

"It's a tornado!" he cried, "and I can't move! . . . I can't do anythin'!"

"Can't we carry him some place?" Roy asked of Sue.

She shook her head. "We're just as safe here as anywhere."

The house rocked as though a giant hand had grabbed the roof and was shaking it. There was a singing roar as the locomotives passed over on invisible tracks, clearing the Kendall hill and whizzing across the valley below. Then came the fusillade of rain, machine-gunning house and roof.

"Thank God!" breathed Matt Kendall, with one of his rare displays of reverence, as he sank back, exhausted, on the cot. "It missed us! Just listen to that rain!"

A moment later, the Dodds were listening to it, too. The blow had gone through above them, but Tom was greatly concerned.

"I wonder, Dad, if it hit the Kendall place?"

"I don't know, son. It didn't miss us by too much," said his parent, soberly. "Some places are certainly catching it tonight!"

"If Kendalls' caught it, they'll be needing help," cried Tom.

"Can't get up their road in this storm," replied Fred Dodds. "It'll be a quagmire by now. We'll have to wait till the worst is over."

A miniature Niagara Falls was running off the roof.

"It's practically a cloudburst," said Tom. "I hope it doesn't flatten my corn."

"It's doing damage," said his father, grimly. "I told you, Anna, I was worried about this one."

A blinding flash lit up every object in the house. It was accompanied by an earth-shaking crash of thunder.

"My, that was close!" cried Mrs. Dodds.

"I saw it go down!" exclaimed her husband. "It struck somewhere up on the Kendall hill!"

"Did it get the barn?" Matt Kendall was moaning.

"I don't know," said Sue. "It hit something out that way."

Through the sound of the rain came a frightened bellowing.

"It's my beef calf!" cried Roy. He ran to the back porch and grabbed an old rain cape off the hook. "I'm going out after him!"

"Stay in here, you fool!" called Matt Kendall. "It's too wild out there yet!"

But Roy was already gone, taking a lantern with him.

"I'm going, too!" said Sue. She dashed in the bedroom and came back with an all-weather slicker.

Her father offered no further protest and she hurried out after Roy, pulling the porch door shut against the wind and rain. It was black and wet but the spot from Roy's lantern was swaying on the familiar path, half-way between barn and house.

Sue sloshed through almost ankle deep water in places, as she followed the light. She caught up to Roy in time to slide back the bolt from the barn door, as he held the lantern. They were both soaked to the skin in this short time.

Inside the barn, the goats and other livestock were whimpering and kicking nervously, in their stalls. A lightning flash explored the interior and went out again, leaving its report down over the valley.

Once more, through the pound of rain on the barn, they heard the cry of the beef calf. Roy opened the door into the feed lot which led on out to the pasture.

"I hope he's not hurt," he said. "I should have brought him in. He may have fallen and broken a leg."

Sue felt suddenly responsible. She had advised against sheltering the steer. It hadn't seemed possible that anything could happen.

They were out again, into the storm, through the muck and mire of the feed lot and into the pasture which was dry no longer. Rain pelted them with stinging drops, and lightning danced all around.

"Look!" cried Roy. "That big hickory in the center of the field! It's *down!*"

It was momentarily dark and everything blotted out. But Sue saw the tree in the next flash, which gave her a fleeting picture of its shattered trunk, with its grand old top bowed down to earth.

"So that's what was hit!" she exclaimed.

The wail of the beef calf sounded once more. It came from that direction. Roy and Sue sprang forward, together. They circled the tree and came upon the beef calf, lying on its side, under one of the boughs.

Roy dropped to his knees, handing Sue the lantern, and cradled the terrified steer's head in his arms.

"You're all right, Your Majesty," he soothed. "Don't worry, boy! We'll get you out of here." He stroked the wet and muddy head as the steer's great eyes looked up at him. An almost relieved sound came from deep within the animal.

"Sue!" cried Roy. "I can't see. Is he bad hurt, anywhere? Maybe he's paralyzed. Do you suppose he was struck, too?"

Sue reconnoitered in the rain. "This limb isn't heavy enough to have hurt him much. His body seems to be all right. I can't quite tell about his rear right leg—but I think he's just down from fright and shock."

The steer struggled and pawed at the softened sod with his front hooves.

"Easy boy," counseled Roy, in a quiet, calming voice. "Lie still. Wait till we lift this limb off of you." He jerked the rain cape from his shoulders and slid it under the steer's head to keep its nostrils out of a pool of water. Then, standing up, he called to Sue: "Set your lantern down on that rock. Do you think we can shift this limb between us?"

"We can try," Sue volunteered.

The lantern started sliding. She caught it just in time and secured it with another rock placed against it. Then Matt Kendall's daughter and the boy from the city grabbed the limb of the fine old hickory and pulled it to one side, fastening it under another branch. The calf lay, unmoving, as Roy had commanded.

"Good boy!" he said, kneeling once more and patting his steer's head. Then, directing: "Sue, get to his rear and watch that right leg. I'm going to try to get him on his feet!"

When Sue was in position, gently patting the animal's flank, Roy spoke, softly: "All right, Your Majesty, we're ready now. You can get up, boy. Come on—get up!"

The animal understood. It pawed the sod for a foothold, doubled its forelegs and rolled and squirmed its fattened body in the slippery grass and earth. The right hind leg came free and, with a great lurch, the heavy beef calf stood on all four feet.

Roy sobbed from sheer relief and threw his arms around his animal's neck.

Sue was near tears, too, as she picked up the lantern. "Can you lead him in?" she asked.

"He'll come," said Roy, confidently. "Won't you, boy?"

The storm was lessening now. A steady rain was falling but the lightning flashes were intermittent and moving further and further away.

With Roy's guiding hand on its shoulder, the steer followed along behind Sue and the lantern, and they made it back to the barn and stall, without mishap.

Once safely inside, Roy said to Sue: "You'd better go in and go to bed. I'm going to rub him down and put blankets on him, and stay with him the rest of the night. Look how he's shivering! He's still scared to death. I want Mr. Carson to look at him first thing in the morning, to see if he's been touched by lightning. I don't know much about things like this but I do know that a bad shock doesn't do an animal any good."

"You'd better look after yourself," said Sue. "I'll go in and bring you a towel and some dry clothes, and a pot of coffee. And I'm telling Daddy that I'm staying up with you!"

Tom Dodds could hardly wait till daylight to get down to his bottom land and see what the storm had done to his corn. Early radio reports told of severe flood and wind damage in other parts of the state. His father was equally concerned, and helped Tom into the saddle of their best riding horse, Old Harry. It was to be his first venture on horseback in over two years and his parent was going with him on foot.

As they left the barn, they could make out the figure of Roy Willard coming down the Kendall hill.

"Let's wait and ask him how they got through last night," said Roy. He urged his horse around the house, out the front drive, and down toward Kendall road. "Hi, Roy!" he hailed.

The boy from the city waved and soon came alongside "Pretty rough last night!" he called.

"It sure was!" said Tom, from the saddle. "Do anything to your place?"

"No, except lightning finished off the big hickory and part of it fell on my calf and gave it a bad scare. I'm going to see Mr. Carson now and get him to come down and take a look."

"Your calf wasn't hurt in any way?" questioned Tom.

"Not that I can see, but he's off his feed this morning." Roy glanced toward the Dodd's home. "Anything hurt on your place?"

"I don't know yet," said Tom. "I'm riding down to my corn now. Have you listened in on the radio this morning?"

Roy nodded. "Yeah. That was a bad blow that went through Walnut Ridge, wasn't it? Guess it took down half the town."

Tom's horse fidgeted as though anxious to be off. "Whoa, boy!" he said. Then, to Roy: "Yes, that cyclone dipped down and did damage in several spots. Batesville and Newport had cloudbursts, too. There are several bridges out and highways washed away in places. We were pretty lucky!"

Roy looked back up Kendall Hill. "The rain didn't help this hill, either," he said. "I'll have to fill it in. Mr. Kendall's funny. He doesn't seem to care whether anyone can drive up it or not."

A busy bee flew close to Old Harry's nose. He reared up and shook his head, and Tom almost slid from the saddle. Roy, nearby, gave a leap and supported him.

"Say," he cautioned. "Aren't you taking a chance on this animal?"

The fellow who had spent almost two years in bed turned his mount around. "I'll get along all right," he said. "Goodbye, Roy. Good luck on your calf!"

Roy started up Stony Creek Route, toward the Carsons, on foot, but turned to call back: "Thanks! . . . Good luck on your *corn!*"

Part of the bottom lands had been flooded and two rows of Tom's corn, both Paymaster and Hybrid, had been washed out, close to Stony Creek. The other rows had taken a beating but stalks were upright and showing renewed vitality from the moisture they had drunk up. The yellowish cast in some of the corn was disappearing and the leaves were losing their curl. Some of Fred Dodds' corn on higher land had been blown down, flattened and bent by the wind, but most of his acreage had also escaped serious damage.

Father and son looked at one another with silent expressions of thanksgiving.

"It's a strange fate," observed Fred Dodds, "how a storm will ruin one man's crops and leave another's free. God doesn't seem to take any account as to whether a farmer's a good church member or not. I've seen some of the finest, most godly people have their homes and barns wiped out by flood or tornado, while other neighbors nearby, who hardly ever saw the inside of a church, weren't even touched."

Tom nodded. "I'm no Bible student," he replied, "but doesn't it say somewhere that 'the rain falls on the just and unjust alike'?"

"It does," confirmed his parent. "And I've a strong suspicion that God gives us pretty much our own way on this earth, after providing us with all we need to make a go of things. I think it's *how* we react to things which happen to us that *counts*."

He looked toward his son.

"I haven't mentioned it before, Tom, but I've often thought that *good* lots of times comes out of *bad* . . . that what seems to us as a calamity can be made God's opportunity. Take yourself, for instance—you could have stayed in bed the rest of your life, but you finally decided to do something about it—and when you did—God began to help you.

"His power is always there, inside you, ready for you to call upon . . . and I think, hard as your experience has been, that you're coming out of it a stronger, finer person, in every way."

This was as completely as the usually taciturn Fred Dodds had ever expressed himself to his son. Tom had sat in the saddle, with his strengthened but still frail hands clasping the pommel, listening thoughtfully.

Some tear drops gathered in his eyes and coursed, unchecked, down his cheeks, to the ground, where they were lost at once in the wet soil. His eyes lifted and strayed over the site he and Sue had picked for their home, then raised to the sky, now bright and shining.

"That's the way I've got it figured, too, Dad," he said softly. "But God knows it isn't easy. I'm doing the best I can."

Local Leader Frank Carson and son, Dave, stepped into *Your Majesty's* stall with the steer's owner, Roy Willard. The animal acted as though it were going to rear and kick until Roy spoke, when the calf quieted at once.

"He's still jittery," observed Rock County's best beef breeder. "Just a minute, now." He circled about the animal, going carefully over its ribs and working up over the back and rump, and examining the legs. "Seems to be in good condition, though," he added, to Roy's great relief. "Say, young man, you've got a wonderful calf here! He's fattened up in the right places these last few weeks—and he shows that you've given him the right care. His flesh is firm and thick, has a good quality *feel* about it." He turned to his son. "What do *you* think, Dave?"

The President of Hidden Valley's 4-H Club, who had also been studying the steer, nodded in agreement.

"It's a fine animal," he said. "You've done a fine job, Roy."

"Thanks," said the boy from the city, mightily pleased.

Frank Carson put his hand on the glossy back of the steer and stood thoughtfully. Then he turned to the animal's owner.

"Roy," he said, "I think you've got a calf here, if he keeps on developing, that has every chance of placing in a livestock show. You need three years of club work to submit your records in most 4-H National Contests but this isn't required in the regular County, State and International Live Stock Shows. If you like, I'll help you enter your calf, along with Dave's, in the County Show at Hidden Valley this October. There will probably be about thirty other entries—but, in my opinion, your Aberdeen Angus is well worth exhibiting!"

Roy's eyes gleamed with excitement. He scratched his steer affectionately behind its ears. "What do you say, Your Majesty?" he asked. "Would you like to compete?"

The steer raised his head and rolled his eyes.

"Okay!" laughed Roy. "If you say he's good enough to show, Mr. Carson, that's good enough for me!"

Chapter XVI

On the fifth day of August, the day Sue was to leave for Fayetteville to attend the Annual State 4-H Club Encampment, Matt Kendall received an unexpected letter which gave him a great deal of personal satisfaction.

"Well, my sister, Ella Bogue, finally got around to writin' me," he said, "after near seven years." He held the letter pressed between his two gnarled hands as he addressed Roy and Sue. Then, as though he owed an explanation to the boy from the city, he went on: "I thought she'd be gettin' in touch with me if I waited long enough. She and her no-good husband done me out of my father's old place, five miles from here . . .

"It don't matter how they done it—but they did . . . and then they sold it and went to Detroit. He died and she's been workin' and roomin' there ever since . . .

"Now here's what she says . . ." He referred to the letter and squinted as he read: "'Dear Brother—It seems terrible for us to be the only two left and not speakin' to each other all these years. I'm writin' to you, once more, to ask you to let bygones be bygones—and patch up our differences and let me come to visit you, my only brother, before one or the other of us dies' . . ."

Matt Kendall looked up to see Sue staring hard at him and Roy gazing off into space. He gave vent to a short, sharp, unpleasant laugh.

"She don't say so, but she thinks I'm goin' to die first—that maybe I've got somethin' saved up . . . well, if I had . . ." and a tinge of venom came into his voice, "she wouldn't get it!" he finished, vindictively.

"I haven't seen Aunt Ella," spoke Sue, "since I was a little girl. She seemed awfully nice to me then."

"Oh, yes, she had a way about her," snapped Matt Kendall. "That's how she was always able to get things out of people

179

. . . But right is right, and what she done to me, years ago, is just as wrong now as it was then . . ."

The boy from the city turned to face Sue's father directly. "Don't you ever forgive anyone for anything?" he asked.

Matt Kendall met his gaze with a bitter look. "I was born to respect the truth," he answered. "And to hate deceit and falsehood. My own sister cheated me—took what was a-comin' to me—and I can't ever forgive that!"

There was a moment of uneasy silence and then Roy, unable to restrain his feelings, said: "Sometimes, Mr. Kendall, I can't understand why you ever took me in."

"You never done nothin' to me," said the chronic invalid. "But my sister did! . . . I treat people as they treat me . . . and you've been doin' all right, so far. I ain't got no complaint."

He dropped the letter on the table and pushed it from him.

"Daddy," said Sue, appealingly. "Aren't you going to answer Aunt Ella?"

Matt Kendall's eyes flashed. "I am not!" he said, decisively. "Not if I was a-dyin'!" Then, deliberately changing the subject, he asked: "You got your things all packed for the trip?"

Sue nodded. "Yes, Daddy. I'm not taking much. I'll only be gone four days. I'll have to be starting down the hill. The school bus will be coming along soon."

"Who all's goin' from here?" asked her father, evincing sudden interest.

"Oh, there's Dave Carson and the Hilton sisters—they're going to sing at the Camp . . . and Tom—his folks are driving him over . . . They offered to take me, too, but I told them I'd rather go with the gang . . ." She hesitated. "I guess that's all from here," she added, glad of her father's show of attention. "There'll be about thirty-four in the bus by the time it's made pick-ups at Melbourne, Marshall, Searcy and Mountain View." Sue's eyes danced. "We ought to have a jolly crowd, don't you think?"

"It wouldn't be for me," said Matt Kendall. "Just a lot of noise and nonsense!"

Sue laughed. "Oh, that's just because you haven't had young people around for so long," she ventured, "if you'd only . . ."

There was the distant honking of an auto horn and Matt Kendall reached for his field glasses.

"There's your bus now!" he said. "And they're havin' to wait on you. Git goin'!"

Sue raced into the bedroom and came out with a little suitcase and her precious dress box.

"I'll take those," volunteered Roy. "I'm seeing you off."

He relieved her of them and she ran to her father's side.

"Thank you, Daddy, for letting me go," she half whispered, as she kissed his cheek.

"Take care of yourself," he said, looking straight ahead. "And don't worry about me. Roy's a good hand."

It sounded as though someone was sitting on the auto horn. Roy was already out of the house and yelling for her to hurry up. She left her father's side but paused at the door to blow him a kiss. There was a pull at her heart as he raised twisted fingers—and returned it.

Great news came to Roy Willard as he was in town for supplies on Friday, the last day of the 4-H Club Encampment at Fayetteville. The Hidden Valley News Weekly was just out, with the headline story which had barely been received in time to make the paper.

Sue Kendall had been chosen State Champion of the 4-H Dress Revue and had won a free trip to the National 4-H Club Congress to be held in Chicago the first week in December. The whole town was talking about it and, within twenty-four hours, it would be the talk of the county.

Roy, buying an extra copy of the paper, ran half the way out Stony Creek Route and then thumbed a ride to Kendall Road that he might get home as quickly as possible and convey the glad tidings to Matt Kendall.

He burst in the door, paper in hand, but breathing so heavily that he could not speak. The emaciated figure in the chair eyed him, his usually severe features stretching the facial muscles in a smile.

"You don't have to tell me," he said. "You wouldn't have run up that hill if she'd a-lost. Let's see that paper!"

Roy, still gasping, grinned as he tossed the paper in Matt Kendall's lap. Sue's father straightened it out with his club-like hands, pressed it against his knees, and read the news account.

"So! She's a-goin' to Chicago next!" he said, and his face hardened.

"Yes," said Roy, dropping on a chair. "She'll get a great kick out of that, Mr. Kendall. That'll be something entirely different. Chicago's not New York, but it's plenty big to anybody who's not been out of this state. I'd like to be there to show her around."

"You can't be," snapped Matt Kendall. "You both can't be away—and I ain't sure I'm goin' to let her go."

"But you'll *have* to!" Roy declared. "She's representing the State now. It's a great honor, Mr. Kendall—and Sue's earned every bit of it. I should think you'd be glad."

Sue's father squirmed, uneasily. "Everythin' she does is takin' her further and further from home. I don't like it!" He turned his head abruptly and shot a questioning glance at Roy. "Tell me this—are you and she up to somethin'?"

The query caught Roy off guard. He stared at Matt Kendall in amazement. "Why, no," he said, "I don't get what you mean. What would we be up to?"

"You're spendin' so much time together," said Sue's father. "I was just wonderin' . . . ?"

"I don't know what you're thinking," said Roy. "But whatever it is, there's nothing to it."

Matt Kendall subsided, satisfied. "I'm glad of it," he said. "I'm mighty glad."

A radiant Sue Kendall returned by bus late that night from Fayetteville and was dropped at the foot of Kendall Road.

"You can't see to go up there alone," said Driver Hank Simmons. "Here—I'll honk and get somebody to come down and meet you."

He gave a blast on the horn before she could stop him.

"I've made it up this hill lots of times after dark," she said.

"And never ran into any snakes?" asked Hank.

"Oh, yes," Sue admitted. "But they don't bother me any."

A light suddenly appeared at the top of the long hill. Hank shifted his gears into low and released the clutch.

"There comes somebody," he called. "You'll be all right now. Goodbye!"

He was anxious to get home himself. He had traveled over three hundred miles this day, returning his various passengers to their county seats, and only the fact that he lived out Stony Creek way enabled him to drop Sue and these few others within easy reach of their homes.

The Hilton Sisters, Local Leader Frank Carson and wife, who had been acting as chaperones, and their son, Dave, waved and shouted as the bus moved off.

Sue, with suitcase in one hand and dress box in the other, could only nod and smile as she called back: "Goodbye, everybody!" She watched the old yellow school bus disappear in a cloud of choking dust. Then she turned to look up Kendall hill and saw Roy swinging down the road, in his familiar overalls, lantern held high.

"Hello!" he shouted, his voice echoing in the night. "Congratulations!"

"Hi!" she answered, in a happy voice.

The reflection of his lantern soon caught up to her and highlighted the sparkling green eyes and glossy black hair.

"Did you have a good time?" Roy asked.

"Wonderful!" she breathed. "The most wonderful time of my life!"

"Well, we're sure proud of you!" said Roy. "Here, you carry the lantern and I'll take your suitcase and box."

They made the transfer and started walking, shoulders almost brushing, up the rough and uneven roadway.

"You haven't seen anything yet," said Roy, enthused. "Just wait till you hit my home town of Chicago!"

Sue laughed. "Fayetteville seemed big enough to me," she said, "And the University of Arkansas . . . and the barracks they put us up in . . . and the big dining hall . . . and the auditorium . . . they were all so huge, they just about took my breath away. I don't know whether I could stand Chicago or not!"

"You could stand it all right," predicted the boy from the city. "I only wish I was going to be there to show you around. What a time we'd have!"

"Maybe Daddy won't let me go," said Sue, face sobering.

"I think he will," assured Roy. "Just so I'm here to look after things."

They were half-way up the hill and neither one of them, despite the lateness of the hour, was disposed to hurry.

"How did Daddy act when he found out that I'd won?"

"Oh, he pretended that it didn't mean too much," said Roy. "But I'm commencing to get onto him now. I think it really made him feel pretty good."

Sue shook her head. "I never know quite how to take Daddy," she confessed. "I'm greatly surprised you haven't had a real run-in with him by now."

Roy gave her an admiring side-glance. "That's because of you," he said, frankly. "I took my cue, that first day, when he lit into me. I was all set to let him have it. But when you gave me the high sign and I realized what you'd been taking all these years, I figured I ought to be able to take it for a short time, *for your sake*."

Sue touched his arm, appreciatively. "You've been swell," she said. "All the way through. And I wouldn't have made out on this clothing project if it hadn't been for you. I wouldn't even have gotten away from home for over-night." Her eyes dimmed with tears. "I wonder if you can ever know how much it means just to get a change of scenery . . . to meet new people . . . to see a tiny bit of the world beyond your hill . . . and to get away from yourself for just a little while . . . ?"

"I think I can," said Roy, feelingly. "Living here with you . . . and with your father!"

They were nearing the house now and were within range of Matt Kendall's field glasses. He would most certainly be having his eyes on them, as always—penetrating, all-seeing, calculating.

"There are some things in life," Sue confided, impulsively, "that I guess you can't change—and Daddy's one of them."

They crossed around to the front porch where they were beyond the reach of his vision. Roy set the suitcase and dress on the top step and turned to Sue, taking the lantern from her.

"I can't help it," he said, in a low voice, tinged with emotion. "There's one promise I've got to break. I'm going to *kiss* you!"

Her lips were half parted in protest as he took her in his arms, pressing his mouth against hers. She did not resist, this time, but clung to him, momentarily, as their hearts hammered against each other.

A dry cough from within the house brought them to their senses. Roy, releasing her, whispered fervently: "I'm crazy about you, Sue! I think you're the swellest girl I've ever known."

She didn't answer but gripped his arm as he turned to pick up her things and dabbed his lips with her handkerchief to remove any possible tell-tale evidence. He caught her fingers and kissed them. She pulled away and motioned for him to hurry.

Roy stood aside to let her open the door while he held the suitcase and dress box. There was a dare-devil look in his eyes and he leaned forward to kiss her hair as she turned the knob.

The door swung open and Roy entered first, Sue following with the lantern. She placed it on the floor and ran across to the figure in the chair, throwing her arms about her father.

"Oh, Daddy!" she cried. "It's good to be home!"

She rested her head on his shoulder.

"Just put her things in the bedroom," he said, giving Roy a meaningful nod. "I'll be seein' you in the mornin'!"

Sue lifted her head and exchanged a startled glance with Roy as he hastened to comply with her father's directions and retired to his own little room off the kitchen.

Chapter XVII

AUGUST DIPPED into September and autumn beckoned a frosty finger, and beef fattened ready for market, and corn ripened, approaching the harvest time. 4-H'ers throughout the country were increasingly busy as their projects neared completion and in Rock County, Arkansas, the first 4-H County Fair was being planned to take place in Hidden Valley late in October. It was to be held the same dates as the County Livestock Show, in buildings at the old Fair Grounds, and President Dave Carson and his Fair Committee were busy concluding all arrangements and working out the program.

Dave was going to be an extremely active young man with his steer exhibiting at the Livestock Show and competing against baby beeves of Future Farmers of America and independent stock raisers. He would have to be in attendance there, running back and forth between the County Livestock Show and the 4-H County Fair, both on the same grounds.

Roy Willard had been devoting all the time he could to filling in ruts and holes in the Kendall road. Its repair was absolutely imperative if he was to get *Your Majesty* off the hill. Local Leader Frank Carson would not risk his stock truck in making a pick-up, otherwise. Dave's father's interest in the beef calf he had sold the boy from the city was equal to that which he held for his own son's entry. He had been outspoken in his praise of Roy's handling of the animal, and had told other livestock men in the state to keep their eyes on this Aberdeen Angus.

Tom Dodds, meanwhile, had stayed with his corn project, displaying almost fanatic zeal in its care. He was being rewarded by two marvelous looking acres of rich "black" corn, which reached well over his head to varying lengths of between six and seven feet.

Two days before the Fair, County Agent Jim Watson and Local Leader Frank Carson visited the Dodds' place and accompanied Tom and his father to the two experimental acres where ears and stalks were to be chosen for the exhibit.

While in the field, Big Jim, examining the yield, said to Fred Dodds, "You know, Mister Man, I think your boy's got you beat! It looks to me like Tom's yield per acre will top yours by quite a bit. Let's do a little figuring."

The three men, with Tom leaning on his crutches watching, paced off a hundred feet in one of his *Paymaster* rows, then snapped off the ears of corn and threw them in the wagon. They next selected the yield from a hundred feet of corn in Fred Dodds' adjacent *Paymaster* acreage. This done, the men moved over to Tom's *Hybrid* acre and repeated the process. Upon completion, they piled in the wagon and drove back to the barn where the individually collected ears were weighed.

"Just as I thought," grinned Big Jim, after he had finished computing the yield per acre in each case, from the sample yields. "The special care Tom's given his corn has upped its production by twenty percent in his *Paymaster* over yours. Of course you didn't plant any *Hybrid* corn, but Tom's *Hybrid* acre is well above his *Paymaster* yield, topping it by almost twenty-five percent. This is really sensational!"

Fred Dodds smiled and put a hand on Tom's shoulder which was now rounded out with evidence of returning firm flesh, beneath his shirt. "It's mighty good news to me," he said. "This *Paymaster* corn of mine has been raised by my father and my grandfather before him. I guess if I want a real yield next year, I'll have to plant *Hybrid* seed like Tom. I was telling him just the other day, I'd never seen such vigorous looking corn in all my life."

"This will make a fine exhibit," commended Local Leader Frank Carson. "If I'm not mistaken, it will be the talk of the Fair."

The young man on crutches accepted the praise, quietly. "I'm glad you think I've done a good job," he said. "But I guess you all know I didn't tackle this project to win a prize. I did it because I wanted to win something for myself."

As his County Agent and Local Leader left, Tom turned to his father. "I haven't won out yet," he said, "but I know now that I've got *more* than a fighting chance."

Roy Willard was as jittery over thoughts of his appearance in the ring and showing off his beef calf as Sue Kendall had been in contemplating her modelling of the dress. He had rehearsed his every movement with *Your Majesty,* time and again, striving for perfection, but always there was something he could find to criticize.

Either his steer didn't leave the stall quickly enough and get into position for showing as he should, or he wouldn't take quite the right stance when he got him in the crude ring he had marked off outside.

Sue, his audience of one, called suggestions or applauded as she thought the animal and its showman merited. This was a serious business and Roy, in an effort to train *Your Majesty* to stand squarely on all four legs, borrowed one of Matt Kendall's canes and tapped each foot as it got out of line. It required eternal patience and control of temper to lead his calf through the paces desired.

"I don't know," Roy would say, in flashes of despondency, "why I ever spent all this time on a dumb animal like this. He'll make a fool of me at the show. I've got him fattened up beautifully but if he doesn't stand still *where* I want him, and *when* I want, I'm sunk!"

Sue would then laugh and reply: "You're working him too hard. You're both of you tired out. Don't start worrying, Roy, or your steer will feel it and it will upset him. Better lay off for today."

And the boy from the city would follow her counsel and give his animal and himself some rest.

But now, the early morning of the County Livestock Show's first day, had arrived and Roy, with Sue helping, was giving *Your Majesty* a last grooming before Local Leader Frank Carson would call with his truck for the trip into town.

They had filled tubs of water from the cistern outside the barn and had let them stand in the sun until the chill was off. Then, before wetting the animal down, they went over it, each on a side, with rice brushes to work out all possible dirt. They looked across at each other, as they brushed, following the natural direction of the hair, and Sue said: "It's fun doing things together, isn't it?"

Roy grinned. "I know some girls in the city who wouldn't think this was fun," he said.

Your Majesty stood quietly as they applied the water and lathered it up with a mild soap solution, and rubbed gently but firmly.

"Now, Mister," said Roy, "You're ready to be rinsed." Then, to Sue: "Get up by his head and hold his ears, face down, to keep out the water. I'm going to douse him."

She did as directed and the calf obediently lowered its head as the lukewarm water ran over it.

"He likes it," smiled Sue, "Don't you, Boy?"

The steer opened one eye, got some water in it, and shook his head.

"I think I'll use a little *dip* to soften his hair and kill any skin parasites," said Roy.

This done, he went over his animal with an aluminum water scraper to remove all surplus solution, then handed Sue a clean brush and took one himself.

"Now smooth his damp hair down," he said. "Stroke from back to front and make straight even lines. That's it!" he added, as he watched.

They brushed for some time, admiring their handiwork, as the hair became soft and glossy. Then they used both brush and Scotch comb to pull the drying hair up, and finally Roy pointed to the calf's tail and said to Sue: "How about your *ending* the job? Give him a large, fluffy tail. Brush just a few strands at a time. Just imagine you're brushing your own hair—and give it the same wonderful finish!"

Sue took the calf's tail and made an impish face at Roy. "I believe you love this animal more than you do *me!*" she said. "Why shouldn't I?" grinned Roy, "I've raised him from a *baby!*"

Competition in this year's County Livestock Show was unusually stiff. As Frank Carson had predicted, there were over thirty entries—thirty-three, to be exact—only two of which were listed as 4-H beef calves. This was only due to the fact that Rock County had been backward in 4-H development thus far, but most other counties in Arkansas had much larger 4-H representations in their livestock shows.

The competition, then, that Dave Carson and Roy Willard were having to meet was coming from FFA members and independent, thoroughly experienced growers of meat animals.

Frank Carson had deliberately stayed out of this contest, not wishing to compete against his son or the boy from the city, and honestly feeling that these two Aberdeen Angus calves from his herd, which they had entered, were as good or better than any others he might have put in the show.

With the stock all on hand ready to be judged, as well as viewed by interested visitors to the show, it was evident that some of the finest baby beeves ever raised in that region were on display. The Hereford and Shorthorn breeds far outnumbered the Aberdeen Angus animals on exhibit, being considered by many breeders easier to raise.

Dave's calf weighed, at twelve months, nine hundred and ten pounds, while Roy's animal, of the same age, tipped the scales at nine hundred and forty-two. The two beeves had been placed in adjoining stalls.

Dave and Roy met there as they cared for their calves, and discussed their possibilities.

"I've taken a quiet look around at the other calves," Dave reported. "And while there's some good stuff here, I really believe, Roy, that we've got the calves the others will have to beat to take the championship. I've talked to some pretty smart breeders, too, and they've got their eyes on our animals. They say it looks almost like a toss-up, and—if that's true—then the judge will have to make his choice on our performance in the ring."

Roy nodded. "I hope it doesn't have to be between *us*. I'd get a kick if I could win out against everyone else in the show but, after the way you and your father have treated me, I'd really hate, as much as I want to win, to see my calf take it."

Dave laughed. "You shouldn't feel that way. A good calf's a good calf, no matter who's showing it. I won't feel badly if my animal edges yours out, so don't you waste any sympathy on me."

Dave extended his hand and, as they shook, Roy said: "Thanks for letting me know how you feel. This is all so new to me, I'd be the most surprised fellow in the United States if my calf won. I've done the best I knew how with it but I have to take the word of a man like your father that it's as good as he says it is. Anyhow—good luck, Dave—and may the best man . . . I mean—the best *steer*—win!"

The arena was packed for the judging at two o'clock that afternoon. Professor Arthur Dowling, head of Animal Husbandry from the University of Arkansas, was to be the judge, assisted by George Regan, beef cattle herdsman from Oklahoma A. & M. College, and Ralph Norris, stock breeder from Little Rock. Their appearance in the ring brought applause from an eager and excited crowd, among whom was the entire Hidden Valley 4-H Club contingent, seated together in the bleachers, directly in front of the judges.

To their right, at one end of the arena, was the entrance from the long, low building which housed the competing steers. This opened onto a small circular track, around which the animals were to be led on parade.

There was a touch of showmanship as a bugle sounded and two experienced cattlemen removed the bars. The first steer's head appeared, followed by its owner, a man of about forty years, in a cowboy hat and plaid shirt. Steer followed steer, after that, accompanied by their showman, each receiving cheers from their individual supporters, and all spectators.

The three judges stood on the far side of the track so they could take a long range view of the animals. Their first job was to be the singling out of baby beeves which obviously were the class of the competition. Dave Carson was seventh in line with his entry, *Carson's Pride,* while Roy Willard was in twenty-third place as he made his appearance with *Your Majesty.* Both of these animals received a great ovation from the enthusiastic 4-H group, which amused the crowd.

"You'd think this was a football contest," a spectator was heard to remark. "But this is one game that can't be won by cheering. It doesn't depend so much on what the contestants do now as on what they've done in all the months past. This is where pedigree, right raising and training count. You can't make a touchdown unless you've got a real all-around animal."

"Line up your beeves!" came the order from Judge Dowling, and the contestants on parade swung their animals around on the track, heads all facing in the same direction, toward the audience. Several of the steers were a bit rebellious but a word or a gentle slap from their owners brought them into line.

"There's a lot of great beef there," said a cattle man.

The judges started walking down the line looking over the back of each steer to determine its spread of rib and uniformity of width and to observe its depth and width of quarter. They handled the animals, beginning over the ribs and working forward, checking the crops and back along the loin, back and rump. They noted the smoothness of covering and thickness of hide and texture of flesh. Then, after conferring together, Judge Dowling went down the line, pointing to different showmen.

"Take yours to the other end of the track," he ordered. "You . . . and you . . . and you—other end of the track!"

The number of competing baby beeves was reduced to eight and those losing out in the preliminary placing were led back to their stalls by their disappointed owners. Those steers remaining were now realigned in the center of the ring for closer inspection.

The judges gave careful time and attention to each animal. Dave Carson's and Roy Willard's entries were still in the running. *Carson's Pride* and *Your Majesty* now stood in number one and three positions, separated by a Shorthorn entry. There were two FFA members with calves, nearby, and the other four were independent entries. But the wise cattle breeders had their eyes on the two easily recognized magnificent Angus specimens of beef flesh, and a murmur went through the crowd that these two animals were the class of the show.

Dave and Roy, hearing the rising tide of comment, glanced at each other and smiled, but their smiles did not last for long. The Shorthorn between their calves suddenly reared and, despite all efforts of its FFA owner, broke the line. This unnerved other animals which showed signs of breaking.

"Steady, Boy!" said Roy, quietly, in *Your Majesty's* ear. "Steady! . . . Steady!"

It was a brutal test of control. Up to this moment his steer's behavior could not have been more perfect and the same was true of Dave's. They were two finely developed animals in temperament as well as flesh and reflected not only the quality of their sire and dam, but the quality of training they had received from their two showmen.

The rump of the unruly steer struck *Carson's Pride* and forced it to break stance. It looked for a moment as though Dave's animal would rear but Dave, with gentle handling, brought it again into line.

A cattle man, seeing that the owner of the Shorthorn could not subdue his animal, came running over to give assistance. As he did so, the frightened calf side-swiped Roy's entry. The boy from the city had his arm about the neck of his steer.

"Hold it, Your Majesty!" he prayed. "Hold it, Old Fellow! . . . Don't move! . . . You're all right! . . . Hold it!"

And *Your Majesty,* paying Roy back for all the long hours and days of loving care he had given him, stood staunch and firm in the face of the panic that was going on around him.

The judges were quick to eliminate the unmanageable steer and have him taken out of line as the crowd cheered a real champion in the making, with *Your Majesty* standing immobile and four-square under command of a young man who now cried unashamedly in appreciation of his steer's marvelous exhibition of poise and obedience.

Dave, looking on, shook his head in admiration.

"I've never seen anything like it," he said. "My hat's off to you, Roy. I can't compete against that!"

The judges proceeded swiftly in awarding first prize to the beef calf owned and exhibited by one Roy Willard, with second place award going to Dave Carson's entry, both calves having been taken from the famous Frank Carson Aberdeen Angus herd. Third and fourth place awards didn't matter as far as the Hidden Valley 4-H'ers were concerned. Their cheers resounded throughout the arena as they realized that, in the very first competition of their members in the County Livestock Show, they had copped the two top prizes.

As Roy was left alone in the ring, with his first place winner, and presented the purple ribbon for "Grand Champion of the Show," he had eyes for only one person in the cheering throng. She was standing up waving to him. Then, when she saw that he had spotted her, she blew him a kiss.

This little by-play was lost to all but the two principals, except one. He was a young man who was seated with crutches between his knees and who now looked away toward the far distant hills as though fighting to control his own emotions.

President Dave Carson was now free to give most of his attention to the 4-H County Fair. County Agent Jim Watson and a staff of judges were going through the various exhibits, representing a diversity of individual projects. The two awards arousing greatest acclaim among visitors to the Fair and 4-H members were the blue ribbons won by Tom Dodds, for his fine quality *Paymaster* and *Hybrid* corn, and Porky O'Connor for his prize hogs—Porky taking first, second and third places, to everyone's amazement but his own.

"Shucks!" he exclaimed, "If I'd entered *myself* in the contest, I'd have taken *fourth* place, too!"

For Tom Dodds, prize recognition came as the outward reward for a gruelling, unrelenting effort, often beset with doubts and fears and moments when he had been grievously tempted to give up the struggle and seek refuge in his isolation of the past. But in periods of blackest despair, his two acres of corn had waved to him from the bottom land, crying out: "We need your care. Are you going to let *us* die, too?" And Tom had somehow found the strength of body and spirit to keep going. He was glad of it now as he sat out of sight behind the booth containing his exhibit, crutches propped against the wall, and heard the compliments passed by those studying his display.

"Well, what do you know—here's some corn raised by Fred Dodds' boy!"

"*Dodds!* . . . I thought he was dead . . . Yes, I'm almost certain . . . he died of infantile paralysis about two years ago."

"No, he didn't—you're wrong. I've seen him around the last few months . . . I guess he was bed-ridden for quite a spell."

"Well, this is *some* corn. It deserves first prize all right!"

These observers moved on and a new group arrived. Tom, with a start, recognized the voices.

"Oh, here's Tom's corn. Aren't those wonderful ears? . . . Look how big around they are and what a fine shape!"

"Yeah, they're big all right, but I wouldn't know what makes prize corn."

"Well, I don't know everything, either—but see those straight rows of kernels . . . that means something . . . Look—these kernels go clear to the tip . . . and they're all regular size . . . those are about the most perfect ears I've ever seen."

The other voice laughed. "The only corn *I've* been interested in is what my calf has been eating."

"You know, Roy, I'm sorry about one thing. I told Tom I'd be back to see his corn when it was full grown but I slipped up. I hope he didn't think I wasn't really interested."

"Well, maybe you'll be seeing him around. I've got to return the milk cow to him pretty soon. I should have done it before. It sure helped me plenty on my project."

Another familiar voice was added to these two. "Hello, Roy. We've been looking for you."

"Oh, hello, Mr. Carson."

"Say, Roy—Mr. Watson and I have been talking about your champion calf. The breeders at this show agree with us that your animal has a chance to take the State and possibly go on to the International at Chicago. Naturally, if anything like that *could* happen, it would mean a great deal to me, as it would to you. I could gain nation-wide recognition for my Aberdeen Angus herd and especially my breeders. If you like, I'll make all arrangements for you to exhibit at the State in November and I'll truck your calf to Little Rock for you."

There was a momentary silence and the winner of the corn exhibit, sitting unseen behind his booth, stiffened with interest.

"Oh, Roy," said a girl's voice. "I can't imagine anything nicer . . . if you *could* win the State that would mean you could go to Chicago, too . . . at the same time I . . . !"

"No, I couldn't . . . that's just it . . . we *both* can't go . . . and *you're* the one . . . !"

A man's voice broke in which Tom recognized as Big Jim's.

"Don't worry about anything like that, Roy. We'll find some way to take care of Mr. Kendall if you and Sue should both have to be away. This means too much to Rock County and to you and to everyone concerned to let anything interfere."

Tom waited suspensefully for Roy's answer which was slow in coming.

"Well, I don't know—what do you think, Sue . . . ?"

"I think you should do as Mr. Watson suggests." Her voice was earnest and full of feeling. "You've worked so terribly hard, Roy, and you might only get one calf like this in a lifetime. I'd rather stay home myself than let you . . . !"

The slender figure behind the booth reached for his crutches.

He swung his body out from behind the partition and suddenly confronted the group as they stood beside his display.

"I couldn't help overhearing," he said, "and I think it's swell that Roy's calf has a chance to go through. I agree that he mustn't miss it . . . and Sue mustn't miss *her* chance, either. I'm sure I can speak for my folks, that they'll be glad to see that the chores are done and Mr. Kendall's looked after, if it works out that Roy goes to Chicago, too."

Sue stood, eyeing the tanned figure on crutches before her. His eyes were sunken no longer. Instead, they reflected a glow of returning health. Fingers clutched about the crutch handles were recovering their grip. She felt powerless to say anything but Local Leader Frank Carson spoke up for her.

"There you are!" he smiled. "Your problem's solved already. That's fine of you, Tom. I'm sure it relieves Roy's and Sue's minds immensely."

"It sure does *mine*," admitted Roy, frankly. "I didn't see how I could go ahead unless . . . but now everything's changed." He looked toward the County's 4-H Corn Champion "I already owe you a lot, Tom. And this just adds more to it. I don't know how I can ever repay you."

The fellow who had been bed-ridden for two years started to back away on his crutches. *"I'll* tell you how," he said. "Bring us home a *winner!*"

Chapter XVIII

No ARMORED CAR containing United States currency or other valuables ever transported its contents more carefully than the truck driven by Frank Carson which conveyed the County's Grand Champion, *Your Majesty,* back to its stall, on the Kendall farm. Dave and Roy also made the ride out from town with the steer and were met by Sue at the barn where their plans were discussed for the trip to Little Rock in November.

Then, as Frank Carson and son drove off in their truck down the still bumpy Kendall road and finally disappeared up Stony Creek Route in the usual cloud of dust, Roy turned to Sue and said: "I never hope to meet any finer people anywhere. What a swell sportsman Dave is! He wanted to win just as badly as I did, but now he acts as tickled over my winning as though he'd won himself. There's a guy for you! I don't think I could have taken it quite like that."

They started slowly toward the house and Sue said, after a moment: "Tom's a great guy, too. In fact, I know *three* great guys," she added, softly, with a sidewise glance at him.

Roy was in a serious mood. "I'm not such a great guy," he replied. "You just don't know the other side of me which I've been trying to hide around here. I'm not out from behind the eight-ball yet . . . not as long as that probation is hanging over my head. It's got about three months to run. But if I get a chance to go to Chicago, that's one of the first things I'll try to clear up."

"How can you go about to do that?" asked Sue.

"Well," considered Roy, "when the time comes, if your father would only write a letter to Judge Braude, giving me a clean bill of health, the Judge might let me off without my having to wait till my case automatically comes up in February."

"Oh, I think Daddy will do that," assured Sue. "I don't know any reason why he shouldn't."

"N-o-o," said Roy, concernedly, "not unless he figured if the

198

Judge released me, that I'd walk out on you folks."

This thought caused Sue to start, impulsively. "But you wouldn't ... I mean ..." She checked herself. "Of course you'd be free to do what you wanted ... and I'd be happy if ..."

They were at the half-way point to the house and in full view of Matt Kendall's searching gaze but the way Sue looked and spoke made Roy stop and place his hands on her shoulders, forcing their eyes to meet.

"You mean, you'd miss me if I left," he said, "and I'd miss *you,* too—but if you'll say the word, Sue—I won't leave—*ever!*"

Sue had half anticipated this moment but she had not expected it to come when it did. There wasn't a romantic setting for it. They were both in their work clothes. Her black hair was loose and uncombed, down her back. The fall air was biting but both were unmindful of that now as Roy pushed her gently against the only large tree, a giant oak, between them and the house. The trunk barely shielded them from being seen by the ever-watchful Matt Kendall.

"I love you, Sue," Roy declared, pressing her back against the tree and his own body against hers.

This time she wanted him to kiss her and she yielded her lips as they clung in a fervent embrace, not caring for the moment what the chronic invalid in the chair might say or think.

His first kiss, stolen from her on impulse, after he had been showing her how to model and fix her hair, had shocked and then awakened in her the long suppressed desire for love and a home which she had crushed within her at the fading of her romance with Tom. Sue had been afraid of the feelings which raced through her that day, and kept her awake that night. She had thought she could never care for anyone again as she had for Tom ... but when Roy had kissed her the second time, so daringly, just outside the front door upon her return from Fayetteville, she had asked herself that night if the feelings which stirred in her could be the birth of a new love.

And, in the days that had followed, she had artfully kept Roy barely at arm's length, the while she had been trying to make up

her mind. Her father had formerly approved of Tom . . .
would he equally approve of Roy? It seemed logical that he
might, regardless of Roy's past, if he was certain the two of
them would remain nearby and continue to look after him.

It didn't seem likely that a girl in her position would get too
many chances to marry. She had been fortunate to have had
this previous opportunity with a fellow as wonderful as Tom.
But fate had ruled against that union and now, in this present
moment, an able-bodied and highly likeable boy from the city,
whom she had seen tested under fire, was offering her his life
and his love.

Perhaps, if she said "yes," it would cure her agonizing rest-
lessness and sense of devastating frustration which struck her
hardest every time her eyes beheld the little site in the pine
grove where she and Tom had planned their home. No doubt
Tom had been fighting similar feelings but it was foolhardy for
her to live out her life on broken and, now, impossible dreams.

Roy's lips upon hers were persuasive. She pushed slightly
away and opened her eyes, looking up at him, mistily. She
tried to speak and couldn't as he whispered against her ear:
"I can't offer you marriage until I've cleared my name—but
just as soon as I can . . ."

She threw her arms about him and pulled him to her. "Oh,
Roy!" she cried. "It doesn't matter to me what you *were* . . . *I*
know what you *are*. Yes, I'll marry you—I'll be *proud* to be
your wife!"

Matt Kendall was sitting upright, drumming the twisted
fingers of one hand on the table, as they came in. This time
neither made any attempt to conceal their feelings for one another, and Roy even sought to be the first to speak, but the
chronic invalid cut him short.

"I'll do the talkin', young man." Then, to Sue: "Go into your
room and shut the door. I want to speak to Roy alone."

"But, Daddy . . . !" protested Sue. "Roy and I want to tell
you . . . !"

"I said—'go to your room'!" commanded her father.

Sue shot Roy an appealing glance but did as she was bidden. The boy from the city steeled himself, not knowing what manner of verbal attack he would have to face.

Matt Kendall fixed his eyes on him, his jaws working furiously. "You've been lyin' to me!" he accused.

"No, Sir!" denied Roy, hotly.

"You told me you two weren't up to somethin'!" said Matt Kendall. "I think you're up to *plenty!*"

"We love each other," declared Roy, staunchly. "And we don't care if you know it . . . we were coming in to tell you . . . !"

Matt Kendall's agitation showed in the peeling of his lips back from his teeth. "I was afraid somethin' like this would happen! I almost didn't take you in for that reason. Throw a tolerably good lookin' boy and girl together and leave 'em alone long enough, and they get notions about each other. I've got to be sure you really love my daughter. She was disappointed once for no fault of hers, or Tom's, either . . . That almost killed her . . . but I ain't a-goin to let her git disappointed ag'in . . . and I'm a-tellin' you right now—Roy Willard, her heart ain't to be played with . . . If I thought you was a-doin' that . . ." He raised a bony fist and shook it, "Why, gol-dang you, I'd *kill* you!"

The boy from the city stood unflinching before the strange protective defiance and indirect tribute to Sue.

"I know my own mind," he said, quietly. "I love your daughter, Mr. Kendall, and when I get my record cleaned up, I'd like to marry her."

There was no immediate sound from the chronic invalid. He sat staring past Roy, unseeing. Then, finally stirring, as though from his depths, he said in a cracked voice: "Were you figurin' on stayin' on here?"

"I was," Roy replied, "with your leave . . . that is, unless you ever got someone else to come in and run the place—in which case, Sue and I might . . . !"

"I'm not ever figurin' on that!" snapped Matt Kendall. "This is her home to have when I'm gone and it's likewise the home of the man she marries . . . You're welcome to stay here . . .

and that's what Tom was plannin' to do—within a good stone's throw, anyway," he added. "But you and Sue don't need to build . . . I'm not too long for this world . . . Then you can have this all to yourselves."

Roy nodded, embarrassed and ill at ease. "There'll be time to decide about those things," he evaded. "I'm glad you approve of me, Mr. Kendall. I'll try to be as good a husband to Sue as I know how."

Sue's father looked down at his twisted hands and then up at Roy. "You're a good worker, I can't deny you that," he said, a trifle grudgingly. "But you're strong-willed . . . you've never really knuckled under to anybody . . . You've been used to gettin' your own way . . . that's your trouble . . . you haven't had to give up enough . . . That's all I can say ag'in you—but I might as well say it now, right at the start, so you know what I think about you."

Roy started to say something but Matt Kendall cut him short and continued: "I been a-watchin' you close. Don't forgit, I've had to be sendin' reports on you to the Judge, and you ain't entirely out of the woods yet. You've been all right around here but you don't bend a young tree for years and straighten it up ag'in in a few months' time. Just the same, if you love Sue and she loves you . . . and you're both willin' to stay on here, I ain't goin' to stand in your way."

Roy's face broke in a relieved smile. "That's wonderful, Mr. Kendall!—Can I call Sue and tell her?"

"No!" snapped her father. "I'll do it!" He cleared his throat and raised his voice. "Sue! Come in here!"

After a moment, the door opened. Sue was red-eyed. She looked from her father to Roy and back again, questioningly.

"Well," said Matt Kendall, eyes gleaming, "go ahead! Take him! . . . I'm not objectin'!"

With a little cry of joyous surprise, Sue flew to Roy's arms.

Now that the 4-H County Fair was over, most of the year's farm and home projects were nearing completion and, at the next regular meeting, held in the Club rooms over the Jordan Drug Store, the majority of the members turned in their carefully kept record books to County Agent Jim Watson.

There only remained the State 4-H Fair and Annual Banquet of outstanding 4-H Club members and their local leaders and county agents, being held the same day as the State Livestock Show in Little Rock—but no one but President Dave Carson was planning to attend this year, and no entries were being made. As for the National 4-H Congress, taking place in Chicago, a little later, Sue Kendall, State Dress Revue Champion, was the single representative of her group qualified to go. But next year an expanded program would enable wider participation of more local members in these outside events.

For the time being, all felt they had gained through the experience of working individually and together, and their accomplishments, as reviewed by them, were adjudged to have been outstanding for a first year effort.

But President Dave Carson wasn't satisfied. One of the purposes for which he had helped organize the Club had not been realized. The 4-H'ers had not taken part, as yet, in the achievement of any civic project.

"As your President," Dave reported, "I have been working behind the scenes, trying to lay the groundwork for us to do something worthwhile for the community, before our first year is over. I told Mayor Brannigan that we 4-H'ers were going to do our bit toward improving this town and county . . . and I want us to make good.

"Not only that, but that 'Civic Improvements' Fund, which Mr. Jordan started, has kept on growing without our even putting on a campaign, which indicates that some citizens in Hidden Valley and in Rock County believe in us and want to back us up in whatever we decide to do."

The 4-H members were listening intently and now, Porky O'Connor, with sublime disregard for rules of order, shouted out: "Well, what *are* we going to do? Let's not just talk about it. Let's get busy!"

The President of the 4-H Club joined in the general laughter.

"All right, Porky," he said. "You asked for it and here it is. What the people in our County need most are good roads and electricity. I've been talking with Roger Bennett—he's head of the Arkansas Power and Light Company, in town, and he tells me that if we can sign up seventy percent of the folks who live on any of the County roads leading out of Hidden Valley, getting them to agree to take electricity, that the Company will put up the poles and string the lines.

"Is *that* all it takes?" called someone, from the floor.

"That's not so easy as it sounds," warned Dave. "It's been tried a number of times before but the *same* ones do the signing up and the die-hards, who have always been sticking their feet in front of the march of progress, keep holding out. It's a simple matter of cost and profit with the Company. They'd be glad to co-operate if they got the necessary co-operation in return."

"Mr. President!" addressed a girl's voice.

"Yes, Carolyn," Dave recognized.

"How do you think *we* can get these kind of people in line if others haven't been able to do it?"

Dave grinned. "You've heard that old saying—'You can catch more flies with syrup than you can with vinegar'! What do you all think of our holding a big Square Dance the Saturday night after Thanksgiving, in our auditorium, and inviting all the farmers on all the Routes leading out of Hidden Valley? We'll get them here, give them a good time, and have petitions on hand for them to sign, not only for electricity, but for good roads, too!"

There were shouts of acclaim for this idea.

"Question!" called a voice.

"Yes, Tom!" said President Carson.

Tom Dodds stood up, supporting himself on his crutches. "As I understand it, getting good roads is largely a matter of politics. It's all tied up between State and County."

"I know," said Dave, "I've been investigating that—but if we get enough signatures from voters and taxpayers, and if we're willing to contribute a good part of our 'Civic Improvements' Fund to help our poor County build these roads, I've been assured by County Judge Middleton that something can be done."

Tom Dodds had remained standing. "That's fine," he said. "But what are we going to do about the terrible condition of the street around the public square? We've got to do a job for the people of Hidden Valley, too—so they'll have something to show for the money they've donated!"

President Dave Carson shook his head. "This project is much tougher," he said. "Mayor Ed Brannigan controls that situation and I haven't found a way yet to budge him. There's only one shadow he hates worse than mine—and that's Sam Jordan's. Under the circumstances, I think we'd better show him up by doing something for the County, if we can, and then—maybe the citizens will be so ashamed that they'll put the pressure on him and he'll have to change his attitude."

"I see," said Tom, still standing. "Well, then—I'd like to put it in the form of a motion that we, the members of the Hidden Valley 4-H Club, hold a big Square Dance on the night of November Thirtieth, for the purpose of securing support for the putting through of good roads and electricity in our County, and that we contribute as much of our 'Civic Improvements' Fund as our President deems necessary, to help get these roads."

"You've all heard the motion," said Dave, "Do I get a second?"

"I second it!" called Roy Willard.

"Motion has been duly made and seconded," smiled Dave, looking down at Secretary Sue Kendall who was busy writing out the resolution. "All those in favor, signify by saying 'Aye'!"

A chorus of "ayes" rang out. It was *unanimous*.

"That's great," said Dave. Then, addressing Porky, he continued: "Reporter O'Connor, it's up to you to get the story of our Square Dance event in next week's paper. We're going to need lots of publicity. Tell Editor Bevins to play it up big. As soon as the news is out, I want to *publicly* invite His Honor, the Mayor, to be *our guest!*"

It was the day before Tom and his father were to harvest their corn that the boy from the city returned the milk cow. He walked her carefully down Kendall Road and turned her in at the Dodds' drive.

On passing the house, Mrs. Dodds saw him and came out on the porch. "Hello, Roy!" she hailed. "Mr. Dodds has gone to town and Tom's taken his horse down to the patch for a last look at his corn. Guess you'll have to put the cow in the barn yourself."

She came down and opened the gate into the barnyard.

"Okay," said Roy, "I wanted to see Tom again and thank him for this favor. I should have returned your cow before but we had good pasture and Tom kept saying you didn't really need her . . . and, to tell you the truth, I'd kind of taken a liking to her." He patted the Shorthorn on her broad flank and she looked around at him with an expression that might have been interpreted as affectionate. "You see," grinned Roy, "I think she likes me, too!"

Mrs. Dodds laughed, "You shouldn't let yourself get too attached to animals," she warned. "If you do, you'll find you won't want to sell or get rid of them, and if anything happens to them, you'll feel almost as badly as though you'd lost a relative."

Roy nodded and, for just a moment, a bitter look came into his face. "Maybe you'd miss them *more* than some relatives," he said impulsively. Then, quickly changing the subject, he asked: "Whereabouts in the barn shall I put her, Mrs. Dodds?"

"Oh, there're several empty stalls—any one will do."

He petted the cow on her shoulder. "All right, come on, Girlie—let's be going."

The cow needed no urging and headed for the barn door.

"I've got something on the stove," said Mrs. Dodds. "So will you excuse me? . . . If you have time, I'm sure Tom would like to see you, and maybe you'd like to see his stand of corn, too. It's really worth a trip down."

"Thanks," said Roy. "I may do it."

He slid the barn door back and spanked the cow on her

rump. She entered and found her own stall. Roy continued on through the barn, to the feed lot, and into the pasture.

It was a beautiful October morning. King Frost had been busy working on his annual leaf painting project. It was a colossal job and Roy fell to wondering, as he saw the maze of brilliant hues everywhere, how this greatest of all artists could take such infinite pains in the exquisite coloring of each individual leaf.

"Man doesn't amount to so much yet," he reflected to himself, as he went down over the hill to the bottom land. "He may think he does but he should get out next to Nature and really see God's forces at work, and he'd realize how much he has to learn—how little he really knows."

Stretching out before Roy, now, were brown acres of corn, ready for harvest. In a few days, the stalks would be shocked, tepee fashion, and the field would take on the appearance of an Indian village.

There was something wonderful about each changing season of the years, as Roy had seen them come and go—from winter to spring and summer, and now—into fall. Changes seemed to be the order of the Universe—nothing was allowed to stand still. Time was the *Simon Legree,* cracking his whip at the heels of all life, saying: "You're here. Start growing . . . develop . . . reproduce your kind . . . move on and make room for others!"

It seemed pretty harsh, on the surface, but if you weren't afraid to face life and put all you could into it and took all you could out of it, there was something majestic about this ever-present change which was taking place in all things, including yourself.

There were *mental* changes, too, as well as physical. Roy reflected now, as he neared Tom's two acres, on the kind of fellow he was when he first met Dave Carson on the train bound for Hidden Valley—"some God-forsaken little hick town at the end of everything for him," as he had so mistakenly supposed.

But here he was, on this bright October morning, with all

things in Nature, their work done, so gloriously dying about him that they might be born anew. Roy sensed, as he felt momentarily attuned to forces greater than himself, that something he had outgrown had died in him, and a finer something was emerging. He had everything now to live for—to strive for—and, best of all, he had not stolen these new things he possessed—he had *earned* them.

He had discovered the joy and dignity of working with his own head and heart and hands. He had reaped the rewards of love and friendship, and there had come to him an inner satisfaction of achievement which had linked him, consciously, with his Creator, and caused him to know that he was part of a great, unfolding cosmic plan. Life was playing sweet music in his soul . . .

Tom was nowhere to be seen. There was his horse, tethered to the great willow tree by the creek bank, and, nearby, a little wooden step, apparently specially built for his rider to mount and dismount. But Tom must be in his corn somewhere.

Roy started down through the rows and suddenly stopped short as he heard a voice. It was just beyond him in the next row but still some yards away. Roy stood in silent wonderment. Could it be possible that Tom had someone with him? He listened. No, it was Tom talking. Roy, with an almost guilty sense of intrusion, stepped softly to the edge of the next row and looked down it.

There was Tom, back toward him, leaning on his crutches, *addressing his corn!*

"This is my last day with you," he was saying, "We've gone through a lot together. When that dry spell hit and you started to shrivel up . . ." he laughed, "I thought you were going to look like *me* . . . but then, when the rain came and you began to grow—*I* began to grow, too . . . We've shared our ups and downs together . . . and now, God willing, I want you to be the first to see me stand alone—and walk without crutches again . . ."

Roy pressed his lips tightly together as he looked and saw the now strengthened form of the County's 4-H Corn Champion slide his crutches from under his arm pits and drop them to the ground beside him. Tom stood, for a moment, wavering unsteadily on legs unaccustomed to supporting his under-weight body. Then, like a scene from a slow motion picture, Tom lifted a foot and put it down ahead of him. He reeled as he did so but he took another step . . . and another . . . and one more—then tottered and fell, face down, upon the hardened ground.

Roy's first impulse was to run forward and help Tom up but he thought better of it and remained where he was, watching with a strange and greatly moved fascination.

The fellow who had been bed-ridden for over two years, lay where he had fallen but Roy now heard him crying out exultantly: "I did it! . . . did you see . . . ? . . . I did it—and I'll do it again . . . I'll keep on doing it! . . . I'll *walk* . . . !" He was pushing himself to his knees. "I'll throw these crutches away!" he was declaring in an ecstacy of spirit. "I'll surprise everybody . . ." He was pushing himself shakily to his feet. "I'll surprise *Sue* most of all!"

Tom was standing on his feet again and beads of perspiration suddenly ringed Roy's face.

Sue! . . . Why had Tom mentioned her? What could he be thinking? Was it possible . . . ? No, it couldn't be! That was all over. Tom had called it off himself. Sue was through with him . . . Tom was a wonderful fellow and all that, but she had made her choice . . . and if Tom was still figuring . . . ! Well, it was just too bad . . .

The fellow who had loaned him the milk cow for his beef project took a few more quick steps and fell again, but Roy Willard did not wait to see more. He stole quietly away out of the bottom land, leaving the silent stalks of corn to witness Tom's struggle alone.

Chapter XIX

NOVEMBER CAME RIDING in like a blustering traveling salesman with samples of the winter to come. It blew and shook the prettily ornamented leaves of King Frost from the trees and shrubs and left their bare limbs shivering. Then it laughed at the denuded landscape as it hustled the leaves into scurrying piles and bedded down the ground so that all sleeping things might rest warmly, undisturbed.

Roy, with the November date of the State Livestock Show at Little Rock approaching, was making all preparations to attend. It was a time of great excitement for him and for Sue, as well. Their hopes were riding high on this event. He had told her so many wonderful things about Chicago, the sights she would see, the things they would do together if he could only make it with her. It would be a bitter disappointment now if *Your Majesty* did not come through.

And, when the time arrived for departure, with the steer loaded on Mr. Carson's stock truck, and Dave and his father and Roy ready to leave, Sue found an excuse to call the boy from the city back into the barn for a moment.

"Are you sure you have everything?" she said to him in the Carsons' presence, and Roy, understanding, excused himself. She was waiting inside the door and locked her arms about him as he entered, giving him her lips. They stood in a close embrace, Roy gently stroking her hair, each reluctant to let the other go.

Your Majesty, missing Roy, and afraid he was about to be taken away without him, as Frank Carson turned the truck around, began calling.

Sue disengaged herself and looked up at Roy, smiling. "Your other love wants you," she said. "But *my* love goes with you, Roy, right into the ring beside you and *Your Majesty* . . . and my prayers go with you, too. If it's right for you to win, I know you will, Goodbye, Sweetheart!"

Her face was wet as she kissed him again and he tasted the salt on his lips.

"We'll win for you if it's any way possible," he said, and ran outside, shouting: "Stop bawling *Your Majesty!* . . . I'm coming!"

He clambered aboard the truck in the seat beside Dave and his father, not trusting himself to look back.

Nor did Sue see his departure. She stood in the barn door, leaning against the casing, with head cradled against her arm, and heard the rumble of the truck as it grew fainter and fainter, down the hill.

But the eyes of Matt Kendall watched until steer and truck and all were out of sight. Then, lowering his field glasses, tremblingly, to his lap, Sue's father whispered: "Good luck, son . . . good luck!"

The boy from the city was to be away for two nights and Sue, up on Kendall hill, would not know how *Your Majesty* fared until the day of his home-coming. She might not know the result, unless the news was carried by radio, until Roy actually got home and told her.

But the second night of his absence, something out of the ordinary happened. A car was heard making the climb up their steep road and when it turned in, her father exclaimed: "Why there's Fred Dodds and Tom!"

Sue, wondering and startled, watched them out the window.

"Tom's getting out but Fred isn't," said Matt Kendall. He lifted a gnarled hand to wave as the elder Dodds hailed him.

"Hello, Matt!" he shouted, his voice loud enough to be heard through the closed window. "I'm coming up to see you soon. Sorry, I can't stop tonight!"

"Funny business," muttered the chronic invalid. "Haven't seen him in months and now he can't even come inside the house. But he's leavin' Tom here. That's even funnier! . . . What d'you s'pose is up?"

Sue started to the door as Fred Dodds backed his car around and she saw Tom swing toward the porch on his crutches.

"I don't know," she called back to her father. "I haven't the slightest idea."

It was a mild November night with a starlit sky and a mellow breeze blowing. Almost a fleeting return of Indian summer. Tom smiled at her as she opened the door.

"Hello, Sue!" he greeted. "Surprised?"

"I certainly am!" she said.

Through the open door, Tom could see Matt Kendall stretched out in his easy chair. He leaned on his crutches and raised an arm. "How are you, Mr. Kendall? Long time since I've seen you!"

"Come in!" barked the chronic invalid.

Tom negotiated the stone steps and crossed the porch as Sue held the door open. He propelled himself inside and stood before the elder cripple. Matt Kendall held out his twisted fingers and Tom's stronger hand closed over them.

"It's certainly great to be up here again," he said.

Matt Kendall eyed him, critically. "You seem to be gettin' along pretty well," he observed. "I thought for awhile I was a-goin' to outlive you. But I'm not so sure of that now." He glanced consultingly at his daughter, then gestured to Tom. "Won't you sit down?" he invited.

Tom acted slightly embarrassed as he looked at Sue and then back to the man in the chair. "No, thanks . . . if you don't mind, Mr. Kendall . . . it's not too cold out tonight . . . I'd like to sit on the porch with Sue for awhile . . . as we used to do . . ."

Matt Kendall cleared his throat, uneasily. "Well . . . all right . . . we've taken our porch chairs in—but I guess Sue can . . ."

"Why, yes—of course . . ." she said, and began pushing two light-weight chairs toward the door.

"I hope to be getting up more often from now on," said Tom, as he turned toward the porch.

Matt Kendall gave no answer to this, but watched as the younger cripple propped his back against the door while Sue slid the chairs out.

"You git around pretty well on those things, don't you?" he

called to Tom, pointing to his crutches.

Tom grinned. "They're not bad at all," he said. "It's almost second nature now. Well," he added, as though anxious to cut Sue's father out of the conversation, "I'll be seeing you." And he closed the door.

The front porch had always been a private domain for Sue and Tom as it had more recently been a secluded spot for Sue and Roy. This was one location beyond the reach of Matt Kendall's eyes, even though it was in fairly close proximity to him. But two people could sit on the porch and talk in low tones and do much as they pleased without his interference or observation.

The door had scarcely closed when Tom, catching Sue by her wrist while depending on his crutches, whirled her about and caught her powerfully in his arms. He strained her to him with all the pent-up feeling of the past two years. She was totally unprepared for this demonstration of affection and recoiled under the bruising force of his lips.

"Tom!" she cried, in a low, frightened voice. "Tom! . . . Let me go!"

But he only held her the closer, hands cupping her head, slender but strong fingers intertwined in her hair, as he continued to kiss her.

"Sue, darling—I didn't dare believe I could do it," he whispered. "But I'm all right now. I've made the grade! . . . See!" He suddenly released her and laid his crutches across a chair. "*I can walk!*"

So saying, to her amazement and delight, he strode the length of the porch and back, and once more stood before her, arms outstretched, smiling.

"Oh, Tom!" cried Sue, choked with feeling. "That's wonderful! . . . I'm so happy for you!"

"I did it all for you!" he said. "I wanted you to be the first person to really see me walk." He seized her again in his arms. "I just couldn't think of your marrying a cripple. I wouldn't have it, but now that I'm back on my feet, the doctors say it will be only a matter of time and I'll be good as new!"

He was hugging her with her head pressed against his shoulder. She didn't know how to face him. She wondered what she could say and how she could say it, without hurting him any more than she had to. She could feel his lips on her hair and little familiar caresses which awakened dear remembrances of long ago. She just couldn't stand it—it was doing something terrible to her—tearing her apart inside.

"Oh, Tom!" she cried, breaking away from him. "It's too late . . . I'll have to tell you . . . you've got to know . . . *I'm engaged to Roy!*"

A sturdy tree, when it is struck by lightning, sometimes stands for an awful moment before it falls. Tom Dodds' reaction was something like that. In the shadows on the porch, the color drained from his face so that he looked white and ghost-like. He felt about for a chair and sat down, unsteadily. Then he put his head in his hands and held it as though it had been split in two. His moan blended with the sighing of the night wind. A sudden chill came into the air. He reached about blindly for his crutches and shoved them beneath his arm pits.

Sue's muffled sobs accompanied him as the rubber tips of his crutches clumped down the stone steps and beat their uneven tip-tap on the gravel walk. He was going down Kendall hill in the dark, by himself, as he had done so many romantic nights in the yester-years, only, this time, his head was bowed and his steps were sticks.

The daughter of Matt Kendall turned in to the house. She hoped she could get into her bedroom and close the door and cry it out without a word from her father, but this was impossible.

"I know what happened," he said, as she reached her doorway. "He's after you to marry him again. But you needn't be a-cryin', Sue. You've made the right choice."

Sue did not answer but threw herself on her bed and burst into full-throated sobs.

Si Hawkins, farm expert, was an early morning favorite with

Matt Kendall. He came on every morning at seven-fifteen from Little Rock right after the news reports. It had been another sleepless night for Sue but she had risen at six, as usual, done the round of chores and was in the kitchen getting breakfast when her father called.

"Sue! Come in here, quick! Si Hawkins has just announced that he's got the winner of the State Livestock Show in his studio and is goin' to introduce him right after the commercial!"

Sue, about to put on some griddle cakes, set down the pitcher of batter and hurried in. "Did he say who he was?" she asked.

"No!" snapped Matt Kendall. "I just told you, he said he was goin' to introduce him, if they ever get through with this gol-danged long-winded sales talk!"

Father and daughter sat tensely while a man's soft and melodious voice tried to charm his listeners into buying an extra potent brand of insecticide which would clean barns and chicken coops of everything but the livestock itself.

"I'd like to use some of that on him!" ranted Matt Kendall. "If he doesn't finish pretty soon, Si Hawkins' time'll be up!"

The commercial announcer finally, reluctantly surrendered the microphone to the featured performer and Si Hawkins came back on the air.

"Well, you raisers and lovers of livestock are in for a treat this morning," he said, "because I have in the studio, not only the man whose steer was crowned 'Grand Champion of the State' but also the beef breeder from whose herd this steer was taken . . ."

The set started fading.

"Oh, damn!" swore Matt Kendall. "It's that bad tube . . . I meant to have you get another."

His twisted fingers fussed nervously at the dials.

"Would that have been Roy and Mr. Carson?" Sue broke in, excitedly.

"Could be *any* two men," clipped Matt Kendall. "Don't count too much on . . ." He finally lost his temper and banged the set with the back of his bony hand. The program came in, loud and clear.

"Thank you, Mr. Hawkins," a voice was saying. "It *was* a great thrill . . ."

Sue couldn't trust her ears. "Is that Roy?"

"I don't know," said her father. "Listen!"

"You had some pretty stiff competition," said Si Hawkins, in his easily recognized voice. "How did you feel when the judges weeded the field down to the last five steers? Did you think then, that your beef was going to win?"

There was a quick laugh as the voice answered: "Well, I figured my chances had improved from sixty to one—to five to one . . . and that made me feel better."

"It *is* Roy!" identified Sue, leaping to her feet with excitement. "Oh, Daddy, it's wonderful! Simply wonderful!"

She flung her arms about his neck and knocked against the radio as she did so. The bad tube sang out, the program disappeared, and the set went dead.

"Now, see what you've done!" charged her parent. "Now we cán't hear a danged thing!"

"I don't care!" Sue exulted as she gave him a quick kiss and turned to straighten up the table. "I know all I need to know now! . . . He *won!* . . . *Your Majesty* came through! . . . That means Roy and I can go to Chicago!"

Matt Kendall stiffened as his face took on a concerned look. "Wait a minute! What becomes of *me?*"

"Oh!" Sue exclaimed, and caught her breath. "Well, Daddy, you see it's all been arranged . . . in case . . . if Roy should win . . . The Dodds have offered to take over while we're gone."

"The *Dodds!*" repeated her father. "Are they goin' to be feelin' so free to come up here and take care of things after what happened last night?"

Sue's face froze with new concern. "I—I hadn't thought of that," she faltered. "It might make a difference . . . we'll have to wait and see."

Your Majesty and the proud boy from the city who owned him, did not get home until late that day. They had been delayed in

Little Rock while pictures had been taken and interviews held with newspaper reporters, farm paper and magazine editors, beef breeders, the State 4-H Club Agent, and livestock specialists, from the Extension Service. Roy Willard had become an overnight new name and personality in the livestock world. He was finding that the State of Arkansas, the Agricultural Department particularly, couldn't do enough for him. And Frank Carson, best beef breeder in Rock County, was the happiest man in forty-eight states. He, in association with Extension Service officials, had already completed preliminary arrangements, via long distance telephone, for *Your Majesty's* participation in the International Live Stock Show at Chicago, which was being held simultaneously with the scheduled National 4-H Congress, the first week in December. This was less than a week away.

"You don't have to worry about a thing," Local Leader Carson had told Roy on the way back from Little Rock. "I'll take care of all details and will carry *Your Majesty* right through to Chicago in this truck."

"That's swell," said Roy, unable to express his gratitude in words. "But there's just one extra favor I'd like to ask, if you don't mind."

"What's that?" smiled Frank Carson.

"That you let Sue ride to Chicago with us, if she wants to travel that way," said Roy. "She's never been to the city and, of course, I've got to stick with *Your Majesty* . . . and Sue's so interested in him, too . . . and . . . well, I don't think she'd want to be separated, knowing we're *all* going, any more than *I* would . . ."

Frank Carson laughed. "Well, this front seat will hold three fairly comfortably, as you and Dave can testify. If Sue would like to come along, she's welcome."

"Thanks," said Roy. "That means an awful lot to me." And then as if to punctuate this fact, he added: "You just don't know *how much!*"

Chapter XX

MAYOR ED BRANNIGAN did not accept President Dave Carson's invitation to be honor guest at the Square Dance. He gave as his excuse that he might be out of town, but when the day arrived he was very much in evidence about his various business affairs.

He had secretly hoped that the weather would be bad and that the much ballyhooed 4-H Club affair would be either rained out or frozen out. There was far more reason for it to be frozen out since an unprecedented cold snap, in the last two days, had chased the equally unseasonal warm weather and driven mercury in thermometers down to the all-time low for November of sixteen degrees above zero.

This temperature nose-dive had given Mayor Brannigan and the city water works department headaches which no amount of aspirin tablets could cure. The city water mains had frozen and burst in several places and it would take at least a week, with an augmented force, to repair them. This alone was enough to keep any half-way conscientious city official in town and on the job.

Actually, these old mains were rotten and needed replacement but who was going to pay for them? They cost money just like new paved streets and all such improvements came mostly out of the hides of the city's biggest taxpayers. This last statement could be further amended to read: ". . . out of the hide of *the* biggest single taxpayer." Every time something went wrong like this, Ed Brannigan suffered an acute attack of jitters in his pocketbook. Sooner or later things would get so bad that something would really *have* to be done and he would have to take the rubber band off his wallet.

Right now there was such a large hole in the gravel roadbed in front of his General Store that cars of low under-carriage were scraping on it, knocking steering knuckles out of place and reshaping rear axles.

Mayor Brannigan had taken to walking past this spot with a

studied air of sublime indifference to the cursing of passing motorists. They swore louder and longer if they were strangers to the region and had made the mistake of wanting to drive off a main artery to see what a little mountain town with the quaint and appealing name of Hidden Valley looked like. They came, they saw, and they were usually confronted with a garage bill.

This was one of the few lucrative businesses, thanks to the gross neglect of the city, that Mayor Brannigan, through some over-sight or other, did not own. He was accused, however, of being a silent partner in Danny's Auto Repair Shop, and outside of Mayor Brannigan, it was true that Danny was perhaps the only other person in Hidden Valley who didn't favor improved streets!

But a little matter like bad roads, either in or out of the city and bad weather thrown in, couldn't keep the farmer folk who loved get-togethers, and especially square dancing, from risking tire trouble and a jolting loose of the vital mechanical organs in their gas horses. They were coming in, young and old, and babes-in-arms, to do a "do-si-do" and a "shoe fly swing" and a "Texas Star" and other old-time cut-ups to the hot fiddle tunes of Uncle Ezry Elkins, who was a great favorite in these here parts. The 4-H'ers had scored a ten-strike in landing Ezry for their first public event as they were assured at the start of the patronage of those who knew and loved his colorful playing and square dance calling.

Even Jud Emery, Frank Carson's hired man, was slicking up to make one of his rare trips into town, to let Uncle Ezry fiddle some of the kinks out of his legs.

"I've never met a woman yet that I felt was good enough to be my wife!" he had said, on many occasions. "But I sure like to dance with all the ladies!"

This form of dancing might be old-fashioned but it was one of the greatest "socializers" in the back hills of Arkansas. You could lock elbows, rub shoulders, bow low, join hands, do the grand right and left, promenade and swing your partner till you got back "home" again, after meeting everybody on the floor. It made no difference whether the girls were fat or lean, old or young—or the boys, either, for that matter. When the fiddle began to scratch such tunes as "Turkey in the Straw" or "Irish Washerwoman", everybody would make a rush for the floor and start going around and around in the contortions and movements demanded of them by the Caller.

Printed invitations had been sent to all farmers in this section of Rock County and the townspeople of Hidden Valley had been generally invited. By shortly after supper time, even though festivities were not announced to start until around nine o'clock, to give those with late chores a chance to get in, the guests began to arrive.

A cold, blustery wind had sprung up out of the north, which made the warm 4-H Club rooms and auditorium seem unusually cozy and attractive, especially when one added the cordiality of the welcomes extended by the reception committee. And Sam Jordan had helped matters by keeping his drug store open to furnish hot chocolate and coffee to those who were too chilled, and ice cream and cold drinks to the warmer blooded. This was a Community Center, the likes of which no man, woman or child in Rock County had ever experienced before.

At nine o'clock a crowd was on hand which over-taxed the capacity of the auditorium and filled the drug store below. It was necessary for the program committee, headed by Carolyn Hilton, to improvise a way by which all who wanted to dance could have a chance to get on the floor. This problem was solved by Carolyn's suggestion, publicly given.

"Hello, everybody!" she greeted, from the center of the floor. "We're certainly happy to see so many of you out tonight and to welcome you to our old-time Square Dance with Uncle Ezry."

There were cheers at mention of his name and the famous old fiddler with the sandy handlebar moustache, his stock in trade, sack cloth coat and bow tie, smoothed down the one remaining lock of hair which curved over his bald pate, stood up, and took a bow.

"But we're a little embarrassed for lack of room," Carolyn

went on, "and right now we have too many of you in one spot. May I suggest that some of you go down stairs or into our reception room in the front and wait till we've run through a dance, and then those who have just been on the floor can change off with the rest, and we'll all have a chance to have fun."

There was a good-natured shuffling of feet as places were taken by those already in position and others obligingly moved out of the way. Uncle Ezry drew his bow across the fiddle strings and things began to happen. There was an instant outburst of laughter and shouts of high glee as onlookers and dancers joined in the rollicking merriment. But, as entertaining as the antics and gyrations of the gay gallivanters was the high-pitched, tremulous voice of Uncle Ezry, singing out an old-time dance call.

"S'lure yer pardner and let her go;
Balance all and do-se-do.
Swing yer gal and run away;
Right and left, the gents sashay!
Gents to the right and swing or cheat;
On to the next gal, and repeat.
Balance next and don't be shy;
Swing yer pard and swing her high!
Bunch the gals and circle round;
Whack yer feet until they bound.
Form a basket and break away;
Swing around and all get gay.
All gents left and balance all;
Lift yer hoofs, let 'em fall;
Swing yer opposite, swing again;
Ketch the sagehens if you kin.
Back to pardner, do-se-do;
All join hands and off you go.
Gents salute yer little sweets;
Hitch and promenade to seats!"

There were wild cheers at the finish and the floor was cleared to permit new dance enthusiasts to take over.

A perspiring Dave Carson, who had been running up and down stairs, trying to keep things under some semblance of control, looked in on the auditorium and gave Carolyn's arm a quick squeeze, as he said: "Things are going great, aren't they, Honey? After we get everybody all warmed up, this'll be a perfect spot to announce our Community Project, and get the petitions signed up. I've been checking with some of the old-timers who know about everybody in the County, and they say we've got the best turn-out of hill people since William Jennings Bryan came through here once on a speaking tour!"

Carolyn laughed, happily. "It's a wonder Mr. Jordan's drugs are staying on the shelves downstairs," she said.

"He's not worrying about that," grinned Dave. "He's just hoping his ice cream and drinks hold out." He looked around. "Is every one of our gang here?"

"I guess so," replied Carolyn. "Sue's been checking them in. She's around here somewhere. Dave, that girl's absolutely gorgeous! She's made herself an evening gown from some plaid feed sack material which is stunning on her. She certainly looks every inch a Dress Revue Champion!"

Dave nodded, catching sight of Sue across the floor. "I should say she does!" he exclaimed. "Everybody's looking at her. Roy Willard, too . . . they make a fine looking couple."

"I wonder what kind of fellow Roy really is?" asked Carolyn.

"Well, I never really got acquainted till the last few weeks," said Dave. "But I've been with him now at two shows and I'm telling you, Carolyn, they just don't come any better. But I'm worried, though. I think Tom's still carrying the torch for her, and it looks to me like she's going overboard for Roy."

The next dance was over and the floor was being cleared again. Dave, taking a sheaf of specially prepared papers from his pocket, started out on the floor.

"Here's where we do our stuff," he said. "Where are your sisters?"

"I don't know at the moment," Carolyn replied. "I can't ever keep track of them."

"Well, follow me," Dave directed, starting toward the stage, where Uncle Ezry had been holding forth. "They'll probably show up when I introduce you girls. I'm counting on you to help me sell everyone here on good roads and electricity before I even give my talk!"

Carolyn laughed. "We'll do our best," she said. "It all depends on how they go for that parody we've written! If they like it—your job ought to be easy!"

She caught his arm and they moved in and out among the crowd on the floor to the stairs leading up on the stage. Uncle Ezry, seeing them coming and having been made a party to this surprise introduction of a civic project, produced some freak sounds on his fiddle to attract attention.

"No more dancin' fer a spell!" he announced. "But gather around here close. Come right out here on the floor, everybody. Some of you in the back run down stairs and get the folks from there . . . We're goin' to have an extra special feature that you'll all want to hear . . .That's right . . . Push on down toward the stage . . . Make room for those comin' in! . . . Now—is everybody here . . . ? That's fine!" He looked the jam-packed auditorium over, with genial-faced, expectant men, women and children almost standing on each others' toes. "Don't all of you take a deep breath at once," he warned, "or you'll push the walls out!" Then, as a general laugh followed, Uncle Ezry motioned to Dave Carson and said: "Everybody, meet the President of the 4-H'ers!"

Dave, smiling, stepped to the front of the stage.

"We're taking this brief intermission," he declared, "to give you a little entertainment and something to think about. But, first, to get you in the right mood, we're going to have a song number from Hidden Valley's famous singing sisters—the Hilton Trio! I've rounded up one of them . . ." He pointed to Carolyn who came from the wings, "and if the other two girls can get through to the stage, I'll be greatly obliged!"

There was a murmur of amusement as Eleanor and Doris were seen to be trying to push through from two different parts of the hall. Boy friends endeavoring to break the way for them, had their difficulties. Finally, however, the girls were passed up over the footlights with Dave giving them a hand, since it was next to impossible for them to reach the stairs at the side.

"I know we're greatly exceeding the capacity of this auditorium," said Dave. "We honestly didn't expect such a tremendous turn-out. But we won't keep you here long. All right, girls! Turn on the music!"

The Hilton sisters *did*—with a popular selection which called for close harmony—and their audience clapped and whistled its appreciation.

Carolyn, spokesman for the trio, bowed her appreciation and then said, smilingly: "For our encore we're singing a little original parody on 'America, the Beautiful', which applies to our homes and our community. We hope you like it!"

Their listeners were all ears—but *what* they heard brought gasps of surprise, as the girls sang, with lilting emphasis:

"Oh horr-i-ble for an-y eyes,
The high-ways that we drive,
The clouds of dust that al-ways rise,
A-wonder we're alive!
A-bom'-na-ble! . . . A-bom'-na-ble!
Oh, what a cry-ing shame!
Let's fix these roads, my breth-er-en,
No matter *who's* to blame!"

There was a roar from the audience, laughter and applause— but, as the attractive Hilton sisters held up their hands and continued, everyone quieted with eager interest.

"Oh, terr-i-ble for our poor eyes,
No 'lec-tric power or light,
Just waitin' for the sun to rise,
Cuz we can't see at night!
How blind we are! . . . How blind we are!
When we could have the light,
Sign up to get your wir-ing done,
And make *your* future bright!"

The reaction of all present to this second stanza was amounting to an ovation. Carolyn glanced happily at Dave who was watching from the wings and he waved his delight at the reception the parody was getting.

The Hilton trio took a step forward, trilled a connecting burst of harmony and went into the third and last verse.

> "Oh, wond-er-ful each day now is,
> The new roads sure are great,
> No smok-ing lamps to flame and fizz,
> With lights we read till late!
> Co-op-er-ate! . . . Co-op-er-ate!
> And make these things come true!
> Just list-en now to your friend, Dave—
> He'll tell you *what* to do!"

As the trio finished, Carolyn, Eleanor and Doris turned in unison toward the wings and beckoned to Dave who came hurrying out to center stage amid tremendous cheers and applause.

"Thank you, everybody! Thank you!" he cried, but they wouldn't let him speak.

"More! More!" shouted the audience. "Sing it again! . . . Sing it again!"

And they brought the Hilton sisters back to repeat the parody, enjoying it even more the second time.

Only then would the crowd let Dave speak.

"I haven't anything to say, folks," he declared, "you've said it for me! . . . I know most of you want good roads and electricity in your homes—and all you've got to do to start the ball rolling is sign up these petitions. I'd like every qualified elector who lives on any of the county roads leading into Hidden Valley, to come forward and put your name on these pieces of paper. They're all made out, legally correct, for every road and every place that needs electricity. And we're turning over to County Judge Middleton a check from our 'Civic Improvements' Fund for five thousand dollars to be used on our road construction. Come on, everybody! Let's finish this thing up right now—and get back to dancing!"

Dave's appeal was contagious. He had the crowd in a revival spirit with a mob urge to do something prevailing. 4-H'ers, with copies of the papers to be signed, began moving through the audience collecting signatures from men and women who hailed them. There might not be electricity in many farm homes round-about, but there was an electrical quality in the atmosphere. Electric, that is, until the *short circuit* occurred.

A booming voice suddenly rang out in the auditorium. "Just a minute here! . . . Just a minute!" said this voice. Its possessor was a tall, heavy-set, beetle-browed individual who was seen to be shoving his way through toward the stage. "Let's not go so fast!" he continued shouting. "They're tryin' to sweep us off our feet here! I got some questions I want to ask!"

The man reached the stairs to the stage and began mounting them where he confronted Hidden Valley's 4-H President. His protest brought a halt to all singing activity on the floor.

"My name's Henry Pringle and I live six miles out on Hollow Run road. I guess most of you folks out there know me!"

"Yes, we know you!" yelled someone from the back of the hall. "You're an old skin-flint if there ever was one! You've been against every decent thing in this community for years!"

The face of the man on the stage inflated with indignation.

"You don't dare come up here and say that to me! I'm a tax-payer, same as anyone else, and I got a right to speak my mind. I thought there was a catch in this here invitation to a Square Dance. People don't do anything for us farmers unless they're plannin' to get somethin' out of us! Now, I admit the roads ain't good and I admit we ain't got 'lectricity, but, by jing, we've got privacy back in our hills . . . nobody interferin' with our lives or trespassin' on our property . . . and that's worth a lot more to me than all these new-fangled modern inventions. Look at the rest of the world—the mess it's in! It's got good roads and 'lectricity and everythin' man could think of, ain't it? I say— bad roads is a protection . . . I say, when it gets dark, God intended for man to go to bed and get a good night's sleep, and get up with the sun.

"It's about time some of these city fellers and real estate pro-moters and fillin' station operators who are tryin' to invade our backwoods country, got told off! I've said it before and I say it ag'in—we don't want 'em here and we don't want the things they want to bring here! We just want to be let alone to live our lives as we see fit!"

There were cries of protest from the floor, growing into a dis-orderly uproar. Dave rushed to the front of the stage and raised his arms, waving and pleading for order, but the meeting was entirely out of hand. Enraged opponents of this Henry Pringle were trying to reach the platform to challenge him, and angry threats and accusations were being exchanged on all sides.

Against this small inferno of sound and fury, there was sud-denly heard the shrill cry of alarm from the town's fire siren atop the Dew Drop Inn. It knifed its way into the hall, cutting short a disturbance which had been about to reach riotous pro-portions.

"*Fire!*" cried someone.

The excited figure of Sam Jordan burst into the auditorium. "Keep calm, everybody!" he called, "But there's a fire broke out in Gibb's Barber Shop down the street—and it's spreading in this wind. There's no water in our mains on account of the freeze. We'll need every man and boy to swing buckets! Report at once in front of Brannigan's General Store!"

There was a general outpouring from the hall. As soon as the sidewalk was reached, the fire could be seen—crackling tongues of flame licking across the street beyond the corner of the square, on the same side as Jordan's Drugs, and directly across from Brannigan's General Store.

Hidden Valley's fire department had not grown with the town. It consisted of one two-ton truck which carried ladders and axes and several hundred feet of hose line. There was no pumper and there were no regular firemen in service. All, including Editor Herb Bevins, who was fire chief, were volunteers. At the present moment, there was no water in the water tower, due to the broken mains. This meant that the fire fighters would have to pull all the wells in town, by means of a bucket brigade.

Dave, one of the first on the scene, ran into a wild-eyed Ed Brannigan.

"My store!" cried the town's most prominent man. "It's going! . . . It's caught in several places. If it burns, I'll lose the whole block!"

"Is anyone on the roof?" asked Dave.

"No—everybody's been at your damn meeting! Fire truck isn't even here yet!"

Dave turned to Porky O'Connor and Roy Willard who had just arrived.

"Round up our gang!" he ordered. "Get anyone else who will help." Then, turning to a frantic Mayor Brannigan who was watching the flames from the burning barber shop peel the white paint off the side of his General Store, Dave asked: "Have you any pails in stock?"

"Yes! Yes!" cried Brannigan, fumbling for his keys and opening the front door. "Plenty! . . . They're in the back, right hand side."

"How about salt?" Dave demanded. "We need some to throw on the roof and wet down!"

"Lots of salt, too!" replied the town's wealthiest man. "Twenty-five pound sacks!" He gave another glance in the direction of the fire. "My God, it's spreading into Bailey's Cafe! . . . Hurry! . . . Hurry! . . . It'll be over here in no time!"

Porky and Roy came running up with all but two of their 4-H fellows and about thirty willing, able-bodied, older men.

"You've got a well out back, haven't you?" Dave asked, as Brannigan switched on the store lights.

"Right beside the door. I'll get pails and salt from other stores, too! . . . Say—it's getting hot in here! . . . There goes one of my windows!"

There was a loud pinging report and the tinkle of falling glass.

"Follow me, men!" Dave cried, and rushed toward the back of the store.

The aisle next the side street, off the square, was warm. Through the windows, now streaked with smoke and flame, Gibb's blazing barbershop could be seen, the red, white and blue barber pole a torch of fire.

"We've got to get a wet blanket over that broken window, first thing!" Dave directed. "Grab these pails . . . Roy, you work the well pump! Porky, stand by to relieve him.'

A line of 4-H members and men helpers seized galvanized pails from a stack in the corner and, as Dave opened the rear store door, rushed outside to place their buckets under the spout.

With the boy from the city pumping, water commenced to flow and volunteers with full pails dashed back into the store.

"Here's some blankets!" cried Dave, "there's a table full over here in the drygoods department. Give me a hand, some of you!"

Ed Brannigan came running in. "My roof!" he moaned. "It's on fire! . . . Get somebody up on the roof! . . ."

Smoke and flames, fanned by the wind, were shooting in the open window. A furnace-like rush of fire could be heard outside.

There was the sound of the fire truck arriving, and Chief Bevins entered.

"Couldn't get the motor started!" he said. "Looks pretty bad, Ed! . . . Like the whole square's going!"

Dave had delegated a group of men to carry sacks of salt up the back stairs to the roof. Others were following with pails of water.

"Can't carry enough water that way!" he decided. "We've got to use *tubs!*"

The tubs were rolled out and filled, Porky now taking over the pumping as Roy, near exhaustion, gasped for breath.

Dave commenced dousing Brannigan's super deluxe all-wool blankets in the tubs of water and having them hung over the windows. The first closed the opening in the broken window and blotted out the flames, reaching for a hold inside. But other windows began popping beneath the heat.

"Better phone Batesville for help!" advised Fire Chief Bevins.

"Tell them to get their pumper over here! We can't throw any water from these wells . . . and the fire's clear out of control now! . . . She'll hit our telephone exchange next!"

Smoke was drifting into Brannigan's General Store as its owner groped his way back to the office and picked up the phone. He dialed "Batesville" and waited anxiously for the operator to come on the line.

"Hello . . . hello! . . . Oh, damn—just when we need some real service . . . ! Hello—Batesville . . . operator—this is Mayor Brannigan—of Hidden Valley! . . . Our town's on fire . . . give me your fire department, quick!" . . .

"One moment, please!"

"One moment!" fumed Brannigan. He looked about him, perspiration streaming from his face.

The interior of his General Store was a maze of activity. Good samaritans in the front were starting to carry out his stock. Men now stood by each window on the fire side of the building, with pails of water ready to reinforce the barrier of the wet blankets. Overhead, footsteps could be heard racing about on the roof. A steady line of men and boys carrying pails and tubs was passing in and out of the back door, coming in full and going out empty.

Ed Brannigan jiggled the receiver. "Hello! . . . Fire department? . . . This is Hidden Valley calling . . . Mayor Brannigan speaking . . . We've got a bad fire here . . . half one side of a block is gone already . . . and we stand to lose the Square unless we get help . . . our mains are out . . . can you send your pumper?"

"Sure! . . . It'll take us about forty minutes to get there . . . if we can make it by then—roads are pretty bad!"

"All right—but hurry! Your pumper's can save us!"

There was a sudden crackling sound in the phone and the connection was lost. Ed Brannigan put down the receiver. His phone commenced ringing. He picked it up again.

"Hello! . . . Hello!" There was no answer—only a loud humming sound. He hung up and the phone resumed its ringing.

"What in sam hill . . . ?"

"You can't use the phone, Mayor!" called a man, from the front of the store. "The telephone exchange is going now . . . and Burden's hardware store, on the alley is next!"

This completed the row of stores on the opposite side of the street.

The wind was carrying firebrands in an angular direction, over Brannigan's General Store, across the corner of the square, with sparks falling all over and around the Courthouse and on surrounding buildings.

There were frenzied store owners and their helpers up on every roof-top, repeating the protective measures Dave had put into operation at Brannigan's General Store. Every possible aid against fire had now been organized and the grim fight was on— to hold the flames to the one side of the street where they had broken out.

Jordan's fireproof drug store, of stone construction, was acting as a fire-break to keep the conflagration from jumping on down the block in that direction—and the real danger area was Brannigan's row of pine-framed buildings. If they could be saved— Hidden Valley could be spared from a major disaster.

But now—despite the herculean efforts of hundreds of volunteers, the General Store was seen to be on fire, over the side doorway and along the eaves. And, as this discovery was made, came the cry: "Well's dry! . . . They've pulled it clean of water!"

There was another well behind Brannigan's Drug Store and weary bucket and tub carriers rushed to it. Roy and Porky had other helpers on the pumping now . . . but this well had no pump . . . it must be operated by hand.

"Can't get enough water, quick enough!" decided Fire Chief Bevins. "You men fan out . . . go to other wells around the square . . . private homes . . . anywhere you can get water . . . and fetch it back here . . . the next half hour will tell the story . . . if this wind gets any worse . . . !"

Dave, just down from a trip to the roof which had been soaked with water and then sprinkled with a covering of salt, seeing the blaze over the side doorway, called for volunteers.

"Six of you men," he said, "Take your buckets of water . . . give me one . . . and let's run through the street and throw our water up as we pass. Maybe we can hit that fire and put it out. If we don't—this building is going!"

"It's too hot! You can't get through there!" warned Chief Bevins.

"We can if we keep moving!" said Dave. "It's worth trying!"

Ed Brannigan, facing a losing fight, grabbed Dave's arm. "Don't risk it, my boy!" he said. "You've all done all you could. Let her go!"

But Dave shook his head. "Are you ready, men?"

One of them handed Dave a pail of dirty water.

"That's from Duncan's old cistern," he said. "Ain't been touched in years!"

The men were standing in line, facing the rolling clouds of smoke and flame.

"Come on!" said Dave, and ran down the side street, close to the General Store, volunteers following.

As Dave passed the doorway, he flung the contents of his pail up at the fire, and kept on going. Everyone in line did likewise. Each man hit the mark and belches of black smoke, turning white, appeared in place of the blaze.

There were cheers from the crowd of onlookers as Ed Brannigan cried: "They got it! They snuffed it out!"

Then new cheers arose as equally daring men on the roof, let themselves be lowered, and dashed buckets of water along the eaves, putting out blazes there.

"It's time that pumper was getting here!" said Ed Brannigan, nervously consulting his watch. "If they can only hold it a few minutes longer . . . !"

A farmer in an old '35 Chevrolet truck wheezed into the littered square, which was now filled with piles of merchandise from many of the stores. He sighted the town's most prominent man and ran up to him.

"Mayor Brannigan!" he cried. "I'm Amos Dill . . . I live two miles out on the Batesville road. I just got a telephone call from the Batesville Fire Department . . . your lines are out here . . . and they told me to come in and tell you that the pumper can't make it . . ."

"Can't make it!" groaned the owner of the General Store. "Why not? . . . What happened?"

"They hit a hole in the road, near a culvert, six miles from here, and wrecked the car," said the farmer. "Say—this is a bad blaze! I wasn't feelin' well tonight and I went to bed early . . . Holy moses!"

Mayor Brannigan, acknowledging defeat, sank down on the curb stone and put his head in his hands.

"All right, boys—you've made a good fight," he said. "I'll never forget it . . . but this finishes us. You're all worn out . . . give it up . . . let my buildings go . . . they should have been fireproof anyway . . . let 'em go . . ."

There seemed to be nothing else anyone could do. A sudden stronger gust sent a great billow of flames swishing up the blackened side of the General Store, and it caught again, in several places.

Then, as all watched, helplessly, someone cried out: "Hey—look! *The wind's changing!*"

Every eye gazed upward, prayerfully, unbelievingly.

Something *was* occurring in the atmosphere. A current of some kind had started to blow the smoke and flame back where it had come from.

New hope surged and worn-out fire-fighters leaped up, spirits revived, to resume the battle. They beat out small flames which could be reached and dashed water on others, and Ed Brannigan, sitting weakly on the curb, could only watch and shake his head as a breeze now fanned his other cheek—the cheek away from the fire.

"The wind *has* changed," he said, almost worshipfully. "It's next thing to a miracle." Then he lowered his head in his arms, too moved and exhausted to say more.

The heroic battle to save not only Brannigan's block but what might have been practically the entire town of Hidden Valley was over. Bleary-eyed, smoke-stained men and boys now looked at one another, with grins of triumph, too weary to lift their voices in cheer. They let the women folks and other onlookers do that . . . but most town and county people felt too reverential to do much shouting. They just stood, facing the flickering glare of the still blazing buildings where the fire had been confined by the last moment whim of Nature, and offered up silent thanks.

Then the town's most prominent man struggled to his feet as though stirred by a tremendous impulse. He made his way through the crowd to the old fire truck, climbed in and stepped up on the seat where he could see and be seen by the throng which filled the Court House Square. He raised his arms for attention, his big figure silhouetted against the conflagration, now under control.

"Friends and neighbors of Hidden Valley and Rock County," he addressed, in a loud voice, tinged with emotion. "I want to make a confession to all of you. I've been a short-sighted, tight-fisted old fool—and it took what happened here tonight to make me see myself as I really am. I've seen you folks demonstrate your love for your town and your community. I've seen you fight to save, not only my property, but Hidden Valley. I've seen what genuine unselfish co-operation can really do. It's a sight and an experience I'll never forget."

His voice broke and, for a moment, he could not continue.

Dave had just reassembled the members of his 4-H Club who had sought each other out, and all were about to return to the Club rooms to close up and go their different ways to their homes. It had been a most unusual night for them—one which had started with such great promise and was ending, as far as their attempted civic achievement was concerned, in uncertainty and confusion. They had helped to win the fight against the fire but they had lost, temporarily, their fight for better roads and elec- trification.

Now, standing near the fire truck, they looked up at the figure of Mayor Brannigan in growing wonderment and surprise, as he levelled a finger at the President of their 4-H Club, and said: "Right here, I want to acknowledge what I owe to Dave Carson . . . !

"Many of you folks will remember the welcome home celebration we gave him. You may recall Dave's getting up and telling us about the starving, suffering peoples in the rest of the world, saying we ought to do something for them. That speech didn't set very well with me or with lots of us back here in the hills. You probably remember that I got up and told Dave, publicly, if he wanted to do something for the world, he'd better start at home."

Ed Brannigan smiled and shook his head.

"Well, Dave took me at my word. He *did* start at home, and he started by organizing this 4-H Club. And he came in to see me to get my co-operation. He began talking about all the things that should be done to make this a better town and county. He criticized the condition of the street you're standing on, and our lack of a sewage disposal system . . . and sanitary rest rooms . . . and the fact that many of you people in the County still didn't have any electricity or telephones or good roads. I got mad and called him a meddler . . ."

He paused and beckoned to Dave.

"I want that young man to come up here on the truck with me," he said, feelingly. "I want to make a public apology to him. I want to do more than that. I want to help Dave Carson and his 4-H Club and the rest of you people in Hidden Valley and Rock County get what you should have had long ago. I opposed the repair and black-topping of the highway to Batesville. I figured, if the roads were kept bad enough, that more of you people would stay at home and shop here. But, tonight, my helping to keep that road in bad condition almost cost us the town, because the pumper the Batesville Fire Department was sending to our aid was wrecked by a hole in the road. If it hadn't been for the fight you folks made and the change in the wind, this whole public square would be in ruins right now."

As if to emphasize his statements, a retaining wall on the

telephone exchange building toppled and crashed, and there was a new flare-up of the fire.

Dave Carson had come quietly forward and was standing by the truck, just below Mayor Brannigan. The town's most prominent citizen reached down a big hand to help Dave up beside him. As they stood on the driver's seat together, someone started applause which broadened into cheers, but Ed Brannigan waved a hand for silence.

"Dave," he said, addressing Hidden Valley's returned war hero, "you're going to get the things you and your 4-H'ers have been working for . . . I don't know how you made out tonight at the meeting . . . but I heard you were aiming to get people pledged to take electricity and signed up on petitions for better County roads. Well, all I can say is—I'm going to Little Rock and see the State Highway Commission. I think I can get them to designate some of these roads 'state highways' and come in and black top them for us. And, just to prove that we're willing to do our part, I'm going to make a contribution of *fifty thousand dollars* toward better roads for Rock County . . . !"

There was a great gasp of astonishment followed by a tremendous outburst of hand-clapping. But again Ed Brannigan gestured for the crowd to be quiet.

"And I'm making my check payable," with a hand on Dave's shoulder, "to the 'Civic Improvements' Fund of the Hidden Valley 4-H Club!"

So saying, he extended his hand to Dave, and two formerly opposing forces joined together, as Ed Brannigan later, humorously but sincerely, declared: ". . . *to make the best better* in Rock County!"

Chapter XXI

THE DODDS' CAR was parked in front of Jordan's Drug Store as Roy and Sue returned to Headquarters with Dave and his group of tired but overjoyed fellow members. They had been whooping it up, down the street, after Mayor Brannigan's electrifying pronouncement and donation which signified the beginning of a new day for town and county.

Tom Dodds, standing without crutches, and with his hand on the door of the car, hailed the daughter of Matt Kendall and the boy from the city.

"We've been waiting for you," he said. It was the first time he had been face to face with Sue since that occasion, such a few nights before, on Kendall Hill, when he had gone off so abruptly to be alone with his grief and disappointment. But now, whatever his inner feelings, he was smiling at them both, as he invited: "Won't you get in? You must be about exhausted, Roy especially. And aren't you leaving early in the morning for Chicago?"

"We *were*," said Sue, hesitantly, as their eyes met, "But I haven't been able to get anyone . . . I mean, we weren't sure . . . well, Roy's going, anyway . . ."

"You're *both* going," declared Tom, taking her arm and giving it a little squeeze as he helped her in the car. "I thought, of course, you were counting on . . . I told you that my folks . . . !" He cut short in sudden embarrassment and confusion.

But Fred and Anna Dodds came cordially to the rescue.

"Why, yes, Sue," assured Mrs. Dodds. "Tom spoke to us about this some days ago—and we told him we'd be glad to help out. I'm sorry if you haven't been planning on us . . . we thought it was all understood . . . !"

Sue's eyes swam in tears and she looked away, biting her lip. "I guess it was my fault," she accepted. "I didn't hear any more from Tom . . . and I thought . . ." Then she looked up at his father and mother and forced a smile. "I appreciate it awfully much."

237

And Roy Willard, who had just slipped in the back seat beside her, added: "Me, too! I didn't see how I could go, either—and leave Sue here—have her give up this Dress Revue contest and a trip to the National Congress, just for me." He kicked Tom's crutches on the floor of the car, and one of them slid out the door. "Oh, pardon me!" he said, as Tom stooped down and picked it up.

"That's all right," replied the fellow who had been bed-ridden for over two years. "I'll soon be able to throw these things away for good."

Roy eyed him, and the flashing remembrance came of that day in the cornfield. He felt a stinging in his throat as he said: "Say, that's great! Good going!"

Fred Dodds started the motor of the car but he could not get the machine under way for it was suddenly surrounded by clamorous 4-H members.

"Hey!" President Dave Carson was shouting. "Hold on, here! Don't go yet! So much has happened, we almost forgot we were going to give Roy and Sue a big send-off to Chicago at the Square Dance." He opened a car door and leaned in, putting out his hand and grinning as he said: "I can't make the flowery speech I'd planned but here's wishing you both . . ." his voice took on an oratorical tone, ". . . on behalf of your 4-H gang and the good people of Hidden Valley—and the even *better* people of Rock County, including *myself*—a wonderful time and may you both come home with the . . . er . . . a . . . *bacon!*"

There were cheers and shrieks of laughter and all four doors of the sedan were yanked open as heads and arms jammed in from every angle—till each 4-H'er had shaken hands with the two state champions, now on their way to seek National Honors.

Once more Fred Dodds prepared to leave but Tom now held up departure. He leaned forward and placed a detaining hand on his father's shoulder. "Just a second, Dad," he said. "I want to speak to Dave a minute."

The 4-H gang was dispersing and Dave was starting off with Carolyn.

"Oh, Dave!" called Tom. Then, turning to Sue and Roy, he said: "Excuse me, please. I just thought of something. It won't take a minute."

He pulled himself forward on the seat, opened the car door, and stepped back on the sidewalk. His step had a returning firmness about it as he strode toward the engaged couple. Meeting them, beyond hearing range of those in his car, he lowered his voice and said: "I just wanted you two to know that I've finally made up my mind. You can have all the building materials I was going to put in my house."

Dave and Carolyn exchanged happy glances.

"Oh, Tom!" cried Carolyn. "How grand!"

"It sure is," said Dave. "There must be a number of truck loads. When shall I make the pick-up?"

"Any time you like," replied the fellow who had been Dave's bosom pal. "Just so you let me know in advance. I don't want to be home when you take it away," he added, with a flash of feeling.

Dave and Carolyn nodded, understandingly.

"I'll let you know," Dave said, and slapped Tom's shoulder, affectionately. "Thanks again, old man."

The muscles in Tom's cheeks were quivering. "I'll be seeing you," he said, and wheeled about, a bit unsteadily, walking slowly back to the car.

The door opened and closed on his figure, and the machine moved off through the Square, past the glowing embers of the now dying fire.

Boys' Court in Chicago was located in the big Municipal Court building on South State Street. Juvenile tragedy of every description was written daily into its records. Boys and young men, white and colored, guilty of all manner of juvenile delinquencies and petty crimes and pranks and misdemeanors, ranging from the defacing of public monuments, purse-snatching, gambling, house-breaking, knifing, speeding, car stealing, sex offenses, run-aways from home, forgeries, and on up to murder.

To these widely differing types of cases, Judge Braude had

given conscientious thought and humane consideration. Wherever possible he had called in parents or guardians or close friends of the youths involved and caused them to assume or share responsibility for the future conduct of this portion of America's citizens in the making.

He was in session now, this cold morning in early December, with a packed court room and an unusually heavy calendar to be disposed of, when the bailiff whispered in his ear.

"Is that so?" said the Judge, aside. "Is Roy Willard in the court room?"

"He is, Your Honor. He's standing in the back there with that swell looking number!"

The bailiff pointed and Judge Braude wiped his moist glasses and replaced them that he might get a better look. Before him stood three badly frightened colored boys, awaiting judgment on a charge of breaking into a South Side Filling Station, holding up the attendant with a water pistol, and robbing his cash drawer of some thirty-seven dollars.

"She *is* a good looker," appraised the Judge, as he studied the trim-figured, dark-haired young woman, who clung to the young man's arm. "All right—look up Roy Willard's case. Get his records out. Tell him I'll see him just as soon as I'm through with these boys here."

In a few minutes, the bailiff stood up and called: "Roy Willard! You're next!"

The young man with the girl on his arm, walked down the center aisle, past the wood benches filled with a motley collection of sober-faced youths and adults, who eyed them curiously. They stood quietly before Judge Braude and looked up at him as he leaned forward, in his austere black robe, and smiled down.

"Well, Roy," he greeted, eyeing the young lady, "it looks as though you'd done pretty well for yourself. May I ask who this is?"

The young man before the bar smiled. "Her name's Sue Kendall, sir," he said, and then added, proudly, "she's going to be my wife."

Judge Braude studied the two of them a moment and then, addressing the girl, he asked: "Are you sure you love this young man?"

There was a moment's hesitation and Sue looked about her in apparent embarrassment, then replied in a low voice: "Why, yes, your Honor, I certainly do!"

"He's told you all about his *past?*" Judge Braude persisted.

The girl before him nodded, her clear green eyes meeting his. "Yes, sir. But that doesn't make any difference."

'What are you doing with him in Chicago?" was the Judge's next question.

"I'm here to attend the National 4-H Congress," she informed. "It's being held at the same time as the International Live Stock Show and Roy's . . . !"

Judge Braude interrupted. "I know about him. I've just had a letter from your father."

Roy Willard looked up, hopefully. "Did he give me a good enough report, sir, so that I could ask you to let me off probation now? You see," he glanced sidewise at Sue, "I don't want to get married as long as I'm . . . !"

"Tell me, Roy," broke in Judge Braude, "How have you liked it on the farm?"

Roy's face lit up. "Very much, sir. I can't thank you enough for giving me the chance to . . ."

The Judge waved a full-sleeved arm. "Never mind that. I understand you've raised a pretty fine beef calf?"

Both Roy and Sue were smiling now, their tension somewhat eased.

"Well, *I* think he's pretty good," Roy answered, slowly, "but I can tell you better after the judging."

The robed figure on the bench evidenced ironic amusement. "That's quite a different kind of judging, isn't it?" he said. "From human beings to meat animals. But I guess, at that, beef raisers take better care of their stock than we do of our human animals." He made a little gesture designed to cover the sorry specimens assembled in the court room, and lines of deep feeling came into his face, as he went on: "We humans don't give any thought to good breeding, we just go on bringing more and more physically and mentally defective boys and girls into the world . . . or making defectives out of them by lack of love, broken homes, poor economic conditions or bad environment. No beef breeder could raise a prize calf under those circumstances! And he couldn't make a winner out of a calf which came from poor stock in the first place!"

Judge Braude brought his thoughts back to the court room and dismissed his serious reflection with a laugh as he said: "Roy, I'd like to trade places with the judges of your beef calf for one day. I think I'd have a cinch compared to what I have to judge here."

The boy from the city, who had been sent to the County against his will, gave Judge Braude a look of sympathetic appreciation.

"I know you would," he said, feelingly.

The Judge picked up the papers on Roy's case and glanced through them.

"Let's see," he said, "Your probation was supposed to run for a year which would take it into next February—and you are requesting that I dismiss you now from court jurisdiction?"

"Yes, sir," said the young man before the bar.

Judge Braude reached in his pocket and took out a letter. Both Roy and Sue could see the large, shaky scrawl of the address on the envelope, recognizable at once as the handwriting of Matt Kendall, who held a pen pressed between his two twisted forefingers and thumbs.

"I'm going to have to base my decision pretty largely on this," said the Judge, "and also upon the opinion this young lady has of you."

He extracted the piece of stationery from the envelope and laid it on the bar in front of him, adjusting his glasses.

"Would you like to hear a little of what Mr. Kendall has to say about you?"

The Judge was talking in a low voice and spectators in the

court room, especially those in the front rows, were trying mightily to glean what was being said, to no avail.

Roy glanced uncertainly at Sue. "Well, I guess it will be all right," he said, uneasily.

Judge Braude fixed his eyes on the letter and started reading: " '. . . and so, Judge, summing it all up—I think the boy has a lot of real ability and good in him. All he's been needing was the opportunity to bring it out. And *that* he's certainly done around here. I guess you can figure my estimate of him when I tell you that I'm willing to have him marry my daughter— and if that's not enough recommendation—then, I'd just like you to know, Judge, that I couldn't think any more of Roy— if he was *my own son* . . . ' "

Judge Braude laid the letter aside and looked down at the young couple standing before him. Both of them were in tears.

Catching the girl's eye, the Judge leaned forward, smiled, and asked, softly: "You think Roy won't backslide, if I let him off?"

Her answer was instant and positive. "I'm sure of it!" she said.

The Judge reached out and shook each by the hand.

"Good luck to both of you," he said, and then added, with a commending glance at Roy: "If the judges give your beef calf as good a rating as I'm giving you here today—you're going to have a *Grand Champion!*"

The National 4-H Club Congress and the International Live Stock Exposition were two mighty magnets attracting some fifteen hundred 4-H Club members and leaders to the city of Chicago, each first week in December. The convention of the 4-H'ers was made possible by co-operation of the State Agricultural Colleges, the United States Department of Agriculture, a great number of farm and business organizations, and the National Committee on Boys and Girls Club Work. Besides competing in the various contests, clubsters were given opportunity to see the International Live Stock Show, the International Hay and Grain Show, and the city of Chicago, itself. Because many of these young men and women were visiting a large city for the first time, this trip to the 4-H Congress was a high and un-forgettable adventure.

It was certainly that to Sue Kendall who had thrilled all the way to Chicago on the long and interesting truck ride in com-pany with Local Leader Frank Carson, the former boy from the city, and their distinguished passenger, *Your Majesty*.

She had seen the prize beef calf safely placed in his stall on the Exposition grounds in the famous stockyards, and left in charge of Rock County's best beef breeder. She had then gone down into Chicago's Loop with the young man she was en-gaged to marry, after having first registered with the Arkansas delegation at the National 4-H Headquarters in the Hotel Stevens on Michigan Avenue, overlooking Lake Michigan.

This beautiful body of water might as well have been the ocean as far as she was concerned. The largest stretch of water she had seen before was the White River. From the room she had been assigned on the twelfth floor, she could see a wide expanse of Lake front, the outer drive along the water a moving line of vari-colored motorized ants, and thousands more of them glistening in the sun, at rest in the parking lots.

Looking straight down, there were still more cars and buses—automobiles everywhere, and countless people scurrying in all directions, all of them seemingly in a terrible hurry.

The tempo of the city had excited her, and the height of her hotel room, let alone the altitude of Chicago's skyscrapers, was almost frightening. Strange sounds, too, bombarded her eardrums. The harsh cough of backfires, the stopping and starting throb of motors, the scream of brakes, the high singing whine of elevators outside her door, voices of gay 4-H'ers running up and down the halls and footsteps running with them, the intermittent far-off roar of airplane engines passing overhead, the shrill whistle of Hotel Stevens' doormen hailing taxis, the almost musical "tweet! tweet!" of policemen directing traffic, muffled locomotives and freight cars barking up at her from the covered yards across the avenue, the distant low-throated summons of a car ferry coming in from the Lake—telling the watchmen to raise the great suspension bridges and stop all traffic so it could get through into the dirty Chicago river and drop its load. All these and many more unfamiliar sounds jabbered in foreign tongues at the daughter of Matt Kendall and did things to her inside.

Because she had been the only girl member from her own 4-H Club in attendance, she had been assigned, as a room-mate, an auburn-haired, vivacious girl named Betty Leslie, from Fayetteville, and who was the State Food Preparation Champion. Betty had dropped her bag in the room and had raced out again after barely having met Sue, to take in some preliminary group meetings before the official program opened.

But Sue had gone with Roy to Boys' Court, to give him what moral support she could in his appeal to Judge Braude to free him from court supervision. After that she had returned happily to the hotel in Roy's company, and he had left her there, hastening back to the Exposition to be with *Your Majesty*.

"I'll be in for you tonight," he had promised. "Mr. Carson's going to stay with my calf, so we can take in a show. I only wish it was summer time so I could treat you to a moonlight excursion on the Lake!"

With Roy gone, and left to herself for the first time without anyone around her whom she knew, Sue felt momentary panic and a queer sensation in the pit of her stomach. She thought of her father, miles away on Kendall Hill, and although she had no doubt he was in good hands, with the Dodds looking after him, she began to worry and wonder if both she and Roy should have come to Chicago and left him.

Then the National 4-H Club Congress reached out its cordial hand and pulled her in to the Grand Ball Room where a sumptuous luncheon was being served to over a thousand members from all of the Forty-eight States. There were also delegates, representatives and guests from other rural organizations from such far-off places as New Zealand, Haiti, Jamaica, the Phillipine Islands, England, Australia, Holland, Belgium, Denmark, Norway, Sweden, Italy, China, Argentina, Mexico . . . oh, it seemed as though there was someone there from almost every country on earth!

Sue forgot her own twinges of homesickness and became lost in contemplation of what a tremendous movement she belonged to! She was thrilled when a group of fine looking Chinese stood up and sang their Chinese farmer song, in their own language, which one of them explained—all Chinese farmers sang while they followed the plow. Poor China—so torn by wars within her borders . . . nothing like the peace and quiet and safety of farming in the back hills of Arkansas!

There were nationally and internationally famous personages seated at the speakers' table, some of whom Sue had heard or read about but had never dreamed of seeing personally. One of these was Thomas E. Wilson, chairman of Wilson & Company, big meat packers, and chairman, also, of the National Committee on Boys and Girls Club Work, which was behind all activities of the 4-H Clubs.

Sue was thrilled at what Mr. Wilson had to say and made notes of his remarks so she could report them to her own club members at the next regular meeting of the Hidden Valley Club. It was past midnight now and she was seated in her bathrobe at the writing desk by the window, copying these notes in her diary as she reviewed the day's events.

"Of more than two billion people on earth," Mr. Wilson had said, "it is estimated that 360,000,000 are boys and girls between ten and twenty-one years of age—about equal to the population of North America, Britain and Russia. Fewer than half—maybe only one third of youth throughout the world have anything like a sporting chance at head, heart, hand and health development which is the key to our famous 4-H Club movement here in the United States. But this favored fraction has the possibility within it to give to all the world the secret of the incentive to progress, prosperity and peace . . .

"When I look at these clear-eyed, intelligent, freedom-loving and achieving youngsters, and then when I consider the tragic perversion and enslavement of equally eager youth of Europe and Asia by the Axis, which conceived humanity its pawn, I am profoundly convinced that the oncoming generation can literally be saved by the projection of this idea into a scope embracing the earth.

"Boys and girls now on the threshold of active life will make or break civilization for centuries to come. Every age has its turning point, where an upheaval of one sort or another breaks down the old and makes way for the new. We may easily lapse into a millenium of mediocrity if we permit destruction to continue; or we can go forward to new heights of achievement, health and happiness, if we exert the intelligence and will power we already have.

"World youth is literally at the crossroads. The choice of its destination must be made now."

These thoughts of Mr. Wilson's opened up new horizons in Sue's mind and she could understand now why Dave had spoken as he had when he returned from abroad and sensed how far removed from what was really going on in the world, most of the home folks were.

The United States was an enormous place, bigger by far than she had ever conceived. But it was reassuring to know that young men and women from Maine to California were meeting and solving many of the same problems which she had been called upon to face on Kendall Hill.

A nerve-exhausted girl from the country, finally crawled between smooth, clean sheets and was almost instantly asleep.

The National 4-H Dress Revue was held at the Eighth Street Theatre, on Wabash Avenue, within a block of the Hotel Stevens. The dresses of the State winners had been displayed for the judges before their makers modelled them at the show. Sue, studying the dresses of her competitors had a sinking feeling. As Roy had said to her on the way to Chicago—she was entering the "big league" now. He was, too, with his beef calf. Any young man or woman who won through to the championship from the pick of the country, really *had* something.

The Dress Revue was to be at ten in the morning, a difficult time for Roy to get away from his care of *Your Majesty*.

"I'll make it if I can," he assured Sue. "But don't count on it. Just go out there, Honey, when your time comes, and do your stuff like you've done it at Hidden Valley and Fayetteville. People are the same, the world over . . . and just because you're in a bigger place, don't let it get you down."

"I'll try not to," she said.

"If I can get to the theatre, look for me standing up in the back," Roy directed. "If I'm not there—I'll phone you at your room in the hotel around one o'clock. Lots of luck, sweetheart!"

Once more Sue was late on the program, and once more she suffered agonies in waiting. The theatre was filled, as expected, and so many were standing that she couldn't distinguish Roy's face from the stage. She couldn't see *any* faces because the footlights were so bright in this theatre that they shut out the audience. But she could hear booming applause as she walked on, smiled, bowed, turned completely around, and with heart palpitating fought the desire to accelerate her steps as she moved off into the wings.

Had Roy seen her? Was he out front now, waiting and wondering with her as to how she had placed—if she had placed at all?

The last girl was on stage now—perhaps just as frightened as she had been—but not showing it, too much, anyway. A girl from Rhode Island . . . the littlest girl from the smallest state. She was getting big applause, too.

And now—it was all over—and the judges were conferring and forty beautiful young women were trying to resist nibbling well manicured nails . . . and, finally, after minutes which were hours and hours—the winners were announced—and her name was not among them.

The daughter of Matt Kendall slipped off the brown dress, made from the material in the gown her mother had never worn. She placed it even more lovingly in the box, for its long trip home. Then she went across the stage, past other losers, some of whom smiled at her, while others were having trouble with the corners of their mouths.

Miss Rhode Island had taken first prize with a dainty little pink creation and she was just slipping out of it when Sue reached her.

"I'm from Arkansas," she said, holding out her hand. "And I'd like to congratulate you."

The blue eyes of the midget-sized but perfectly formed blonde from Rhode Island, shone.

"You're the girl who wore that lovely brown dress, aren't you?" she identified. "I really picked *you* to win."

Sue smiled, with an ache in her throat and an even deeper ache in her heart.

"I guess I was quite a bit out of my class here," she said. "But it was worth it—to get a chance to make this trip. I'm learning a lot."

She slipped away, picked up her dress box and hurried out the stage entrance, running along the side street to the hotel. The Revue had taken almost three hours. It would soon be time for Roy to be calling . . . the phone was ringing when she entered her room.

"Hello, Honey," said his voice, when she took down the receiver. "How'd you make out?"

"Oh, Roy," she cried, her voice breaking. "I lost—I didn't even place."

She smothered a sob through biting into her handkerchief.

"You've placed with *me,*" said the former boy from the city. "You're in first position, Sweetheart—and you always will be!"

"I looked for you, like you told me," she said, making conversation, hanging onto him, now that she had him on the wire. "I was so hoping . . . !"

"I just couldn't get away," said Roy. "Mr. Carson has been talking to the judges and big stock men here. My steer is causing a real sensation, even before he's been judged. Apparently *Your Majesty* has developed into an unusual all-around animal. He weighed in at eleven hundred and one pounds—but it's not his weight . . . it's his quality of flesh and everything that goes with it . . . They all say that I can't miss getting one of the first three awards."

Sue's spirits lifted. "Why, Roy, that's marvelous! Oh, you just must win with *Your Majesty*. Now that I've lost—you've got to uphold the honor of Hidden Valley!"

Roy laughed. "If I can just practice what I've been preaching to you," he said. "And not get too nervous . . . Judging starts this afternoon. By tomorrow at this time, I should know my fate! Buck up, Sue—don't feel too badly—take in the 4-H programs and forget about it. The pressure's all over for you but I've still got to sweat it out. I'm staying here tonight so you won't see me till I know the result. Goodbye for now!"

"Roy!" she cried, suddenly unnerved. "Don't hang up! . . . Talk to me! . . . I never felt this way before! . . . I'm scared . . . I wish you were here with me . . . I—I'm almost sorry I ever left home . . . !"

"Take it easy, Honey," said Roy's voice, in soothing tones. "You've just been under tension for so long, taking care of your Dad . . . carrying all that responsibility . . . you're getting a natural let-down that's all . . . Lie down for awhile . . . skip lunch . . . don't eat when you feel upset . . . I wish I could jump on the elevated and come into town but I . . . !"

"No, no—you can't do that—but, Roy, I'm coming out to you . . . I'm coming right away . . . !"

"But you don't know how to get around."

"I'll take the elevated . . . can't the motorman put me off?"

"Yes, he can," said Roy, concernedly. "Tell him to let you out at the main stockyards stop and I'll meet you."

"How long will it take me?"

"About a half hour!"

"Then be there for me in about an hour. Oh, Roy—I think I'll die if I can't see you and *Your Majesty* soon! . . . I know the 4-H meetings mean a lot—but feeling as I do—I just can't miss being with you—when they announce the awards . . . I want to be the first to congratulate *Your Majesty*—if he wins!"

Chapter XXII

It was all *Your Majesty* at the International Live Stock Exposition. The beef calf owned and developed by Roy Willard, former Chicago boy, and taken from the famous Frank Carson Aberdeen Angus herd of Hidden Valley, Arkansas, performed with the perfection expected of all Grand Champions. Once back in his stall, surrounded by an admiring crowd after having patiently held his prize winning stance for impatient photographers, *Your Majesty* seemed to enjoy the fuss being made over him. But if a steer could blush, he did so when a beautiful dark-haired young woman threw her arms about his neck and kissed him.

Frank Carson, standing nearby, laughed and said: "I feel like doing that myself!" Then, placing a hand on Roy's shoulder, he added: "You've reached the end of a long road, son—and no one knows better than Sue and I what a climb it has been. But it's been worth it all now, hasn't it?"

The former Chicago boy nodded, with a lump in his throat which wouldn't come out.

"I'll say it has . . . do you mind sticking around, Mr. Carson . . .? I'd like to run off with Sue for awhile and do a little celebrating on our own."

"Go ahead," smiled the man who was now being talked about as the finest breeder of Aberdeen Angus herds in the United States. "It's all over now but the shouting—and the auction tomorrow."

"The *auction!*" exclaimed Sue, and turned questioningly to Roy. "You're not going to sell *Your Majesty?*"

Roy nodded. "We sure are—and I've been tipped off . . ." he looked around cautiously and lowered his voice, ". . . that The Firestone Tire and Rubber Company is all set to bid a record price per pound to get it."

"How much might that be?" asked Sue.

"Mr. Carson tells me," said Roy, "that they might go as high as ten dollars. If they did, *Your Majesty* would bring around *eleven thousand* bucks!"

Sue gasped. "What would you do with all that money?"

Roy took her by the arm. "Come on," he said, "and I'll tell you!"

They rode the elevated down into the Loop, past row on row of smoke-begrimed, squalid frame and brick dwellings, through colored and white districts, with little to distinguish between them.

"So this is the way people live in the city!" said Sue.

"Part of them," Roy replied, "but you should see some of the swanky apartment houses on the Gold Coast!"

Sue looked bewildered. "Gold Coast! What's that?"

"That's a section on what we call the Near North Side, over-looking the Lake," informed Roy, "where lots of rich people live."

Sue sat silently for a moment, then turned to him, distressed. "But there are lots more poor people than rich in Chicago—and is this the way most of them have to live? No yards? No trees? No real place for children to play? All this dirt and noise? And air that almost chokes you to breathe? And the water—I can hardly drink it!"

Roy laughed. "That's because they put chlorine in it to purify it," he explained.

"I never heard of such a thing!" said Sue.

"I know," replied Roy, sympathetically. "But there's so much sewage dumped in Lake Michigan, we have to protect ourselves here. I agree it's not like on your farm where that water comes out of the ground fresh and clear and cold and soft—just like nature made it."

Sue shook her head. "The city may be wonderful," she said, "but I don't like it."

Roy looked at her. "You'd get used to it after while," he said. "Lots of folks from the country do." He hesitated a moment, then added, testily: "I was hoping you *would* like it a little bit. I met a man today who offered me a job—a mighty good one, too—in his packing house."

Sue stiffened. "Who was he?" she asked.

"Thomas E. Wilson," said Roy. "Don't suppose you ever heard of him."

"Heard of him!" Sue exclaimed. "Of course I have . . . he spoke at the Congress . . . I copied down what he said . . ."

"You did!" cried Roy. "Then you know—I don't have to tell you—he's one of the finest men in the business . . . !"

"Yes," Sue admitted, deeply impressed. "What kind of a job did he offer you?"

"A Junior Cattle Buyer," said Roy. "It's something I hadn't dreamed of—but it pays very well."

Sue looked away and gazed reflectively out the window. The elevated train was winding into the Loop, passing the second and third stories of buildings, so close that she could catch glimpses of intimate scenes through their windows. A mother changing a kicking, squalling baby in a little two-by-four bedroom with droopy, gray curtains hanging at the windows . . . an elderly woman in a faded blue dress, watering a pathetic looking potted plant behind the window pane . . . three pallid-faced youngsters, a boy and two little girls, their noses pressed like round balls of putty against the glass, watching the train go by— *her* children, perhaps, ten years from now—if she ever answered the call of the city with Roy.

Sue suddenly put her face in her hands, fighting to control her emotions.

"Why, what's the matter?" the owner of the year's Grand Champion asked.

"I don't know," she cried, softly. "All I know is—I want to get home to Daddy and all my friends there . . . and, if you're really thinking about leaving the farm and coming back to Chicago . . . to work . . . then I . . . !" She couldn't finish.

The former boy from the city studied the girl who had promised to marry him. If they had not been riding a public conveyance, he would have liked to have taken her in his arms and to have comforted and reassured her, but there were unfeeling passengers on all sides of them and no opportunity for the expression of any real sentiment. It all had to be dammed up inside.

Everyone living in the city had his privacy invaded. Right now, at this time of year, he couldn't get off the elevated with Sue and take her to a public park along the water-front, and find a secluded place and talk it out. He would have to escort her back to the hotel where they would be forced to sit in an unromantic lobby and try to fit the changing conditions in their lives together.

The impact of what a city was doing to the emotions of people, young and old, who craved the uninhibited enjoyment of love and companionship but who could find few intimate places and moments for their realization, hit Roy with stunning force. Some temperaments just couldn't stand this four-walled, cooped up, high pressure way of living. He could see now what had happened in the home life of his father. Living room, bedroom, kitchen and bath—himself sleeping on the davenport at night. No wonder his step-mother hated him. How could she get any real chance to be alone with her husband when he or anyone else was around? . . . It was like this all over Chicago —in all the Chicagos of the world. Congestion, no escape from it anywhere—people sacrificing their personal freedom of body, mind and spirit—and living almost on top of each other for the sake of making a few more dollars a week.

Was this happiness? It had only brought trouble and misery in his life . . . He had never experienced any real joy of living until he had been forcibly shipped to the country. Something was terribly wrong with civilization. There was going to have to be a great change some day soon because most humans just couldn't go on this way without cracking up.

Roy knew now that whatever the business opportunities offered him, he couldn't remain too long in a city—a new something within him was responding to the call of land and air and sunshine and rain and just the boundless feeling of space, into which his expanding spirit could rise, reaching out toward communion with all things in nature . . . the things preachers meant when they talked about God.

The boy from the city turned to the girl from the country.

"This is our stop," he said.

He took her by the arm as the elevated slid into the station and came to a jolting halt. They got off with some hundred others, and the platform gate clanged shut behind them as the train rattled and banged on its way. They walked down the wooden steps worn thin by millions of footsteps, descending to the street where taxicabs snarled and barked at them as they dashed across in front.

It was late afternoon when they reached Michigan Avenue and turned down toward the Hotel Stevens. The Avenue was a maze of traffic, most of it outgoing. There were endless lines of buses, jammed with homeward bound office workers and shoppers. Their gasoline fumes, even on the sidewalk, penetrated Sue's nostrils and caused her to cough. She tried to speak to Roy but he could not hear her against the drumming of passing motors.

He piloted her inside the drug store at the Stevens and found a lone stool for her at the soda fountain.

"Don't mind me," he said. "I'll stand."

A harassed appearing man next her was ordering a Bromo-Seltzer.

"Mix it up strong," he ordered. "I've got a killer-diller of a headache."

Sue ordered a chocolate ice cream soda and asked Roy what he wanted.

"I'll take one, too," he said.

The gum-chewing redhead behind the counter threw the ingredients together, slopped the soda water over the sides of the glasses, stuck in some carelessly washed longhandled spoons and shoved the concoctions their way, with balls of ice cream mangled on top.

Roy reached over Sue's shoulder to take his soda standing up.

"Next!" called the feminine soda jerker. "Who's next?"

The man who had brought in a headache, left apparently

without one, and Roy captured his stool by an eyelash over a later arrival, a sleek-haired young man who had spotted this attractive dark-haired girl and wanted to sit beside her.

"Pardon me!" he said, when he saw that Roy was with her, and slunk to the end of the counter.

Sue, with her lips to the straws, took a sip and then raised her head, saying in a low voice to Roy: "This doesn't compare with the sodas we get right at home—in Jordan's drug store!"

Roy grinned. "I'm afraid," he said, "it's going to be rather difficult to wean you away from Hidden Valley!"

Sue looked down at her soda, pushing the ice cream down inside the glass, with her spoon. "I'm afraid it is, too," she said. And, then, feeling that she must give voice to her feelings, whether in a public place or not, she half whispered: "Maybe we should forget our plans . . . and you should take this job with Mr. Wilson's company . . . it sounds to me like a wonderful opportunity . . . you're used to the city and I'm not . . . and Daddy still needs me . . ."

Roy felt his stomach roll up into a tight ball. He pushed the soda from him.

"You don't mean that?" he said, forgetting anyone around him, eyes only on the girl seated beside him, the girl he wanted more than Grand Champions or anything else in the world.

But Sue had her courage up now. She was going to say what was in her heart to say. She must say it—so there couldn't be any misunderstanding come up between them, so if their lives were to go on together, Roy would know how it had to be.

"I haven't any choice, Roy—but you still have," she said. "I've got to stay on the farm—or near it, anyway, as long as Daddy lives. I wouldn't be happy if I felt you had turned down something you very much wanted to do . . . So, perhaps it would be best—since we haven't gone too far in our plans . . . for you to go your way . . . and I'll . . . !"

"But, Sue!" said Roy, leaning toward her as she lowered her head and poked the straws around in her soda, bringing up lumps of ice cream on their tip ends. "You don't want to live your life out that way . . . without love . . . or marriage . . . or—or anything . . . !"

"No," said the girl from the country, "but you can probably find someone else . . . and I . . . well, maybe some day, when he gets stronger . . ."

A knife drove into Roy's heart and turned painfully in it. *"Tom?"* he whispered, hoarsely.

She nodded, not looking up. "He proposed again while you were in Little Rock."

"He *did!*" Roy exclaimed, impulsively. "What did you say?"

"I had to tell him we were engaged," she confessed.

Roy's mind flashed to the day in the cornfield when he had come upon Tom trying to walk and had overheard him mention Sue's name. Could it be that Sue, herself, cared, too? Was *this* what she was hinting at?

"You don't need to worry about that job I was offered," said Roy. "I just mentioned it as a matter of interest . . . but I promised your father that I would stay on the farm as long as he needed me . . . and *you* mean more to me than any job Mr. Wilson or anyone else could ever offer . . ."

There was a look in Sue's eyes which Roy couldn't quite fathom. She was trying to say something when the redhead behind the counter broke in on their hushed conversation.

"What's the matter? Don't you like your sodas?" she demanded. "There's others waiting!"

Sue and Roy glanced up and saw a line of men and women standing behind each place at the counter. Most of them were staring their way, curiously.

"Come on," said Roy, taking Sue's arm and grabbing up the check. "Let's get out of here!" Then, over his shoulder to the redhead, he fired: "Yes, sweetheart—we loved them!"

The feminine soda jerker tossed the unfinished sodas in the sink. "Some people!" she exclaimed, in a voice dripping with disgust. "What's yours, Madam? . . . What'll *you* have, Mister?"

"A bromo!" said a worried looking man. "Boy, what a headache!"

Chapter XXIII

"THIS IS *Your Majesty*—the grandest of all Grand Champions!" barked the auctioneer, before the most distinguished group of baby beef buyers ever assembled in the arena. "He was sired by *Black Beauty*, one of the two leading Aberdeen Angus sires in Frank Carson's famous herd. His dam was *Sweet Alice, the III*, who in turn was sired by *Ozark Glory*, Carson's other top Aberdeen Angus herd bull.

"This wonderful meat animal was fed and raised by Roy Willard, a boy from our good old home town of Chicago. He bought his calf of Mr. Carson when it was five months old, never having had any experience before in developing meat animals. But this young man, who picked his own calf from the Carson herd, learned mighty fast and did a great job.

"*Your Majesty* stands here in the ring beside his proud master, a living model of the perfection which has been reached in beef cattle breeding. He weighed in this morning at eleven hundred and four pounds. I don't have to give you any sales talk on a magnificent piece of quality flesh like this. Gentlemen, the bids are open! What am I offered?"

Roy Willard, with his hand resting on the neck of his beloved *Your Majesty*, listened to the offers per pound as they were shouted to the auctioneer from different sections of the arena. The bidding was high, purposely so, in appreciation of the prize Exposition beef, and several big companies were anxious to capture *Your Majesty* for use in public relations and education. Roy heard the bids go up and up and listened unbelievingly as Russell A. Firestone stayed in there with the ten dollar level reached, and three other bidders still holding on.

"Do I hear $10.25?" shouted the auctioneer.

"You *do!*" said Russell Firestone.

"$10.30!" called another buyer.

"This beef comes high," said the auctioneer. "It's already past

258

the all-time record but let's keep going! Who will say $10.50?"

There was a moment of silence. Most buyers had gone as far and even further than they had been authorized to bid in order to get *Your Majesty*.—But now a familiar voice was heard again. "I'll go $10.50!"

"$10.50, going once ... going twice ... Who'll make it $10.55?" boomed the auctioneer. "... No takers? ... $10.50 going for the third and last time ... Gone to The Firestone Tire and Rubber Company—sold for the highest price per pound ever bid!" He turned to the clerk of sale who was standing nearby. "I'm no good at mathematics. What's the grand total of this buy?"

The clerk, rapidly computing on a piece of paper, looked up and shouted out, excitedly, so that all could hear: *"Eleven thousand, five hundred and ninety-two dollars!"*

"There you are!" beamed the auctioneer. "Thank you, gentlemen for the tremendous tribute you've paid *Your Majesty* by bidding up your price to this record height. I think most of you know that The Firestone Tire and Rubber Company, now that it owns *Your Majesty,* plans to take the Grand Champion on a nation-wide educational tour in a streamlined specially designed truck which will cover approximately twenty-two thousand miles before it gets through. This will make the fifth Chicago Grand Champion purchased by The Firestone Company and taken around the country in the interest of better purebred beef raising."

The auctioneer turned to Roy Willard and put out his hand. "My congratulations, young man. You can lead *Your Majesty* from the ring now and turn him over, outside, to his new owner—and, last but not least, *collect your check!"*

There was laughter and applause as Roy Willard, leaving the exhibition ring for the last time, was met at the exit by Frank Carson and the buyer for Firestone. The details of the transaction were simple and Roy was soon holding his check. Some cattle handlers for the Firestone Company had backed up a truck and one of them said to Roy: "He'll probably mind you better than us. Will you get him in here?"

The former boy from the city looked at *Your Majesty* who,

in turn, looked trustingly at him. The moment for parting had arrived—a moment Roy had not realized was going to be so difficult. There now raced through his mind all of the little intimate, personal experiences which had been woven around his life with the beef calf since the day he had pointed it out in Frank Carson's herd. It suddenly came over him with heart-tearing force what raising *Your Majesty* had meant in his life. The days and nights of unceasing care and worry and work . . . that night, especially, of the great storm and Sue and he down in the pasture, in the mud and rain and lightning . . . and Tom's friendly help with the loan of the milk cow . . . and Frank Carson's ever-ready guidance . . . and Matt Kendall, too, with all his pretended indifference, showing a rough surface interest . . . These and more memory pictures went through Roy's mind as he gently urged *Your Majesty* up the ramp into the truck.

"At least," he said, fighting to conceal his feelings, "I'm not selling you to be lead off to the slaughter."

He slipped an arm around the short, well-set, firm neck and gave *Your Majesty* an affectionate pat of farewell. The steer seemed to sense the impending separation and raised his head to nose Roy's cheek.

"Goodbye, *Your Majesty,*" his owner whispered, huskily, then turned and left the truck, running from the scene to the seclusion of the Grand Champion's empty stall.

Dave Carson was surprised and almost dumbfounded, as he was coming from the large barn where the prize Aberdeen Angus herd was stalled, to see the familiar figure of a young man running up the drive-way.

"Hello, Roy!" he greeted. "I wasn't expecting you back for a couple of days yet. Where's Dad? Did something happen to the truck? What brings *you* home?"

Roy Willard was breathing heavily. "I've come right out here from the train," he said. "I left Chicago last night by myself. Sue's driving back with your father tomorrow."

Dave stared at Roy, bewilderedly. "I still don't get it," he said. "That was great news about *Your Majesty!* Why didn't you stay until things were over? Are you in trouble?"

"No," said Roy, his eyes alight. "But I've got a job to do back here—and I need your help!"

Dave grinned, relieved. "Don't tell me you've come back with all that dough, and want to buy some more beef calves!"

"Cut it out!" Roy replied. "This is serious. You probably don't know it—but Sue and I have been engaged."

Dave nodded, wisely. "I've suspected it," he said.

"Well," said Roy, rushing on as though eager to confide, "I've found out she doesn't really love me—she loves Tom. She has all along. There's nothing that she or I or anyone can do about it . . . and I happen to know that Tom loves her—and he's eating his heart out for her right now!"

Dave took hold of Roy's arm and shook him. "Not so fast, Roy . . . Calm down! You may have this thing all wrong . . . Here's something you *don't* know." Roy eyed him questioningly. "Remember the night of the fire when you were going home in Dodds' car and Tom got out to speak to Carolyn and me?"

Roy nodded. "What about it?"

"Simply this," said Dave. "Tom offered to sell us his barn full of materials for the home he and Sue were going to build. He wouldn't have done that if he still . . . !"

"Oh, yes he would!" broke in Roy. "He proposed to Sue a few weeks ago and she told him we were engaged . . . that was just his way of stepping out of the picture."

Dave looked at the former boy from the city, debatingly. "Well, if that's the case, it could be," he conceded. "But what do you think you can do about things now?"

"*Plenty!*" declared Roy, "if you'll help me."

"Okay—shoot!"

"Here's the plan," fired Roy, then checked himself: "First—one question. Have you picked up Tom's housing material yet?"

"No. I was going for it as soon as Dad got back with the truck."

"Then it's perfect!" cried Roy. "You'll have to get your home somewhere else because we're having a *house-raising party* for Tom and Sue and we're putting their home up, right where they've wanted it, all in *a day's time!*"

Dave gave Roy a look of unbounded admiration. "You city fellows think *big,* don't you? That's a community project if I ever heard one! . . . Raising a beef calf is nothing compared to this!"

Roy smiled for the first time. "I'm glad you like it," he said. "It's the one great chance I've got to pay back the two most unselfish people I'll ever know."

"When do you plan to pull this all off?" asked Dave.

"I have every step figured out," said Roy. "I sat up all night on the train, thinking about it. We've got to do it this Saturday. Your father and Sue won't be back till late that afternoon and you'll have to find some excuse to take Tom away with you for the day so I can get some trucks from town to carry the materials up to their building site. We'll have to let Tom's folks in on the plan so they'll co-operate—and I'll take care of Mr. Kendall."

"You've got a big order there," said Dave. "I wouldn't want that assignment."

The boy from the city nodded, grimly. "Now let's see," he said. "I want to check everything. Oh—could you call an emergency meeting of the 4-H Club and put them to work on this?"

"I sure can," said Dave. "I'll have them all rounded up for a meeting yet tonight! They'll do everything they can but they're not carpenters. How're you going to solve that problem?"

Roy grinned. "I'm counting on you to go with me to see Mayor Brannigan—and selling him a bill of goods," he said. "He's got enough influence to get us all the carpenters in town and everything else we need!"

Dave slapped Roy on the back. "Just let me change my clothes and I'll be with you," he said. "Here's where we collect interest on that little fire-fighting job we did!"

Matt Kendall's field glasses were focused on the Carson car as it stopped, several hours later, at the foot of his road, on the way back from town, to let Roy Willard out. He was carrying his suitcase.

Sue's father was as surprised to see him back as Dave had been. The Dodds had brought him word late yesterday of Roy's great triumph with *Your Majesty* and a short letter had arrived from Sue, telling him that she had lost out in the Dress Revue. But Roy's return home *alone,* ahead of schedule, had an element of mystery and alarm about it.

"I don't like this," said Matt Kendall, addressing himself. "There's somethin' gone wrong!"

He could hardly wait until the hurrying figure was up the hill. Maybe Roy had gotten in trouble back in Chicago. Maybe he'd run into some new charges against him.

"Maybe my letter to Judge Braude miscarried," he said, aloud. "My handwritin' ain't so good . . . and maybe the Judge, if he didn't get my letter, wouldn't let Roy off probation."

When the boy from the city walked in the door, Matt Kendall, as he thought, had steeled himself for anything. Roy set down his suitcase. His face had a look in it that Matt Kendall had never seen before.

"Hello," he greeted. "How'd you make out since I've been gone?"

"Not bad," snapped the chronic invalid. "You sick or somethin'?"

"No," said Roy, pushing up a chair and sitting down directly facing the man whose daughter he loved. "I came back early to have a talk with you—and to fix up some things the way they *should* be."

Matt Kendall's eyes commenced to narrow defensively.

"I'm not followin' you just yet," he said, cautiously.

"Well, there's several facts I've got to tell you—and then you will," Roy replied. He took a deep breath as though what he was about to say hurt him. "First thing you need to know is—Sue doesn't love me—she still loves Tom."

The frail figure on the easy chair started, convulsively.

"No!" he said. "That ain't so—it can't be!"

"I wish it *wasn't* so," said Roy, grimly, "but it is . . . Oh, she thinks a lot of me . . . and she'd have married me as long as she felt Tom wouldn't marry her . . . and she'd marry me even now if I insisted on it, because she promised . . . but when she found that Tom really cared, that changed everything."

Matt Kendall sat, with lines hardening around his eyes. "She doesn't know her own mind any more," he said. "I'll have to make it up for her when she gits back!"

The wills of the two men met head-on.

"You're not going to do any such thing," said Roy. "Sue's marrying Tom on Saturday and they're going to live in their new home!"

Matt Kendall's eyes opened wide. His whole being seemed to explode at once as he pounded the table with a bony hand.

"What kind of talk is that? She's not marryin' because I won't allow it . . . and there ain't any new home!"

Roy met his broadside with a smile. "There *will* be, by then," he said. "Right in the pine grove where they planned it. Just about all the folks in this part of Rock County and Hidden Valley are going to build it for them!"

The chronic invalid sat upright, an expression of utter unbelief on his face.

"Roy Willard, you're as crazy as a loon!" he blasted.

"Crazy or not," grinned Roy, "that's what going to happen. Early Saturday morning, Dave Carson, according to plan, will pick up Tom and take him away for the day. Then I'm moving in, with a fleet of Brannigan's trucks, and transferring all of Tom's building materials up the hill to the pine grove . . ." He pointed out the window overlooking the Dodds' place and Stony Creek Route below. "You'll be able to see the whole operation right from here," he continued as Matt Kendall sank back, staring, in helpless amazement. "Sue isn't due to return with Mr. Carson until late Saturday afternoon, which makes it just right. By that time, Tom's and her new home will be up and we'll be ready to hold the wedding!"

Matt Kendall was being hit so hard and so fast that he had,

thus far, been given no time or opportunity to form an adequate line of defense, but now he began to collect and organize his shattered forces.

"Hold on here, boy! Whose outlandish scheme is this—*yours?*"

Roy nodded, still smiling. "It's the best idea I ever got," he confessed. "And it's going to work," he added. "Mayor Brannigan's declaring Saturday a half holiday. The merchants are closing up at noon at twelve o'clock. Every carpenter and every able-bodied man who knows how to use a hammer or a saw is coming out here the first thing in the morning, with his wife and children. It's going to be the biggest community event you ever saw— a *real,* old-fashioned house raising party, with the women folks serving the meal at noon and everybody staying for the wedding at night."

Matt Kendall's inner rage was mounting into a fury.

"I don't thank you for this, Roy Willard!" he said, bitterly. "You've started somethin' that ain't goin' to pan out and it's goin' to boomerang right in your face! You mean to tell me you intend to keep Tom and Sue from knowin' anythin' about this and spring it on 'em at the last minute?"

Roy nodded. "That's the plan," he smiled.

"I'll put a stop to it!" declared the chronic invalid. "Nobody's a-goin' to come in my home and tear it apart like this." He had a sudden thought and eyed Roy sharply. "Did Judge Braude let you off probation?"

"Oh yes," said Roy, with appreciation. "I meant to tell you . . . and I can't ever thank you enough for that letter you wrote—it was swell . . ."

Matt Kendall's jaws clamped together and opened again.

"You mean, you *read* it?"

Roy met his questioning gaze. "The Judge read it to me. You've been like a Dad to me, Mr. Kendall . . . and I'm glad you felt that way."

"I take it all back! I wish I hadn't said it!" stormed the father of Sue Kendall. "You're a home wrecker, that's what you are! You've ruined your father's home . . . and now you're ruinin' mine . . . you've taken my daughter away from me—and I s'pose *you'll* be leavin', too!"

The boy from the city nodded, quietly. "Yes, Dad," he said, and the impact of the word shook Matt Kendall. "I suppose I *will* be leaving when things get straightened out here. I don't think you'd want to punish me by making me stay in sight of the girl I love when she's married to another man. But if you love her as much as I do, then you should be willing to give her up, too—if you know it will make her happy."

For once in his life the ravaged physical temple of Matt Kendall was split open, laying his soul bare. The fight was gone now, the bitter hatred engendered by his condition in life, the everlasting railing against people and circumstances, the hollow pretense of hardness. His tightened features relaxed as he lowered his proud head against the chair rest.

"What's goin' to become of me?" he whispered.

Roy's eyes were glistening as he said: "You don't know it yet but your sister is coming to live with you—and take care of you!"

This was the last stirring of smoldering embers and a final flash of bitterness flared up in his eyes.

"No, no—not that!" he protested, involuntarily. Then, suspiciously: "Did you send for her?"

Roy shook his head. "No, but *you're* going to, because it's the only way to really free Sue—and from that letter your sister wrote, I know she wants to come."

There was a long moment of silence as the sufferer from arthritis looked far into his past and traveled painfully back into the present. Then, with a look of profound resignation in his eyes, he gestured, weakly: "Bring me my writin' paper . . . !"

Chapter XXIV

IT WAS URGENTLY necessary, so Tom Dodds thought, for Dave Carson to take all of Saturday, with his assistance, to make an inspection of the roads in Rock County. As Dave had explained it, they needed to turn in a report on their condition to Mayor Brannigan so he could pass it on to the State Highway Commission when he went to Little Rock.

"We've got a lot of ground to cover," said Dave. "So you be ready to leave at sunrise."

And Tom was.

There were other things ready to happen at sunrise. Roy Willard had been up an hour before. As soon as he saw Dave drive away with Tom, he turned to Matt Kendall and said: "Well, Dad, I've got to be going. Have you everything you need, within reach?"

The father of Sue Kendall nodded. There was a sparkle of excitement in his eyes and the field glasses lay in his lap.

"Everythin'," he assured. "I feel the best today I've felt in years!"

Roy stopped at the door and looked back. "Don't you worry," he said. "I'll pick you up in time for the wedding—chair and all!"

Matt Kendall smiled. "Go to it, Son," he said, with feeling. "I can hardly wait!"

The boy from the city ran down Kendall Hill to the Dodds' place. It was a glorious December morning, turned mild again, with the rising sun shining through a fluffy lace curtain of clouds. Fred and Anna Dodds were awaiting him.

"Have you got the blue prints of the house and Tom's old marriage license for me?" were Roy's first questions.

"Yes," said Mrs. Dodds. "Here they are!" and she handed them over. "I had to wait until Tom was asleep to get a-hold of his wallet and take out the license. It's pretty badly worn. See! . . . It's even turning yellow."

Roy laughed. "He'll have a brand new one tonight. Then he can frame this one," he said. "Well, folks, this is going to be a terrific day." He turned to Tom's father. "I guess, Mr. Dodds, you'd better be getting me right into town. I'll take care of everything there if you'll come straight back and help the men load the trucks and get the people started on the job as they arrive."

"I'll do it," said Fred Dodds. "I'm ready."

"So am I," said Mrs. Dodds, pointing to her kitchen. Every available dish and all silverware was laid out in preparation for the invasion of housewives which was soon to come. "And here's something else," she announced, happily, opening a pantry door. "Look—Tom doesn't know it—but that's his wedding cake! I baked it yesterday."

The two men laughed and Fred Dodds, stooping over, kissed her on the cheek. "I thought, for a long while, Mother, you'd never have a chance to bake it."

He hastened from the room with Roy.

She watched the car leave the drive and then turned to look up toward the hill and the pine grove. It was the one warm spot of green in a now rather brown and barren landscape. But the morning sun was spotlighting it as though it, too, was interested in the home building project, so soon to take place.

Willing heads and hearts and hands performed a labor of love that day under the fascinated gaze of a man who sat in an easy chair and looked out on their doings from his house on Kendall Hill. No colony of ants could have been better organized or more industrious. Upon the stone foundation already laid, to the singing of saws and the rhythm of hammers, the framework of a little home mounted in view, as Matt Kendall watched.

"Never seen anythin' like it," he said to himself. "And I never will ag'in." Then his voice broke. "Thank you, God, for lettin' me live to this day!"

In the home of the Hiltons, further out on Stony Creek Route, the sewing circle group of 4-H girls was busy. Each was having a hand in the remodelling of Carolyn's white evening gown.

"I'm so happy this could be made over for Sue's wedding dress, instead of mine," said Dave's fiancee. "I think it will be ever so much prettier on her than on me. I can just imagine her now with her wonderful dark hair, against this white lace at the throat."

Sue liked that dress so much, too," reminded Eleanor. "Remember at our Dress Revue, when she told you she'd never seen anything prettier? And she thought you'd surely win the prize."

Carolyn nodded, thoughtfully. "She lost out at the Congress—but she gets two prizes today—a fine new home and a wonderful fellow for a husband . . ."

"And if I catch her bridal bouquet," added freckle-faced Sally Eiker, "the nearest man to me had better watch out!"

The sun was setting in a bank of golden clouds when Roy Willard came back up the hill with Tom's father, in a light truck, to call for Matt Kendall. Sue's father greeted them, excitedly.

"How's everythin' goin'?" he asked.

"Couldn't be better," answered Fred Dodds. "House is all up, fireplace is in, roof is all on, they're just finishing the first coat of white paint, and they're putting the furniture in it now."

"*Furniture!*" exclaimed Matt Kendall. "Where'd *that* come from?"

Roy smiled. "That's a gift from Brannigan's General Store," he informed. "Everything a bride could want for living room, bedroom and kitchen—including a kerosene ice box which Mr. Brannigan says they can change for electric as soon as they get electricity out here!"

Matt Kendall shook his head and eyed Fred Dodds, his voice trembling as he said: "I don't know what our two kids have done to deserve all this—but it's pretty grand, just the same."

Tom's father nodded. "Matt," he said, "you haven't seen anything yet. If anyone ever tries to tell me we don't have the best neighbors and friends in all the world, I'll run them out of the County!"

Roy walked impatiently about the room. "I hate to be rushing you, Dad, but we'll have to be getting back. We want to get you to the pine grove and all set before Sue arrives. She's due most any minute."

Matt Kendall slipped a blanket from around his shoulders. "I'm ready," he said, "except I'd like you to go into that drawer there and take a white shirt and black tie . . . and you'll find the coat to my old blue serge suit hanging up in the closet . . ." Then, with a self-conscious half-laugh at Fred Dodds, as Roy sought out the articles mentioned, he added: "I guess I ought to look the best I kin, for this occasion."

Roy came back with the coat, shirt and tie. He helped Sue's father out of his bath robe and held the shirt as Matt Kendall slid withered arms into the sleeves.

"You'll have to tie the tie."

Roy's sure fingers made the loop and pulled it in place. In another moment he had the coat on.

"Now do you want your bathrobe?" he asked.

"No!" snapped the man in the easy chair. "Just wrap the blanket around me." He looked down at his coat, reflectively. "Last time I wore this," he said, "was another great event in Sue's life—she'd just graduated from the Eighth Grade!"

Roy and Fred Dodds each took hold of a side of the easy chair and shoved it across the floor with Matt Kendall in it. It was a tight squeeze through the door but they made it. And then, lifting both chair and occupant, they carried it to the truck and set it in the back. Roy stood holding the chair in place as Fred Dodds drove carefully down the Kendall Hill to the turn-off between their properties which led up to the pine grove and the new little white house, gleaming among the trees.

It was dark enough now so that the house raisers were working by lantern light—several hundred lanterns, in fact—brought by the volunteer builders. The occasional sound of hammers was still heard as the truck swung into the little clearing and the crowd gave a cheer of welcome when the father of Sue Kendall was sighted and recognized.

The trip home from Chicago was not a happy one for the girl who had participated in the National 4-H Club Dress Revue. Frank Carson, ordinarily an entertaining companion, soon discovered that Sue preferred to be alone and undisturbed with her thoughts and reflections, so he drove, for the most part, in silence.

This return journey was so much different from the one going when Roy had been seated beside her and *Your Majesty* was riding just behind. What a change just the last few days had brought! Now *Your Majesty* was gone and, with his going, all the fun and excitement and heartache she had had helping Roy raise him. Roy, himself, was mysteriously gone, too, leaving her without explanation the night *Your Majesty* had been sold, saying only that he couldn't stay around the Exposition any longer, and that he wanted to get back to her father.

Sue had tried to analyze her own feelings about Roy on this ride home. She would have to be ready to say something definite but just what she could say or do seemed now, almost beyond her. It was dark when they passed through Hidden Valley, but Frank Carson, exclaimed in some surprise: "That's funny. It looks like the stores are closed!"

But there was nothing to stop for and Rock County's finest beef breeder was as anxious to get home as Sue was. They were just opposite the Dodds' place when a group of girls, waving lanterns, stopped the truck and shouted: "Hello, Mr. Carson! . . . Hello, Sue! . . . Mr. Carson, drive into the Dodds', will you? . . . We're having a little party here—and you and Sue have got to attend!"

Frank Carson laughed, looking out upon many of his 4-H girls. "But I'm tired and dirty and I want to get on home!"

"You can clean up here," ordered Carolyn Hilton. "This is important!"

Local Leader Frank Carson surrendered. When his truck reached the turn-around in Dodds' yard, the girls following seized a wondering Sue and hurried her into the house to a downstairs bedroom, where fresh dainty underthings and a made-over white evening gown were laid out on the bed. There was warm water in the tub in the adjoining bathroom and everything in readiness for a lady's toilet, with a row of beaming ladies-in-waiting!

"Hold on, girls!" gasped Sue, her eyes taking in all this array.

"What kind of a party *is* this?"

"It's your *wedding party*," announced Carolyn, "And this is your *wedding dress!*"

Sue stood, bewildered and hurt. "It's beautiful . . . and it's been made from your own gown," she identified, "but—you're *joking!*"

"Oh, no, we're not!" assured Carolyn, as the other girls joined, in chorus. "You're marrying Tom and you'll have to hurry and get dressed because he's not supposed to see the bride till the ceremony—and he's apt to be getting home any moment."

Sue sank down weakly on a chair. "But I'm still engaged to . . ." she started, and placed a hand to her head, then asked: "Where's Roy?"

"He's around," smiled Carolyn. "It's all right, Sue. He's arranged all this."

Quick tears shone in Sue Kendall's eyes. "But why all this hurry?" she asked. "I can't think . . . there're so many things . . . my Daddy . . ."

There was a knock on the door and Eleanor, nearest it, answered. "It's Roy now," she announced. "Come on out, girls—he wants to see Sue a minute alone."

The young women followed her into the living room and the boy from the city stepped in.

Sue faced him, eyes flashing. "Roy Willard—what on earth are you up to?" she demanded.

Roy smiled, quietly. "The one thing in life you want most," he said.

Her eyes faltered and she burst into tears, dropping down upon the bed beside the wedding dress. Roy stepped over and tenderly placed his arm about her. She rested her head against him and muffled her sobs. He stroked her hair as he said, soothingly: "Don't do that, Sue—unless you're crying because you're happy. It's all right with me. I'll be happy knowing you're happy . . . I was just the fellow who came along when your world was all upside down and when my world was pretty confused, too . . . but we've helped each other get back what we thought we'd lost . . . and that's what counts most of all."

Sue lifted her head and looked up at him, a new light in her eyes. "Oh, Roy!" she cried. "You've just said what I never could have said . . . you've said it so beautifully . . . it's just how I've been feeling inside—and I couldn't put it in words . . ."

The boy from the city nodded. "I know . . . you didn't have to tell me . . . I was sure of it or I wouldn't ever have arranged this . . ."

Sue glanced down at the wedding dress and her mind came back to the immediate present. "But, Daddy!" she protested. "How will he . . . ?"

Roy grinned. "He's all taken care of. I'm staying on for a few weeks . . . and his sister's coming to live with him."

"Aunt Ella!" exclaimed Sue, unbelievingly. "No, Roy!" There was joy in her face. "How did he ever . . . ?"

"Oh," smiled the boy from the city, "He was just waiting for an excuse. He really wanted her to come all along."

Sue stood up and placed her hands on Roy's shoulders.

"I hope, some day, you'll be as happy as I am," she said, and kissed him.

Roy gave her face a little pat and backed away. "I'm pretty close to that now," he said. "You'd better hurry. Everything's gone off without a hitch so far—and we don't want the bridegroom to have to be waiting for the bride!"

Sue caught Roy's arm as he started to slip out of the room. "Where *is* Tom?" she asked, suddenly concerned.

Roy grinned. "He's been out inspecting the county roads with Dave all day," he said. "He'll probably be *all in* by the time he gets back."

"Roy Willard!" cried Sue. "You mean to tell me he doesn't know anything about this yet?"

The boy from the city retreated to the door. "Not yet," he said. "But we're figuring on giving him five minutes' notice!"

He shut the door as Sue rushed at him.

Dave Carson was out with a flashlight, and under his car. "What do you suppose is the matter?" asked the fellow with him. "That's the third time your motor's died on you."

"It's either a bad connection somewhere or a weak battery," said Dave. "What time is it, anyway?"

"It's almost seven o'clock," said Tom, looking at his watch. "And I've had a day I'll never forget. I've recorded every bump in these county roads, not only in my notebook, but on my sitter!"

Dave got back in the car and tried the starter. The motor caught on and he grinned in apparent relief. "Well, maybe we can limp home."

Half an hour later the Dodds' place was in sight but, instead of turning in at the drive-way, Dave proceeded to Kendall Road and swung up it until he came to the turn-off which led to the pine grove.

"Hey!" cried Tom. "What's the big idea? . . . Where're you going? . . . What's up?"

Dave said nothing, keeping his eyes on the rough road. As they hit a bad rut, Tom groaned: "Cut it out! I've had just about all those I can take!" He suddenly looked ahead and gasped at what he saw. There were cars and trucks parked all along the sides of the road in front of them and on into the clearing. Inside a circle of lantern lights, a small white house glowed among the majestic pines. Tom rubbed his eyes and looked again, and then, with a choked feeling in his throat, he turned to Dave and said: "I didn't give you permission to build your home on my land."

Dave, still looking straight ahead as he drove the car past the parked machines, up toward the house, replied: "That's *your* home, Tom. We figured you might be needing it pretty soon, so we thought we'd get it up for you."

The fellow who had been Dave's bosom pal, clasped his hands and sat rigidly as they swept into the clearing and he saw the home he and Sue had designed together some two years before. He saw more than that. He saw a great crowd of smiling townspeople, most of them in work clothes, assembled to greet him. He saw Mayor Brannigan and Sam Jordan, standing together near the front porch, their faces beaming. He saw his father and mother next to them and the whole 4-H Club gang . . . and as he slid his tired and cramped body from the car and stood without crutches, surveying the scene, the Hilton sisters began singing, softly:

"My home must have a high tree above its open gate,
My home must have a garden where little dreamings wait;
My home must have a wide view of field and meadow fair,
Of distant hill, of open sky, with sunlight everywhere . . ."

Tom put out a hand and placed it on Dave's shoulder, and together, they walked toward the house, as the girls continued singing.

"My home must have a friendship with every happy thing,
My home must offer comfort for every sorrowing . . ."

Tom's face was wet now but his footsteps were firm as he came within the circle of his friends from Hidden Valley and all over Rock County, and the sheltering circle, too, of the sweet-scented pine trees which gently dipped their boughs in welcome.

"And every heart that enters shall hear its music there
And find some simple beauty that every life may share . . ."

Tom was standing now in front of the entrance to his home, and he found some words from deep down within him to say to Dave, "This is all wonderful . . . wonderful . . . it only lacks one thing . . . the girl to go with it."

But before Dave could answer, the Hilton sisters commenced humming a melody—an old familiar refrain which has guided the feet of countless lovers . . . and the crowd at one side of the house broke ranks and formed a lane . . . and, in a pathway lighted by lanterns, Tom saw a vision—a lovely bride in white, floating dreamily toward him.

Dave gently slipped Tom's hand from his shoulder and gave him a little pat on the back. The sweet-throated music of *Mendelssohn's Wedding March* tugged at his feet and he started toward the girl he had loved and lost and found again. They met at the steps leading up to their front porch and Reverend

Hascom suddenly appeared before them, with Dave and Carolyn each standing on a side.

And then there was a momentary pause while two men carried a smiling figure, seated in an easy chair, and placed him down nearby.

Reverend Hanscom was saying: "You are here to be joined in the bonds of holy matrimony." And now he was looking up and at the man in the chair. "Who gives this woman in marriage?"

And the voice of Matt Kendall rang out, with a joyous quality in it. *"I do!"*

It was all a glorious haze to Tom after that: Dave pressing a wedding ring in his trembling hands at the right moment and his placing this ring upon Sue's finger . . . and the minister finally saying: "I now pronounce you—man and wife!" . . . and his taking her in his arms and their clinging to each other as they kissed amid a growing chorus of congratulations.

And now everyone was drifting away, taking their lanterns with them, and leaving only the lights within their little home. There was the sound of motors being started and car after car going down the hill . . . and farewells from Dave and Carolyn . . . and the 4-H gang . . . and his father and mother . . . and Roy . . . and from Matt Kendall, as he was carried away in his chair, to be taken back to his home on the hill . . . while, in the valley, the two of them, standing in the doorway of their home, could hear the voices of the Hilton sisters, once more raised in song.

". . . And every heart that enters shall hear its music there . . ."

Without a word, Tom lifted his bride in his arms and carried her happily across the threshold.